Proceedings
of the U.S. Forest Service
Centennial Congress

Proceedings
of the U.S. Forest Service
Centennial Congress

A Collective Commitment to Conservation

January 3–6, 2005 ♠ Washington, D.C.

Edited by Steven Anderson

Forest History Society *Durham, North Carolina*

The Forest History Society is a nonprofit educational and research institution dedicated to the advancement of historical understanding of human interaction with the forest environment. It was established in 1946. Interpretations and conclusions in FHS publications are those of the authors; the institution takes responsibility for the selection of topics, competency of the authors, and their freedom of inquiry.

This book is published with support from the Lynn W. Day Endowment for Forest History Publications and with additional funds from a cooperative agreement with the U.S. Forest Service.

Printed in the United States of America

Forest History Society
701 William Vickers Avenue
Durham, North Carolina 27701
(919) 682-9319
www.foresthistory.org

First edition

Design by Zubigraphics, Inc.

Cover: The cover image and centennial logo were created by the USDA Visual Communications Center (Now USDA Creative Services Center).

Library of Congress Cataloging-in-Publication Data

U.S. Forest Service Centennial Congress (2005 : Washington, D.C.)
  Proceedings of the U.S. Forest Service Centennial Congress : a collective commitment to conservation / edited by Steven Anderson.-- 1st ed.
    p. cm.
  ISBN-13: 978-0-89030-067-1 (pbk. : alk. paper)
  ISBN-10: 0-89030-067-4 (pbk. : alk. paper)
  1. United States. Forest Service--History--Congresses. 2. Forest policy--United States--History--Congresses. 3. Forests and forestry--United States--History--Congresses. 4. Forest conservation--United States--Congresses. I. Anderson, S. (Steven), 1956- II. Title.
  SD565.U43 2005
  354.5'50973--dc22
                        2006003027

Contents

Preface

In the first week of January 2005, the U.S. Forest Service celebrated the one-hundredth anniversary of its establishment and anticipated its next century by hosting what it called the Centennial Congress, held at the Grand Hyatt Hotel in Washington, D.C. This was the same week, one hundred years before, that the second American Forest Congress was held, also in Washington, D.C., under the auspices of the American Forestry Association. The 1905 Congress set the stage for President Theodore Roosevelt to transfer the forest reserves from the Department of the Interior to the Department of Agriculture and establish the U.S. Forest Service under the leadership of Gifford Pinchot. In the intervening hundred years, five additional American Forest Congresses have been held—in 1946, 1953, 1963, 1975, and 1996.

Although the Forest Service Centennial Congress was not formally counted as the "Eighth" American Forest Congress and was not organized by the American Forestry Association (now American Forests), like its 1905 predecessor, it sought to bring together a diverse group of public and private national leaders who would consider the challenges that face our nation's forests. In 1905, delegates represented the lumber, mining, grazing, irrigation, and railroad interests—then the primary users of the forests. During the past one hundred years, the national forests have acquired new stakeholders. One hundred years from now, historians of natural resource policy will look back and find among the delegates to the 2005 Congress representatives from environmental groups, timber investment management organizations, hunting and fishing associations, off-road-vehicle groups, trail and skiing associations, a forest management certification standards program, even an association for nude recreation, among other entities, plus urban foresters, environmental justice advocates, and minority students. No doubt, the new demands and uses have brought new complexities to those who manage the national forests and grasslands.

The preface to the proceedings of the 1905 meeting indicates that it was "the most important meeting ever devoted to forestry in the United States," and that as a result, "forestry has come to have a new meaning to the American people." Similar claims for the 2005 Congress are certainly premature, but in any case, this meeting was not orchestrated to advocate for specific political objectives. Rather, it was designed so that thousands of individuals across the nation who care greatly about our national forests could listen to one another and exchange ideas. It should take its place in history nevertheless, perhaps as an example of the public participation and collaboration that characterize public land management in the early twenty-first century.

To maximize participation, eleven regional centennial forums were conducted in advance of the 2005 Congress where delegates provided regional perspectives on the potential issues and challenges for the future of the national forests and grasslands. Their findings were reported at the Washington meeting, and summaries are contained in these proceedings. At the 2005 Congress, participants had the opportunity to create a framework for discussion as the Forest Service embarked on its second century of service. Twenty breakout groups, each with about fifteen people, explored ways that the Forest Service and its partners could collectively meet the challenges and opportunities facing the national forests. A brief summary of the breakout groups' discussions is included in the proceedings; a much longer document, published separately, details the eight key themes, twenty-three topics, and 727 recommendations for new approaches that participants proposed to help the Forest Service prepare to meet the long-term needs of the land and the public.

Similar to the 1905 Congress proceedings, the intent of this publication is to provide a record, not necessarily verbatim, of the sessions. Most of the papers contained in these proceedings were submitted by the presenters themselves, either before or following the event. A few addresses were adapted from closed-captioning efforts, and others were transcribed from video recordings. All the papers experienced a light editing by Sally Atwater, an editorial consultant and former editor of the *Journal of Forestry*. Jamie Lewis, Forest History Society historian, transcribed several presentations from video and assisted with photo selection and captioning.

The Forest History Society is pleased to publish this documentation of a historic event recognizing the centennial of the U.S. Forest Service and the men and women who have served the agency and the nation in furthering its conservation goals.

Steven Anderson, *President and CEO*
Forest History Society
Durham, North Carolina

Centennial of the Forest Service, 2005
By the President of the United States of America

A Proclamation

In 2005, the Department of Agriculture's Forest Service celebrates a century of service to our Nation. After President Theodore Roosevelt established the Forest Service as part of the Department of Agriculture in 1905, Secretary of Agriculture James Wilson wrote to the First Chief of the Forest Service, Forester Gifford Pinchot, the "all land is to be devoted to its most productive use for the permanent good of the whole people." The Forest Service has now upheld this noble charge for 100 years, and America's forests remain vibrant because of the hard work and dedication of our foresters.

Beyond serving as places for recreation, our forests are also sources of paper products, building materials, chemicals, and many other resources that drive our economy. Over the last century, the Forest Service has combined this ethic or good stewardship with sound science and a spirit of innovation to cultivate and sustain our forests in ways that benefit our entire society.

Today, Americans continue to be responsible stewards of national forests and grasslands. Through the commonsense management approach of my Healthy Forests Initiative, the Forest Service is working with state and local governments, tribe, and other federal agencies to help prevent destructive wildfires, return forests to a healthier, natural condition, and maintain a full range of forest types. The Forest Service is also providing important work, education, and job training to citizens in need. This commitment to "Caring for the Land and Serving People" contributes to our country's success in conserving our environment and ensuring that our natural resources remain sources of pride for our citizens, our communities, and our Nation.

NOW, THEREFORE, I, GEORGE W. BUSH, President of the United States of America, by virtue of the authority vested in me by the Constitution and laws of the United States, do hereby proclaim February 1, 2005, as the Centennial of the Forest Service of the Department of Agriculture. I call upon the people of the United States to recognize this anniversary with appropriate programs, ceremonies, and activities in honor of the Forest Service's contributions to our country.

IN WITNESS WHEREOF, I have hereunto set my hand this first day of February, in the year of our Lord two thousand five, and of the Independence of the United States of America the two hundred and twenty-ninth.

George W. Bush

Centennial Congress Planning Committee

Partners

Lowell Baier, *Historian, Boone & Crockett Club*
Robert Model, *President, Boone & Crockett Club*
Deborah Gangloff, *Executive Director, American Forests*
Rachel Brittin, *Communications Director, American Forests*
Michael Goergen, *President, Society of American Foresters*
Steven Anderson, Ph.D., CF, CAE, *President, Forest History Society*
Al Sample, Ph.D., *President, Pinchot Institute for Conservation*
Patricia Woods, Ph.D., *President, The Woods Institute*
Mary Mitsos, *Vice President, National Forest Foundation*
Jack Ward Thomas, Ph.D., *Boone and Crockett Professor of Wildlife Conservation, College of Forestry, University of Montana*
Doug Crandall, *Staff Director, House Resources Subcommittee on Forests and Forest Health*
Derrick Crandall, *President, American Recreation Coalition*
Max Peterson, *Forest Service Chief Emeritus*
William H. Banzhaf, *President, Sustainable Forestry Board, Inc.*
Jim Gasser, *Meeting Planner, National Park Service*

Greatest Good Team

David Steinke, *Producer*
Steve Dunsky, *Producer*
Ann Dunsky, *Producer*
Alana DeJoseph, *Distribution Manager*

Forest Service Employees

Tom Thompson, *Deputy Chief, National Forest System*
Gloria Manning, *Associate Deputy Chief, National Forest System*
Dan Harkenrider, *Incident Commander*
Jacqueline Leonard, *Planning Chair*
Erin Newman, *National Forest System*
Debbie Pressman, *National Wildlife Program Leader*
Stana Federighi, *State & Private Forestry*
Bill Helin, *Business Operations*
Gerald W. Williams, Ph.D., *Forest Service Historian*
Teri Cleeland, *Legislative Affairs*

Floyd Thompson, *Recreation Heritage Resources*
Linda Brett, *Policy Analysis*
Denise Ingram, *International Programs*
Catherine Karr, *International Programs*
Jeff Waalkes, *Senior Special Agent, Security*
Denver James, *Pacific Northwest Research Station*
Pipa Elias, *Conservation Association Intern, Conservation Education*
Jonathan Stephens, *Congressionally Designated Areas*
Ralph Holiday Crawford, Ph.D., *National Program Leader for Rangeland Ecology*
Don Hansen, *Volunteer Coordinator*

Agenda of the Forest Service Centennial Congress*

January 3–6, 2005
Grand Hyatt Hotel, Washington, D.C.
*Adapted agenda as made available at the Congress

Monday, January 3, 2005

12:00 pm **Registration (until 8:00 pm)**

6:30 pm **An Evening with Pinchot and Roosevelt**

6:55 pm **Purpose for Centennial Congress**
William Possiel, *President, National Forest Foundation*
Tom L. Thompson, *Deputy Chief, National Forest System*

7:00 pm **EXPO Opens**

7:05 pm **Light Hors-d'oeuvres and No Host Bar**

Tuesday, January 4, 2005

6:00 am **Registration**

7:00 am **EXPO**
Continental Breakfast

7:45 am **Video Presentation**

8:00 am **Job Corps Color Guard Presentation and National Anthem**
Chuck Leavell, *The Rolling Stones*

8:20 am **Welcome Address**
Dale Bosworth, *Chief, USDA Forest Service*

8:40 am **Administration Welcome**
Ann Veneman, *Secretary of Agriculture*

9:00 am **Historic Perspective on the Forest Service**
Ed Brannon, Jr., *Former Director, Grey Towers Natural Historic Landmark*

9:30 am **Reflections and Visions from Forest Service Chiefs**
Sally Collins, *Associate Chief, USDA Forest Service (Moderator)*
Max Peterson, *Eleventh Chief, USDA Forest Service*
F. Dale Robertson, *Twelfth Chief, USDA Forest Service*
Jack Ward Thomas, *Thirteenth Chief, USDA Forest Service*
Mike Dombeck, *Fourteenth Chief, USDA Forest Service*

10:40 am **Break**

11:05 am **Outside Perspectives on the Forest Service: Social, Economic, and Environmental Benefits**
Jo Ellen Force, *Forest Resources Department Head, College of Natural Resources, University of Idaho (Moderator)*
Mavis C. Hill, *Executive Director, Tyrrell County Community Development Corporation*
Debra Shore, *Director of Development, Chicago Wilderness*
Robert Model, *President, Boone and Crockett Club*
John Shelk, *Ochoco Timber Company*
Todd Davidson, *Chair, Western States Tourism Policy Council*

12:15 pm **Lunch (on your own)**

1:30 pm **Public Policy Panel: The Multiple Use Challenge**
Patricia Limerick (*Moderator*)
William H. Meadows, *President, The Wilderness Society*
Paul Hansen, *Executive Director, Izaak Walton League of America*
John Heissenbuttel, *Vice President, American Forest and Paper Association*
Butch Blazer, *State Forester, New Mexico Forestry Division*
Robert E. Douglas, *President, National Forest Counties and Schools Coalition*
Lyle Laverty, *Director, Colorado Division of Parks and Outdoor Recreation*

2:45 pm **Break**

3:15 pm **Premier Screening: *The Greatest Good: A Forest Service Centennial Film***
Introduction by Char Miller, *History Professor, Trinity University*

5:30 pm **Special Presentation by *Greatest Good* Production Team**

6:00 pm **Evening Reception**

Wednesday, January 5, 2005

7:00 am **Registration**

7:00 am **Continental Breakfast**

8:00 am **Congressional Views on the Nation's Forests and Rangelands**
Mark Rey, *Under Secretary, Natural Resources and Environment (Moderator)*
Greg Walden, *U.S. Representative, Oregon*
Larry Craig, *U.S. Senator, Idaho*

Pete Domenici, *U.S. Senator, New Mexico*
Mark Udall, *U.S. Representative, Colorado*
Norm Dicks, *U.S. Representative, Washington*

9:15 am   **Break**

9:30 am   **Forest Service in a Changing World**
Ross Whaley, *Chairman, Adirondack Park Agency (Moderator)*
Emilyn Sheffield, *Chair, Department of Recreation Administration,*
    California State University, Chico
Gifford Pinchot III, *President, Bainbridge Graduate Institute*
James Gustave Speth, *Dean, Yale School of Forestry and Environmental*
    Science
Sally K. Fairfax, *Professor, Department of Environmental Science,*
    Policy and Management, University of California, Berkeley

11:00 am   **Charge to Breakout Sessions**
Liz Agpaoa, *Chief of Staff, USDA Forest Service*

11:10 am   **Lunch**
Box lunches provided for informal discussions in breakout rooms

12:30 pm   **Report on the Centennial Regional Forums**
Forum Delegates
Deborah Campbell, *Anchor, Regional Forum Reports*

1:40 pm   **Break**

1:55 pm   **Report on the Centennial Regional Forums**
Forum Delegates
Deborah Campbell, *Anchor, Regional Forum Reports*

3:10 pm   **Breakout Sessions**
(Predetermined groups and rooms assigned at registration.)

5:30 pm   **Break**

6:00 pm   **Buses Depart for Whitten Building Event**

6:30 pm   **Awards and Recognition**
Sally Collins, *Associate Chief, USDA Forest Service*
The evening will also include special visits from Lassie, Jon Provost
    (Timmy from *Lassie*), Smokey Bear, Woodsy Owl, and Roosevelt
    and Pinchot

8:15 pm   **Buses Begin Returning to Hyatt** (last bus at 9:00 pm)

Thursday, January 6, 2005

7:00 am   **Registration and Continental Breakfast**

8:00 am   **Lessons for a Future Forest Service:**
    Assistant and Under Secretaries' Views
    Jim Moseley, *Deputy Secretary of Agriculture (Moderator)*
    M. Rupert Cutler, *Former Assistant Secretary of Agriculture for Conservation, Research, and Education*
    James R. Lyons, *Former Under Secretary of Agriculture for Natural Resources and Environment*
    George Dunlop, *Former Assistant Secretary of Agriculture for Natural Resources and Environment*
    John B. Crowell, Jr., *Former Assistant Secretary of Agriculture for Natural Resources and Environment*

9:00 am   **Break**

9:15 am   **The Power of Participation, the Power of Partnership**
    David Bell, *Chairman of the Board, National Forest Foundation (Moderator)*
    M. Hosny El-Lakany, *Assistant Director-General, Food and Agriculture Organization of the United Nations, Forestry Department*
    James B. Hull, *State Forester, Texas Forest Service*
    Rob Keck, *CEO, National Wild Turkey Federation*
    Ann Linehan, *Division Director, Program Support, Head Start Bureau*
    Majora Carter, *Founder and Executive Director, Sustainable South Bronx*

10:45 am   **Break**

11:00 am   **Conservation Leaders: Today and Tomorrow**
    Jim Oftedal, *Director, Central California Consortium (Moderator)*
    Alba Mercado, *Student, College of the Sequoias, Dinuba, CA*
    Jessica Farrar, *Student, Illinois Wesleyan University, Bloomington, IL*
    Terry Baker, *Forester Trainee, Apalachicola National Forest, Marianna, FL*
    Alyse Charley, *Student, Reedley High School, Dunlap, CA*
    Daniel P. Delgado, *Student, Cuba High School, Cuba, NM*
    John T. Vogel II, *Student, Jesuit High School, San Antonio, FL*

12:00 pm   **Summary Review**
    Dale Bosworth, *Chief, USDA Forest Service*

12:15 pm   **Break**

12:45 pm   **Awards Ceremony Luncheon**
    A Uniquely Forest Service Gala Featuring the Fiddlin' Foresters

2:30 pm   **Adjourn and Travel Safely**

Purpose for the Centennial Congress

January 3, 2005
6:55 pm

William Possiel
Tom L. Thompson
Jeffrey Stine

january 3-6
2005
washington dc

US Forest Service

Centennial Congress

A Collective Commitment to Conservation

William Possiel
President, National Forest Foundation

It is a great pleasure to welcome you to the Forest Service Centennial Congress. Let me start by wishing you and your families a happy New Year!

One hundred years ago, a group of people concerned with the future of our nation's forests gathered for the American Forest Congress of 1905. The goal was clearly stated: "to establish a broader understanding of the forest in its relation to the great industries depending upon it; to advance the conservative use of forest resources for both the present and the future need of these industries; to stimulate and unite all efforts to perpetuate the forest as a permanent resource of the nation." As we all know, a very special organization was born of that meeting, to take on that task, "to stimulate and unite all efforts to perpetuate the forest as a permanent resource of the nation."

President Theodore Roosevelt came to the Congress in 1905 and said, "Your coming is a very great step towards the solution of the forest problem…." So there is continuity from 1905 to 2005. Your coming is a great step towards finding solutions to the increasingly complex array of challenges that face our nation's forests.

The group gathering in 1905 represented numerous interests in our nation's forests. Today, a very different group has gathered. We recognize that our nation's forests are vital to economic development, healthy communities, and maintaining representative examples of our nation's flora and fauna. We know the importance of the fresh, clean water that our national forests provide. We recognize the role public lands play in the nation's physical fitness. And the very imagery of America is formed not only by the great cities, communities, and agricultural landscapes, but by the mountains and valleys, the rivers and streams, and the vast and inspiring vistas that we enjoy when looking out over the Monongahela, the Wasatch-Cache, the Superior, the Cherokee, Buffalo Gap, and the Lewis and Clark, just to name a few of our 155 national forests and 22 national grasslands.

As our nation has grown, and continues to grow, we have encroached upon these ever more precious lands. The value of these lands and waters, the fish and wildlife they harbor, and the renewable resources they provide is incalculable. They become more valuable each and every day.

The people who lead this agency, from the Chief to the district ranger, have enormous responsibility. These folks often feel like they are caught between a rock and a hard spot when making decisions that benefit the greatest number over the long run. This agency is made up of an exceptionally talented group of natural resource professionals who strive to make the best decisions within an environment of conflicting demands.

The Centennial Congress is an opportunity to reflect on the past—to share the lessons learned, both good and bad. It is also a chance to recognize the thirty-three thousand individuals who believe that caring for our nation's natural legacy is much more than just a job. We celebrate these people tonight, this week, this month, and this year, as we—together through hundreds of partnerships across America—begin a new century of service.

This Forest Service Centennial Congress, ladies and gentlemen, is about the future.

Tom L. Thompson

Deputy Chief, National Forest System

The National Forest Foundation has been instrumental in planning and preparing for this gathering this week. We thank them and look forward to many, many years of support and partnership with them.

To each and every one of you I extend our thanks and a sincere and warm welcome this evening. It is my pleasure to represent leadership and employees of the U.S. Forest Service and say that we truly appreciate that you have chosen to be here as delegates to this special Centennial Congress. This is a congress intended to commemorate those who have worked so hard to create an institution, an organization, and a spirit that embody the dreams and hopes of forward-looking conservation leaders of a century ago.

The purpose of this Congress is to pause, to reflect, and to think about the successes, the service, the stewardship, and the accomplishments of a century of work of the Forest Service. It is our hope and most importantly our desire that we look ahead and think about the possibilities, the challenges, the issues, and the realities that we face together in the world that we find ourselves in today. It is our intent that over the next few days we can take advantage of the information and perspectives that will be shared by the outstanding panelists to help explore the concepts that will help the Forest Service to better serve the diverse and growing public of this great nation.

In short, we believe this is an opportunity to renew our Collective Commitment to Conservation for the new century that lies ahead of us. It is a unique chance that we have. It is a chance also to take stock of the strength we have when we engage all our partners and cooperators. You make us stronger and more relevant to the people whom we serve.

I want to take just a moment and tell you how proud we are, all of us who are a part of the Forest Service in 2005, and how lucky we know we are to have this opportunity to be a part of the agency as we celebrate our first hundred years—the chance we have to help frame some of tomorrow and together with you identify how we might better approach the challenges ahead.

We know that there are many, many people who wanted to be here but could not. You are here. You are the delegates who have the opportunity to participate, to listen, to think, to share, and to use the time we have together at this Congress to help shape the future. I am certain the week will be a memorable event for all of us, but what I truly hope is that the week will prove to be a meaningful event that helps influence in a positive and helpful way what happens in the future as the Forest Service adjusts, adapts, and works to meet the needs of the people and provides the stewardship of the land and resources entrusted to our management and influence.

A number of you had the opportunity to participate in one of a dozen regional forums in November, and some of you are delegates representing many others from those forums. Others of you are here representing partners, organizations, cooperating agencies, and other institutions who share in some way responsibilities with the Forest Service. No matter whom you represent, it is our hope that you will be able to influence in some way the outcome of the Congress.

Before I yield the podium, I would like to officially recognize some of our honored guests.

First, I would like to recognize Chief Dale Bosworth and Associate Chief Sally Collins.

Second, I would like to recognize four other Chiefs who are with us this week and whom you will hear from tomorrow morning—former Chiefs Max Peterson, Dale Robertson, Jack Ward Thomas, and Mike Dombeck.

Third, I would like to note that around the hall you will notice a number of people in uniforms similar to the one I wear tonight. These individuals represent the top leadership of the Forest Service. They are other deputy chiefs, associate deputy chiefs, the regional foresters, the research station directors, the area and institute directors, and several other members of the National Leadership Team. This is the first time these uniforms have been worn, and we wanted to usher in our new century with this new dress uniform.

Fourth, I would like to recognize several honored guests from Canada, Mexico, and the United Nations: Brian Emmett, Assistant Deputy Minister, Natural Resources of Canada; Yvan Hardy, Chief Scientist, Natural Resources of Canada; Manuel Reed, Director General, Mexico National Forest Commission; and Dr. Hosny El-Lakany, Assistant Director-General, Forestry Department, FAO, United Nations.

And lastly, I would like to recognize each of you who are delegates. Take a moment to look around you, shake a hand or two, and give yourselves a round of applause to recognize your Collective Commitment to Conservation. We are so glad you are here and are excited to hear your thoughts about the future of the nation's forests and grasslands.

The Centennial Congress will open officially tomorrow morning. The opening will be at eight A.M. Please be in this room and seated as the program will begin on time, and the doors will closed at eight-ten A.M. For security reasons, please wear your nametag at all times in the building. Throughout the week, please do all you can to be prompt for the start of each session and enjoy the special opportunities we have planned.

Now, enough of the formalities. It is time to get to know each other, have some food and refreshment, and visit the Expo next door. There are also tables that you may have noticed in the foyer, which provide information about each of the regional forums. Have a great evening.

Jeffrey K. Stine

Historian and Curator, National Museum of American History,
Smithsonian Institution

As a historian who works directly across the National Mall from the Forest Service headquarters, it is a special privilege to stand before you on this opening night of the Centennial Congress. My only regret is that my Smithsonian colleagues will *never* believe me when I tell them that I followed President Roosevelt and Gifford Pinchot on the program!

I'm here to introduce the trailer you are about to see for the remarkable Forest Service documentary, *The Greatest Good*, which will have its world premiere tomorrow afternoon at three-fifteen in the hotel's Independence Ballroom.

Anniversaries provide us with important opportunities to celebrate, to reflect, and to look ahead. The creation of the U.S. Forest Service—and the national forests themselves—were acts of supreme wisdom and foresight. Their enduring legacy of societal benefits is difficult to overestimate. Yet there was nothing inevitable about those contributions.

Guided by the goal of providing the greatest good for the greatest number for the longest time, the Forest Service's history was forged over the years by men and women much like yourselves who argued in good faith about the agency's—and the nation's—future. The documentary unveiled tomorrow conveys this story in ways that are enlightening, entertaining, and inspiring.

I can't say enough good things about the three filmmakers—Ann Dunsky, Steve Dunsky, and Dave Steinke—as they have done an unsurpassed job in portraying the ongoing debate in American society over how best to manage the nation's natural resources. It is a debate that reflected the perpetual tension between development and preservation, between special interests and the national interest, between the advances of technology and the retreat of the natural world.

As you will see in the trailer, this beautiful and compelling film sets out to capture the sweep of the Forest Service's past and to root it firmly in the larger framework of American history. So let's watch this teaser, and I'll look forward to joining you tomorrow as we make up the first audience to see *The Greatest Good* on the big screen.

Welcoming Remarks

January 4, 2005
8:00 am

Chuck Leavell
Dale Bosworth
Ann M. Veneman
Gale Norton

january 3-6
2005
washington dc

US Forest Service

Centennial
Congress

A Collective Commitment to Conservation

Chuck Leavell
Tree Farmer and Keyboardist, the Rolling Stones

I love birthday parties! Who doesn't? But a hundredth birthday—that's a long, long time. Even the Red Sox managed to win two World Series in less than a hundred years.

We folks who live and work with trees, of course, are patient people, even more patient perhaps than Red Sox fans. Just a few weeks ago, my wife Rose Lane and I planted some long-leaf pine on our Tree Farm, Charlane Plantation, down near Macon, Georgia. I expect that those trees will still be growing when you folks get together to celebrate your next hundredth birthday.

But that's O.K., because Rose Lane and I are in it for the long haul. We'll enjoy watching the seedlings take hold, and our daughters will see them grow. And their kids will be grown up when the trees become mature. And maybe *their* kids—Rose Lane's and my great-grandchildren—will come to Charlane and start the cycle all over again.

That's our dream for our little piece of America's forest. And happily, it's a dream that's still within reach for us and for the millions of other folks who own nearly half of America's forestland. We want to keep our forests green and growing. We want our neighbors to enjoy the clean water, the clean air, the wildlife, and all the other great things we produce: pianos like this one, great books, daily newspapers, comfortable homes…. (Gosh, I expect all together we produce almost enough paper every year to handle two, maybe three forest plan appeals.)

There's a special pride in knowing that this is a family legacy, not just Chuck's or Rose Lane's. We're taking care of land that Rose Lane's family has owned for generations. And we're preparing our family to continue that heritage of stewardship.

This heritage of family stewardship is a powerful force, and there are millions of families like ours who share it. That's a good thing, because what happens on family-owned forests over the next decades will shape our nation's forest history for the next century.

We family forest owners are your allies, in many ways your true constituents. We know you share our commitment to the land, and to our communities. And we're ready to do all we can, working with you, to assure that *our* forests remain part of our nation's future.

So, on behalf of the American Forest Foundation and the fifty thousand families who are members of our American Tree Farm System, happy birthday and many, many more!

Dale Bosworth
Chief, USDA Forest Service

Centennial Congress: A Historic Opportunity

Welcome! I am honored and privileged to be here at this Centennial Congress together with so many of our partners and collaborators. Let me start by thanking all of you for being here. This is a difficult week, coming as it does right after the holidays. Your being here is a real tribute to your dedication to conservation.

I'd like in particular to thank the secretary of Agriculture, Ms. Ann Veneman, for taking time from her busy schedule to be with us today. Secretary Veneman has given us the strong support and leadership we needed in the last few years, and I deeply appreciate everything she has done to help us better fulfill our mission of caring for the land and serving people.

Unique Moment in History

This is a unique moment in time. Exactly a hundred years ago, a similar group of people gathered here in Washington, D.C., for the first American Forest Congress. The delegates came from all over the country—and from as far away as the Philippines. Some of them gave up their holidays to be here.

That first American Forest Congress faced daunting challenges. President Theodore Roosevelt addressed the Congress, and he spoke of forests in trouble. He spoke of timber profiteers whose only idea was—and I quote—"to skin the country and go somewhere else." He spoke of a possible timber famine.

But he also spoke of hope. He challenged the delegates to figure out how they could continue using the nation's resources without destroying them, because if they destroyed them, then they themselves would be destroyed.

But they were not destroyed. Instead, they flourished because they took the opportunity to change the nation. They set the stage for generations of Americans from all walks of life to practice conservation, both in their professional lives and in their personal lives.

When I look around this room, I see the same sort of opportunity here today. A great many interests from all over the country are represented here. There are folks from industry…from the environmental community…from the outdoor recreation community…from all sorts of user groups. Groups we collaborate with are here. Universities and the academic community are well represented. Our partners in government at every level are here—tribal, local, state, and federal. Heads of federal and state agencies are here, and my special thanks to them. There are also representatives from Capitol Hill. Many young people are here, our future conservation leaders. And, of course, there are folks from the Forest Service family…from the National Forest Foundation…from the regions and stations…from State and Private Forestry…and from the ranks of our retirees, including several former Chiefs—Max Peterson, Dale Robertson, Jack Ward Thomas, and Mike Dombeck.

Proud Forest Service Record

Speaking of the Forest Service family, let me say a few words about the Forest Service. This year, the Forest Service is a century old. I have worked in the agency for more than a third of that time, and because my father was in the Forest Service, I have really been part of the agency for my entire life. That's more than half of our entire history as an agency.

I cannot begin to tell you how proud that makes me feel. I've known Forest Service employees all my life. I've seen them go through some ups and downs as times have changed, and I've drawn inspiration from their tremendous dedication to conservation. I've seen how hard they've worked and the things they've accomplished for the land and for the people we serve. I've seen them take the lead in dealing with emergencies going way beyond wildland fire— after 9/11 at the Pentagon and at Ground Zero in New York; after the *Columbia* shuttle disaster in Texas; and now, after the tsunami disaster in South Asia, we're again involved in our nation's emergency response through our International Programs staff. And I can honestly say, after a lifetime of experience with Forest Service folks: I cannot imagine a finer bunch of people. It makes me proud to be one of them.

But this Centennial Congress is about more than just the Forest Service. What brings us together from so many different backgrounds is something we all have in common: our public spirit and our collective commitment to conservation. We sometimes have strong differences of opinion, but I see those differences as positive, partly because they reflect the same passionate commitment to conservation we all share. Every one of us here wants to do what's right for the land and for the people we serve.

This Centennial Congress is an opportunity for joint reflection on what that means. It's an opportunity to recognize our successes, to celebrate our collective commitment to conservation, and to look to the challenges ahead. At this historic moment, I see a real opportunity to renew a national dialogue on the conservation idea.

Conservation Successes

What is conservation? Gifford Pinchot famously said it's "the greatest good for the greatest number for the longest time." Today, we tend to use the terms *sustainable forestry or sustainability* as the equivalent of *conservation*. I think our Forest Service mission sums it up pretty well: "To sustain the health, diversity, and productivity of the nation's forests and grasslands to meet the needs of present and future generations."

"The greatest good"…"the needs of present and future generations": it sounds great. But what I might think is a "good" or a "need," someone else might not. My "good" or "need" might conflict with theirs, and the next thing you know we're in court—*unless* we remember our collective commitment to conservation. That's partly why we're here for the next few days: to build trust…to promote dialogue…to rediscover our common ground.

And I think we have had some remarkable successes over the last century. The whole idea of conservation has given us a lot of common ground. A century ago, Theodore Roosevelt spoke of the old pioneer days, when—and I quote—"the American had but one thought about a tree, and that was to cut it down." Through that attitude, we lost about a quarter of America's entire forest estate in the first three centuries of our history as a nation.

Thanks to conservation, that wasteful attitude has totally changed. We no longer think of a tree as an obstacle to progress or even as just standing timber. In my lifetime alone, we've seen a huge shift in values and attitudes. Today, thanks in part to new scientific insights, our focus has broadened. We now focus on the long-term health of entire forested landscapes.

As a result, the way we go about managing forests and harvesting trees today is light-years ahead of where it was a century or two ago. And it's truly paid off: in the last century, America's forest estate has stayed roughly the same, with little or no net loss nationwide.

Skinning the Country

Does that mean we no longer just "skin the country and go somewhere else," as T.R. put it a century ago? Yes…and no. Today, the cut-and-run logger of the nineteenth century would be hard to find in the United States. But we've found subtler ways of skinning the country.

If you drive in any direction from here, you will soon see signs of it. Farms, fields, and forests are giving way to development. Nationwide, we're losing more than four thousand acres of open space to development every day. Our families are getting smaller, yet we're building bigger houses, mostly from wood. And more and more of that wood is coming from overseas.

The "land skinner" today is no longer the American timber producer. Professional forestry in the United States is one of the twentieth century's greatest conservation success stories, and I think you'll see some of that story told in the film *The Greatest Good*. Our forests today, especially on public land, enjoy the world's greatest environmental protections.

But I'm afraid we still might be skinning the country—*somebody's* country, anyway—when we import lumber from places with fewer environmental protections. Out of sight, out of mind—but that doesn't mean it isn't happening. When we import wood from some places, I'm afraid we promote unsustainable forestry practices…illegal logging…deforestation.

Challenges to Conservation

Those are some of the challenges to conservation. There are other challenges, too, and they are huge. Here are some of them:

- *Dealing with a growing population.* In the last hundred years, we have more than tripled our population to 275 million, and it just keeps on growing. By the turn of the next century, we are projected to have 571 million Americans. Think about what that means for our water resources alone. Some of our fastest-growing areas are some of our driest.
- *Expressing the changing face of America.* As you know, Americans are growing ever more urban and more ethnically diverse. Conservation belongs to all of our citizens, yet the face of conservation has traditionally been rural and white. We need to give Americans from every background more opportunities to participate in conservation.
- *Supporting our land ethic with a strong consumption ethic.* Americans want it all—recreation opportunities, access, clean water, wildlife, and scenery, plus inexpensive two-by-fours and printer paper. Last year, Americans consumed wood products at record levels, and we remain the largest wood-consuming nation on earth. Yet we don't want any changes in the landscape or any commercial operations on public land. If we truly believe in a land ethic, then we must also demonstrate a consumption ethic. That goes especially for the Forest Service. Others will follow our leadership only if we practice the conservation we preach.

- *Restoring our fire-adapted forests to something more resembling their condition at the time of European settlement.* Many of our most pressing problems are related to fire and fuels in forested landscapes that, by their very nature, are dynamic. Our goal is not to keep landscapes unchanged for all time—which is impossible, anyway—but to restore, or at least to account for, the dynamic ecological processes that our forested landscapes evolved with. That includes disturbances such as fire.
- *Responding to the realities of a global economy in a culturally diverse world.* One of those realities is that invasive species are moving around the world with growing ease. It's a huge threat, both to our native ecosystems and to our pocketbooks.
- *Better managing outdoor recreation.* We're in growing danger of loving our public lands to death. We have to get to the point where visitors get the high-quality experiences they want without compromising the health of the land or the ability of future visitors to get those same high-quality experiences.
- *Restoring the health of so many of our watersheds, along with our deteriorating infrastructure.* We have a huge backlog of watershed restoration projects on national forest land alone. We've got thousands of deteriorating culverts to replace. We've got roads to restore, abandoned mines to reclaim, watersheds to repair, vegetation to treat, and all kinds of deferred maintenance and ecological restoration to catch up on.
- *Understanding and coping with long-term and large-scale climate changes.* Climate change at various scales is undeniable. For example, we're in a much drier period out West than we were thirty years ago. This has huge social, economic, and ecological implications.
- *Finally, working better together across boundaries on a landscape scale.* That includes better engaging our publics in managing national forest land. Partnerships and collaboration are absolutely crucial. I believe they hold the key to everything else.

Hope for the Future

These challenges are enormous. But as I look around me at the people gathered here, I believe we are up to the task. I am filled with hope—the same hope for the future of conservation that inspired Theodore Roosevelt a century ago.

Partnership will be key. In the last few months, together with many of you, we held regional forums all over the country to prepare for this Centennial Congress. At those regional forums, we opened a dialogue on the future of conservation. Here, you will have an opportunity to build on that dialogue. Tomorrow, we will hold breakout sessions where you can express your own perspective on conservation, on the role of the Forest Service, and on how we, together, can seek "the greatest good for the greatest number for the longest time."

I ask you to remember one thing: this is not just another meeting. This is a historic occasion, and we are lucky. Celebrating this moment is a privilege denied other generations, both past and future.

You stand on the shoulders of giants—people like Theodore Roosevelt, Secretary of Agriculture James Wilson, Gifford Pinchot, and all the others who set the stage for conservation a century ago. Through their collective commitment to conservation, they gave us common ground. That common ground is represented here in this room, and I believe it gives us reason for hope today.

At this Centennial Congress, you have a historic opportunity to build on that common ground by setting the stage for a new century of service…for another hundred years of caring for the land and serving people…for a whole new era of conservation. Please take that opportunity and use it well.

Ann M. Veneman
Secretary of Agriculture

I want to thank all of you for being here today. I'm very pleased to join all of you, and thank you, Chief Bosworth, for those very good remarks and for your leadership of the Forest Service through the past four years. You've been an excellent leader during these times.

I also want to thank Mark Rey, who is here, and Dave Tenny, both of whom have played a very, very crucial role in leading our resource agencies over the past four years, and they've done a tremendous job. And it's great to see my good friend Chuck Leavell here. I'm sorry I missed you playing the National Anthem. We really very much appreciate your support of the Forest Service and all you do for us.

I want to welcome all of you who are visiting from out of town, welcome you to Washington, D.C., and to this Centennial Congress. And congratulations to all of you on this tremendous milestone.

When we mark important anniversaries, we often do two separate things: we spend time reminiscing, looking back at our accomplishments and at how things have changed. But we also use times like this as a chance to look to the future, to how things are and how they ought to be.

Looking backward and forward at the same time might seem contradictory, but these two impulses complement each other perfectly. After all, our history can help us shape the future, and the history of the U.S. Forest Service is a very rich one indeed.

Fully two years after the Wright Brothers made their famous flight and before Oklahoma, New Mexico, Arizona, and Alaska were even states, on that day one hundred years ago, here in Washington, D.C., one of history's great conservationists, President Theodore Roosevelt, stood before the American Forest Congress and closed his eloquent remarks by saying, "I believe in the future of this movement."

The people in this room are that future, and if he were here today, I hope and believe that President Roosevelt would find his optimism well founded.

Today, the state of our national forests is strong. When the Forest Service was created, there was a genuine fear that our great forestlands were in danger of being destroyed in the name of progress. It is often said that vision is the art of seeing that which others do not, or cannot. Indeed, one of President

Roosevelt's most powerful and important visions was one in which forests could be conserved without sacrificing that same progress.

It is interesting to note that President Roosevelt directed several of his remarks a century ago at industry, particularly the forest products industry. Teddy Roosevelt had no intention of shutting down what was then, and still is, a vital part of our economy. His views were summed up in a phrase that we all know well today: *sustainable resource management.*

We work to sustain our forests both for their vital, natural values but also because of the resources they provide. Throughout its history, the Forest Service has worked to maintain this balance with a legacy of success to look back upon.

Back at the beginning of the twentieth century, the United States was home to about 76 million Americans and 760 million acres of forestland. Our population today has nearly quadrupled, and the number of forestland acres has changed by only slightly more than one percent. By virtually every measure—population, standard of living, technology, geography—our nation has grown in ways that President Roosevelt could never have dreamed of. But through it all, we have conserved our forests in no small part because of his bold action and the dedication of people who shared his vision—people like his secretary of Agriculture, James Wilson, and Gifford Pinchot, the first Chief of the Forest Service. That dedication is mirrored by the people in this room today.

If there is one thing that has not changed over the last century, it is the passion that Americans feel for their natural heritage. And for the men and women of the Forest Service, this is not just another nine-to-five job. For them, conserving our national forests is a lifetime cause.

It is personal for me, too, because I grew up near the Stanislaus National Forest, one of our country's oldest national forests. My visits there every summer helped me to develop a love of our national forests, of the natural beauty, the history, and the sheer fun of it all. Not to mention Smokey Bear, someone many of us knew from a very early age. Little did I know that I would one day be, in the words of my niece, "Smokey Bear's boss."

The opportunity to serve as secretary of Agriculture has been more than just an honor; it has also been an opportunity to be part of something that has been such a big part of my life, from the very first days. It's also an opportunity to give something back. And I think the record of the past four years speaks to enormous success, thanks in part to leadership that begins with President Bush and extends through the many people and partnerships that make effective stewardship possible.

For example, one of the President's priorities when he came into office was protecting against catastrophic wildfires. As you all know, 2000 was one of the worst wildfire years on record, and 2002 followed closely behind. Forest fires have been around as long as the forests, but their frequency, size, and devastation were more recent problems—and something that had to be addressed. In 2002, President Bush announced his Healthy Forests Initiative. It was a new way of looking at forest management. The key to the initiative was to give local experts the flexibility and tools needed to treat forests, curbing the hazardous and unnatural buildup of undergrowth through thinning procedures and controlled burns. The Healthy Forests Initiative changed the terms of the debate, replacing deadlock and stalemate with bipartisanship and progress.

In December 2003, President Bush came to the U.S. Department of Agriculture to sign the Healthy Forests Restoration Act, the centerpiece of the Healthy Forests Initiative, which was approved by Congress with large, bipartisan majorities. In 2004, the first year under that law, USDA and the Department of Interior together treated a record 4.2 million acres of land, an increase of 1.6 million acres over the previous year's total. And in the four years that President Bush has been in office, federal land management agencies have treated hazardous fuels on 11 million acres of public lands, twice the pace of the previous eight years. These are not just statistics to me or to any of us. I will never forget visiting the sites of wildfires or areas that had been burned and seeing firsthand the ecological and social devastation that catastrophic wildfires can cause. I have seen stands of dead and diseased trees, some of which, not long after, burned to the ground.

And I am proud that we are changing the equation. We are not doing things the same old way, and because of that, we hope that devastating forest fires can soon be the exception rather than the expectation. We have made important strides in other areas as well. We have streamlined restoration projects by helping federal, state, and local officials work together. We have intensified the fight against invasive pests, treating 1.1 million acres to protect against devastating infestations. We looked to the long-term, developing a ten-year strategy to protect western lands from wildfires, a strategy that seventeen western governors endorsed. Under the Healthy Forests Initiative, we have implemented policies that result in improved wildlife habitat, better air and water quality, and less erosion. These improvements are coming not just on our national forests, but on the vast landscape of America's private forests that are owned by ten million individuals and families, the stewards that we all depend upon. We are working with state foresters, private landowners, and tribal and local governments to develop guidelines that promote the use of forestry practices to sustain healthy watersheds. We are also consulting with landowners and private organizations to help develop a Healthy Forests Reserve Program that will help restore and maintain biodiversity and the habitat of threatened and endangered species.

We can all be proud of these initiatives. They honor our past and illuminate the pathway to our future. And just as we take pride in the one-hundred-year history of the Forest Service, we are also proud of the people who are behind that legacy. The men and women whose passion is the protection of our forests have touched so many lives. They were, and are, people of vision, people who made the first American Forest Congress a success, like Gifford Pinchot.

Chief Pinchot was an early architect of the Forest Service, and from the beginning he had a clear vision of the agency and its mission that has stood the test of time. As I said at the beginning of my remarks, I believe that the future and the past are linked. The Forest Service will not have a "first century" and a "second century," divided artificially. The past informs the present and it shapes the future.

A hundred years ago, President Roosevelt, Secretary Wilson, and Chief Pinchot had a vision for national forests that were sustained and conserved yet still contributed to the growth of our economy and our nation. It is a vision that lives on today and continues to guide us at the U.S. Department of Agriculture. It animates the policies and decisions of President Bush, who sits at the same desk that was occupied by Teddy Roosevelt in the same West Wing, which President Roosevelt built. President Bush often says that those who make a living off the land are also the best stewards of the land. What the government can do is offer support and incentives. USDA does this through the activities of the Forest Service, our conservation and Farm Bill programs, and implementing the President's initiatives, such as Healthy Forests, his wetlands initiatives, and the Great Lakes Interagency Task Force.

The past hundred years has taught us many lessons—among them, that conservation and progress can be complementary goals. Finding the proper balance can pose challenges especially as new opportunities and threats emerge. I know that you will be spending the next three days discussing many of the specific issues relating to the future of our national forests and the Forest Service. I offer my best wishes, but also my hopes that your discussions are guided by first principles—the founding ideals of the Forest Service—and the successes we have enjoyed because of them.

Sustainable resource management and progress can go hand in hand, and like President Roosevelt, we should all believe in the future of this movement. The opportunity to serve my country as secretary of Agriculture has been one that I could hardly have dreamed of in my days going to 4-H camp in the Stanislaus National Forest. I will remember much about the last four years. I will remember the honor of serving a president I admire tremendously, a man whose dedication to the conservation of our natural resources has been a personal inspiration to me. I will remember attending more than two dozen Forest Service events in fourteen states and meeting with families, workers, and children whose lives the Forest Service have made better. But most of all, I will remember the men and women who have helped make the past four years such a success.

Chief Bosworth has been an outstanding partner and friend and a visionary in his own right whose dedication to the Forest Service has made it a stronger agency. Dale, thank you for all that you do. And thanks also to Sally Collins, our associate chief, who does an excellent job day in and day out, our deputy chiefs, and our regional foresters, many of whom I have developed a great working relationship with. I am touched by the support I have been given and by the leadership that they all have provided our department. And I am grateful for the thousands of Forest Service professionals across the country, the rank-and-file, without whose service and dedication our success would never be possible.

I often remind people that it is from this corps of professionals that the concepts embodied in the Healthy Forests Initiative were born, rather than some government programs, which come from the top down. I will also remember our partners across government and in the private sector, the people in this very room who are here because they care so much about our nation's forests.

Thank you, all of you, for your expertise, for your dedication, and for your friendship. God bless you, God bless America, and best wishes for the next one hundred years.

Gale Norton
Secretary of the Interior

I am pleased to be here on this one-hundredth anniversary of the Forest Service.

Admittedly, this is a bit of a bittersweet occasion, marking the time that the Forest Service was separated from my department. You have done great work since then. While the newborn Forest Service left the Interior family, it has matured into one of our most valued partners, and we share one of the closest working relationships in the federal government.

In "Plant a Tree," poetess Lucy Larcom observed, "He who plants a tree/plants a hope." For the past one hundred years, the Forest Service has been planting trees and growing hopes. The Service was premised on the promise of the seedling—that acorns would grow into great oaks, even as seeds of stewardship would grow into prosperity, healthy forests, and enjoyment.

Gifford Pinchot and Theodore Roosevelt repeatedly proclaimed that the national forests were to be conserved for continual use. It was understood then, as it is understood now, that forest resources would be continuously enjoyed only if they were constantly renewed.

Years from now, when historians look at the history of the Forest Service, I believe they will regard these four years of stewardship by Secretary Veneman, Under Secretary Mark Rey, and Forest Service Chief Dale Bosworth as years of great accomplishment. Under their watch, some of the most sweeping policy changes have been made that improve the health of our national forests. These changes include…

- Helping President Bush and Congress create the Healthy Forests Initiative that calls for active management, not passive neglect, of our national forests. President Bush's Healthy Forests is enabling us to reduce the risks from catastrophic fires. It is empowering us to reduce the years of built-up underbrush and overly dense stands of trees that have made our forests vulnerable to destructive fires. The bipartisan Healthy Forests Restoration Act and our other administrative changes are allowing us to begin the forest and rangeland restoration process. Federal land management agencies, working with states, tribes and local communities, now have new tools to help protect families and habitat from the enormous risk of devastating wildland fires. Since 2001, federal land management agencies have treated eleven million acres of hazardous fuels on public lands.

- Making communities and ecosystems safer from catastrophic fires through this record amount of fuels treatment projects.
- Managing together the worst fire seasons in history in a way that saved countless lives and millions of dollars of property.
- Creating the Wildland Fire Council with representatives of all federal land management agencies and state and local partners to ensure coordination of fire management.

It was great to work with the secretary and all those at the Forest Service on these issues.

For one hundred years, the Forest Service has successfully fulfilled its mission. Last year (2004), the agencies of the Interior Department and the U.S. Forest Service treated almost 4.2 million acres, more than 110 percent of their goal for the year; 2.4 million of those acres—more than half of those treated—were in the wildland-urban interface. We are continuing the work of making our forests healthier. Funds for the Healthy Forests Initiative in this year's budget should enable our federal land managers to make even greater progress in reducing hazardous fuels from public lands.

Our two departments also collaborated in establishing the Interagency Wildland Fire Leadership Council. The creation of the council almost three years ago formalized the efforts previously underway at the Agriculture and Interior departments to ensure the implementation of the National Fire Plan. That plan, developed in the summer of 2000, continues to guide us in reducing risks to communities from catastrophic wildfires.

Invasive species have been compared to slow-moving wildfires. They often spread after fires. Invasive plants present many dangers to the forests. So too, do epidemics of diseases and parasites, such as bark beetles and the fungus that causes sudden oak death.

Those predators and parasites do not distinguish between federal, state, or local agency boundaries. Secretary Veneman and I serve as co-chairs of the Invasive Species Council, an interagency effort committed to coordinating dollars and activities in addressing the challenges we face from invasive species.

The Forest Service's Forest Health Program is primarily responsible for minimizing the spread of established invasive species and lessening the damage caused by native insects and diseases. The program usually funds about ninety percent of the twelve to fifteen proposals made annually by the National Park Service. My department's Bureau of Land Management has teamed up with the Forest Service to fight another invasive threat, the saltcedar. A single saltcedar tree can produce up to five hundred thousand seeds each year, crowding out native vegetation along ecologically significant stream corridors.

A different kind of partnership that benefits our fellow citizens is the Service First Initiative between the Forest Service and my department's Bureau of Land Management. Through Service First, the Bureau of Land Management and the Forest Service share offices and develop common business practices. So far, the two agencies have collocated more than twenty facilities in nine states and hope to combine twenty-two more by the end of this year. As a result, millions of dollars will be saved, and citizens will have more seamless service.

We are also working closely together through our recreation fee programs. The Federal Land Recreation Enhancement Act, which President Bush recently signed into law, will allow cooperating agencies to develop a national pass to all federal lands and water where a fee is charged. That legislation will benefit visitors to public lands in several ways. It will reduce the confusion over differing fee programs, and it will allow the reinvestment of a majority of fees back into the sites of collection. The legislation will also ensure that I and the secretary of Agriculture continue to work together for the benefit of all who enjoy our public lands.

I will miss Secretary Ann Veneman. She has been a friend and a fellow steward. We have worked closely together on many issues. I look forward to working with Secretary-designee Governor Mike Johanns. Together, we will continue the work of cooperative conservation; we will continue to plant seedlings of hope through the forests.

Ultimately, the health of our forests depends on all of us. This anniversary is an important occasion to recommit ourselves to the work begun one hundred years ago.

Chuck Leavell, who played the National Anthem, is not only a keyboardist of some note—namely his notes with the Rolling Stones—he is also a passionate landowner. In his book, *Forever Green*, Chuck wrote,

> *Maintaining our forests requires a delicate balance, where all the players have to be playing the same tune. A few people alone can't save, conserve, and protect our forests. It takes arborists, loggers, foresters, mill operators, environmentalists, private landowners, wildlife enthusiasts…and all of us to get it right. We can't play solo on this one, for the forests are too fragile and the stakes too high…. Each tree—each forest—has its own song, and we must listen.*

I agree. We must continue to listen to the forest; we must continue to act in concert. We must continue to steward the forests if we hope to enjoy them for the next one hundred years. For the past century, the Forest Service has been planting seeds and growing hopes. I hope that you will continue to plant those trees, and grow those hopes, for the next one hundred years.

Historic Perspective on the Forest Service

January 4, 2005
9:00 am

Edgar B. Brannon, Jr.

january 3-6
2005
washington dc

US Forest Service

Centennial Congress

A Collective Commitment to Conservation

Edgar B. Brannon, Jr.
Former Director, Grey Towers National Historic Landmark

Setting the Foundation for the Second Century of Service

On a cold day in January 1905, Gifford Pinchot stood on the steps of the Executive Office Building with the other delegates to the American Forest Congress. As the photographer worked to make sure all were in the right position, Pinchot may have been having his own thoughts on positioning: "Are we now positioned to bring *forestry* to America and put foresters in charge of the *forests*?"

He need not have worried, if in fact he did. Everything changed for Pinchot when Theodore Roosevelt became President. Roosevelt and Pinchot were of like minds, especially when it came to forestry and forests, agreeing that both needed to be brought together—and the sooner the better.

The American Forest Congress was the last piece of window-dressing Pinchot needed to establish the U.S. Forest Service. His skillful maneuvering of public opinion toward forestry and the need to transfer the forest reserves finally was reaching fruition. Congress passed the Transfer Act of 1905 not more than a month after the American Forest Congress, essentially creating the Forest Service. The forest reserves became national forests and were to be managed by the Forest Service, just as Pinchot had envisioned. But the story begins earlier.

Fatherly Advice

Gifford grew up in a family with influence and the will to use it. On his twenty-first birthday, while he was still a student at Yale, his family opened their new country home, Grey Towers, in the town of Milford, Pennsylvania, along the Delaware River—a town their family had settled in after fleeing France following Napoleon's defeat in 1816. His brother, who was a young teenager at the time, gave him a gift—a very important gift—which essentially changed his life. This gift was the book *Man and Nature, or the Earth as modified by Human Action*, by George Perkins Marsh.

Marsh's book is often referred to as the fountainhead of conservation—or more accurately, what David Lowenthal has tagged *utilitarian optimistic conservation*. He defined the two great evils facing conservation: overcoming ignorance, and overcoming greed. But after regaling the reader with the horrors of waste and land abuse, he gives us a message of optimism: *it does not have to be this way. The earth can be like a garden.*

At Gifford's graduation address at Yale the following year, he spoke of his intent to make forestry his life's work. No matter that no one in the audience probably knew what he was talking about, because forestry was not practiced to any extent in the United States. Pinchot wasn't exactly clear about his career path, either.

Gifford's father, James, suggested that he visit Europe to learn a bit about the scientific forestry that was being practiced there. He met Sir Dietrich Brandis, the retired Inspector General of Forests in British India, who suggested that he enroll in the French Forest School in Nancy, France. A few weeks later, Pinchot was a student at Nancy.

In addition to the formal schooling in Europe, Pinchot also traveled with Brandis to see forestry being practiced. He was most impressed with the Silhwald, the municipal forest of Zurich, Switzerland. This municipal forest becomes, in a very real way, a model in Pinchot's mind of what forestry could be in America's democratic society.

Pinchot never does complete his studies at Nancy. He is too anxious to get back to America to put what he has learned to work. So, with Brandis's blessing and encouragement, he leaves Nancy for home and hangs out a shingle as "forester" in New York City.

Within a short few years, Pinchot has made a name for himself in America. His reputation became such that in 1898, Secretary of Agriculture James "Tamma Jim" Wilson convinced Pinchot to take over the tiny Division of Forestry, which was headed by Prussian-trained forester Bernhard Fernow. Pinchot brought his friend Henry Graves with him and, with just eleven people, the Forest Service begins to take root.

Early Leaders

Pinchot had a real knack for identifying true talent. Within his first six years of building the Forest Service, he gathered a leadership cadre that continues to astound us today. To mention only a few:

Raphael Zon. A Russian Jew imprisoned by the czar, Zon escaped to America, where he practiced forestry. A brilliant thinker, Zon, more than anyone, is responsible for establishing the system of forest experiment stations in America, as well as setting the standards for forest research. He was extremely devoted to Pinchot.

Henry Graves. Graves's administrative and political savvy held the agency together after Pinchot's departure in 1910. He "set the bar" for competent managers.

George Woodruff. A Yale crony and Forest Service lawyer, Woodruff picked fights and won each of the eleven cases that he took to the Supreme Court. Without Woodruff's skillful use of the judicial system, the authority of the young Forest Service to even control the use of the national forests would be in question.

Overton Price. The organizational genius behind Pinchot, Price followed Graves as associate chief. With Pinchot on the road for most of his tenure, Price was responsible for the agency's organizational structure, operation, and its high level of performance.

Albert Potter. Pinchot needed a leader who would take responsibility for complex and politically sensitive issues in order to address the first really significant challenge the agency faced: managing sheep and cattle on the western reserves. Potter was genius at bringing order from chaos and was the progenitor of the field-hardened leader.

Herbert Smith. Smith established the government public affairs job in a way that never before existed. With a swift and competent hand, he made the Forest Service front-page news across America. Forestry and conservation became household words, and more information flowed from the Forest Service than all other government agencies combined.

Nothing Is Forever

When Taft became President, Pinchot lost more than his connection to the White House…he lost his job, too. Taft fired Pinchot in 1910, just five short years after the agency was first established. By then, Pinchot had built up not only a number of powerful and supportive friends, but also an equally impressive group of enemies.

What kept this infant agency alive and functioning? To some degree, it was the skill and adeptness of Pinchot's successor. But more importantly, it was the credibility that the Forest Service had already gained with so many.

Pinchot returned home to Pennsylvania, where he carried on a full and active life in politics. But he never lost contact with the agency that he fathered, and was actively involved until his death in 1946. On the last days of his life, he put the finishing touches on his autobiography, *Breaking New Ground*, which was published posthumously.

What does this mean for the second century of the Service? The entire story (at least, two hours' worth) of the Forest Service's first century will be told in the film *The Greatest Good*. I know you will find it as informative and inspiring as I have. So I will leave the full story to later in the day. But I would like to end by going back to the beginning.

The idea of conservation and our commitment to it (possibly first planted in Pinchot's mind through Marsh's *Man and Nature*) continues unabated. Marsh's concern for overcoming ignorance and greed will never completely be resolved, but we have made real progress. Today, these threats to our forests have been linked to a desire for sustainability, beauty, and social justice. In the broader sense, we see a desire to link communities and our wants and desires together with the land in a way that restores our relationship between man and nature. As stewards of America's forest resources, we continue that sense of optimism for the future.

It is the people, the Forest Service employees themselves, who continue to build on this legacy of integrity, competence, and commitment. It is a part of the culture of the organization (and sometimes it does get us into trouble). We continue with a sense of optimism about the future, of hope that we can make a difference and that solving the problems is worth the sacrifices we all make.

Perhaps the most important factor in perpetuating this legacy is America's forests themselves. We face challenges and threats that are unique to our era, and it is unlikely that there will ever be a time when there are no issues or threats. But the natural resources of our land definitely are not lying in waste, and we have an incredible legacy that we can embrace and enjoy.

Reflections and Visions from Forest Service Chiefs

January 4, 2005
9:30 am

Sally Collins *(Moderator)*
Max Peterson *(1979–1987)*
F. Dale Robertson *(1987–1993)*
Jack Ward Thomas *(1993–1996)*
Mike Dombeck *(1996–2001)*
Question-and-Answer Session with the Former Chiefs

january 3–6
2005
washington dc

US Forest Service

Centennial
Congress

A Collective Commitment to Conservation

Trying to cover seven and a half years in a few moments and also make it interesting is a daunting task. I hope the four of us can give you a glimpse of the twenty-three years that spanned our time as Chief that will be helpful for the future of the Forest Service.

I succeeded John McGuire as Chief on July 1, 1979, after serving five years as deputy chief for Programs and Legislation. That gave me an opportunity to be quite familiar with Forest Service people and programs as well as with people in the Department [of Agriculture], the Office of Management and Budget, Congress, cooperators, and critics. I had also been involved during those five years with Forest Service legislation, budgets, and major policy questions.

I told several people that it was the easiest transfer we ever made. I only had to walk about one minute down the South Building third-floor hall, taking my nametag from my door with me. That must have been a great learning experience, though, because all kinds of people now paid a lot more attention to what I had to say!

Chief McGuire told me he thought it was a good time for him to retire, particularly since basic legislation concerning all the Forest Service programs—National Forest System, Research, Cooperative Forestry, and International Forestry—had been enacted, and the large and complex Roadless Area Review and Evaluation (RARE II) had been completed. Also, the major reorganization of federal agencies, including sending the Forest Service to Interior, where we would "subsume" the Bureau of Land Management, had been withdrawn by President Carter after spirited congressional opposition. By the way, no one I talked to at either BLM or the Forest Service had the slightest idea of what *subsume* meant, but some said it had something to do with a snake swallowing a rat.

Chief McGuire concluded with the thought that it appeared to be a rather quiet and stable time for the Forest Service, and with Doug Leisz continuing as an experienced associate chief, we could make good progress in implementing the new legislation and getting the first round of national forest land management plans completed.

We began that effort with enthusiasm. With an experienced associate chief, deputy chiefs, regional foresters, and directors, we were ready to move ahead. We had a set of informal goals in mind in addition to implementing the long-range program set forth as part of the Resources Planning Act process. Those goals we called "A Forestry Agenda." Those fourteen items are [appended below].

What neither of us knew was that future events would unfold quite differently. Let me give you a glimpse of major unpredicted events during the first eighteen months.

1. About six weeks after I became Chief, a prescribed fire in Idaho that had been completed without incident came back to life under strong winds and escaped. It burned a large area of public and private land, including a large amount of forage, fences, etc. The escaped fire was criticized by the governor and by armchair experts on national television. We had other prescribed fires burning in Idaho and other western states which were called into question. You could call that my baptism by fire.

That was a good learning experience. I went to Idaho and met with Governor Evans, and we flew over the fire areas and discussed both the escaped fire and other prescribed fires. We had a joint televised news conference the next day. The end result was a much better understanding of what we were doing. An important lesson is that a critic who is interested and concerned can become a friend.

2. Next was an adverse court decision on the RARE II effort that found the environmental impact statement to be inadequate. That threw the whole effort up in the air, which was a bitter disappointment to many people who had worked very hard on that effort, launched under the direction of Assistant Secretary Cutler and completed while John McGuire was Chief. We had to look to Congress for action. So I spent a tremendous amount of time for the next several years on what was called shuttle diplomacy, working with congressional committees and individual members of Congress fashioning state-by-state bills that would designate certain areas as wilderness, hold some for further study, and "release" other areas for management for multiple uses other than wilderness under normal Forest Service land management plans, at least for the first generation of plans. Fortunately, Congress did move ahead after reaching agreement on release language on individual state bills, except for Idaho and Wyoming. The Montana wilderness bill passed Congress but was vetoed. In most cases the Congress followed the RARE II recommendations rather closely. By the way, one of our critics once told me that *rare*

obviously meant "not well done," and the Forest Service has done three of them, including the latest, which has also been enjoined by a federal court. Some issues seem to persist.

3. Next, Mount St. Helens came to life on March 20, 1980, after 123 years of dormancy. Initial eruptions were rather small, but a large bulge appeared on the north side of the mountain, causing great concern about public safety for both residents and visitors. After consultation with earthquake and volcanic experts at the U.S. Geological Survey and with other state, federal and local agencies, the Forest Service and Washington Governor Dixie Lee Ray closed the mountain and surrounding area and evacuated many people, including our own ranger station, amid substantial press criticism that we were overreacting. We did let people go into the area under police escort and in fact let a group go into the area on Saturday, May 17, and planned on another group going in under escort on Sunday, May 18. Because of substantial increase in tremors on Saturday night, the Sunday trip was canceled. Unfortunately, several people went around the roadblocks and entered the area for various purposes and were killed, along with Harry Truman, [an octogenarian innkeeper] who refused repeated requests to evacuate.

On Sunday morning the mighty earthquake and eruption occurred with unbelievable force, estimated to be equal to five hundred Hiroshima atomic bombs. The massive slides, as well as rock, ash and pyroclastic flow, spewed from the mountain and devastated two hundred square miles, blocking the mighty Columbia River and sending ash around the world. Fortunately, evacuation of the area plus the disaster plan prepared in advance by Forest Supervisor Bob Tokarczyk and cooperating organizations was put into effect and not only saved many lives but sped up the search, rescue, and recovery effort. President Carter in a visit to the area three days after the major eruption said the area looked like the craters of the moon.

4. About eighteen months after I succeeded Chief McGuire, I had the great privilege of making a transition from Assistant Secretary Rupert Cutler, who had come from the Wilderness Society, to John Crowell, who had been the general counsel for a major forest products company. That change was made even more interesting when incoming Secretary [of Agriculture] John Block asked me to serve as acting assistant secretary for four months until John Crowell was confirmed.

A few years later I said to the two of them that it would have been a whole lot easier if we could have put the two of them in a sack, shook it up, and worked with the average. Even though a change of administration in a democracy is somewhat messy, confusing, and sometimes stressful for all concerned, we were fortunate that all four of the assistant secretaries as well as USDA secretaries I worked with during my tenure respected and used the professional input of the Forest Service in making decisions. That didn't mean they always agreed with us, but they demonstrated a commitment to the professionalism of the Forest Service. This was reflected in analyses and policy proposals coming from the administration as well as those we developed. In return, they deserved and received professional, timely, and competent implementation of policy by the Forest Service.

Those four examples of unexpected events in the first eighteen months I was Chief point out the importance of having a dedicated, professional, can-do organization that not only can handle the challenging task of managing 192 million acres of national forests, conducting research, cooperating with the states, and meeting important international forestry responsibilities, but can be proactive in handling the unforeseen events. So my first "lesson learned" is that leaders and managers must prepare for an unpredictable future and must help prepare the organization to be flexible, creative, and resilient. My fellow Missourian Mark Twain once observed that predicting the future was difficult because it is largely unknown. I am an advocate of doing all we can to see and prepare for the future even though there will inevitably be surprises.

During the next six years, the Forest Service was involved not only in managing national forests, conducting a broad program of research, and cooperating with the states in a many-faceted effort, but also in worldwide international forestry efforts to improve management of forests and the lives of people throughout the world. The Job Corps Civilian Conservation Centers and the senior citizen programs continued as important parts of our effort. I was delighted to see the members of the Job Corps providing the color guard for the opening of this Congress. I have seen first-hand the results in the lives of young people who have participated in Job Corps programs.

Let me mention just a few of the major challenges and opportunities during that time:

1. The massive Alaska Lands Act not only designated a large amount of land for management by various federal organizations but also provided millions of acres to the state of Alaska and native tribes. Working with them on land selections, land management, and land exchanges was a major challenge to everyone.

2. The Forest Service-BLM Interchange was an effort taken on cooperatively by BLM and the Forest Service. The goals were rather clear: interchange lands

so that each agency could better "care for the land and serve people." That effort failed for many reasons, including the fact that it was launched by OMB as part of the President's budget, which meant it was secret until the budget was released. It became too large, and closing an office in a small town where both the Forest Service and BLM had offices may be good business but it does not garner local support.

3. The major depression, particularly in the housing and timber industry, which followed the huge increase in interest rates, caused significant unemployment and even many bankruptcies. Congress and the administration had a difficult time in deciding what, if anything, to do. The Forest Service inevitably was called on to analyze many different options, including whether the President should sign the legislation.

4. Implementing major legislation, including the National Forest Management Act, the Endangered Species Act, the National Environmental Policy Act, the Clean Water Act, and myriad other legislation, came together in the field, where people were trying to get work done while reducing the workforce by twenty-five percent and adding to workforce diversity. The goals behind these individual acts are laudable, but no one figured out how the acts related to each other in managing large areas of public land.

Unfortunately, the courts added to the confusion by case-by-case decisions, which in many decisions said that more analysis and more time should be devoted to even rather small decisions. Over time those seemingly desirable pieces of legislation caused what has been called paralysis by analysis. Unfortunately, not much has changed. As a bit of trivia, I had the chance recently to read my daily diary kept during my first six months working for the Forest Service. It is quite clear that many things we started and completed or at least got started during those first few months would take at least five to ten years today. Most were completed at less cost in dollars and time than the paperwork to get them started today. That is *not* progress. It is more important for trained people to spend time in the field to be sure quality projects are done than to sit at a computer screen cranking out long statements.

5. A nationwide information-processing and e-mail system was undertaken and completed, which dramatically changed how the Forest Service functioned. Prior to that time the Forest Service had a few large computers, which were centralized and behind closed doors but available to the experts for major tasks. Meanwhile, at the field level, most Forest Service people were laboring with very obsolete equipment and in many cases assembling and reassembling reports by hand as they moved up the ladder to meet reporting

requirements. After I saw that in the field, I challenged our people to come up with a system that would put computer technology in the hands of our field people we depended on to get work done. The rest is history. The Forest-Level Information Processing System, called FLIPS, was developed and put in place in about three years. That was the first civilian agency system to combine information technology and e-mail into a national system.

6. In 1985 the Congress, at our request but with some skepticism, gave us permission to undertake a cost-sharing challenge grant program which permitted us to cooperate with others to get work done. It required at least a match by the cooperator. It was my privilege to sign the first of those grants with the National Wild Turkey Federation in 1986. I am pleased to see that program grow and prosper over time.

7. Keeping Forest Service programs strong was a constant challenge, particularly in a time of decreasing budgets and people, with more expected of the agency to meet increasing needs. Maybe because I started at the bottom rung of the Forest Service career ladder and spent thirty years mostly in field assignment moving up the ladder, I was particularly concerned about keeping Forest Service programs strong in the field, where it is most important. That meant trying to move as much money and authority down the ladder as feasible and rely on delegation and some guidance to get quality work done. That principle applies not only to the National Forest System but to Forest Service Cooperative Programs, Research, and International programs. A primary reason President Theodore Roosevelt gave in 1905 for transferring the Forest Reserves from Interior to Agriculture was to bring all forestry together. Many do not realize that research and private forestland assistance in USDA predates the transfer of the Forest Reserves.

Let me note in closing that many things have changed in the almost eighteen years since I left the Chief's job. Surprisingly, many things have not changed that much, and unfortunately, some things have gotten worse. Let me mention just a few.

1. The question of what to do with roadless areas has been around for more than sixty years. The Forest Service has long recognized the value of such areas for many purposes. For example, the first [designated] wilderness was administratively set aside by the Forest Service in 1924 as the Gila Wilderness in New Mexico, some forty years before the passage of the Wilderness Act. The Forest Service has made three major attempts to reach a solution as to future management of roadless areas: RARE I, RARE II, and the latest roadless rule, or RARE III. Absent a comprehensive solution, the Forest Service has been rather

careful not to change the character of such areas. If that were not the case, there wouldn't be millions of acres of roadless areas to argue about today!

2. Heavy fuel accumulations resulting from a variety of causes, including older and more dense forests, insect and disease epidemics, many dead trees as well as limbs and other fuels, plus the in-growth of shade-tolerant trees, has created very dense and unhealthy forests. Couple that with a long drought and many people living both inside and adjacent to those forests and there is a recipe for disaster. Unfortunately, there are no easy or inexpensive solutions. Even current, very expensive efforts will take time and will solve only a portion of that problem.

3. Completion of forest land management plans has been and continues to be a complex, expensive, and many times polarizing experience. The initial land management planning regulations adopted by the Carter administration to implement the National Forest Management Act were issued in 1978, before I became Chief, after considerable work by a special Committee of Scientists, chaired by Dr. Art Cooper. The regulations were revised slightly by the Reagan administration in 1982, when I was Chief, and clearly needed revision many years ago. In fact, before I retired, we asked several people both inside and outside the Forest Service to critically review the experience to date and recommend how to streamline and simplify the regulations. After several unsuccessful attempts over the years to substantially revise the regulations, new ones were issued recently. Time will tell whether the new regulations will be of help to streamline the time-consuming, costly process and—equally important—produce quality plans while retaining adequate participation by the public that are the owners of these forests.

4. Heavy use of many forests by many types of users has created not only resource and land damage but also conflicts between those who "share" the forest. Traditional conflicts between so-called commodity users and noncommodity users remain, but conflicts between different types of other users, particularly recreationists, have intensified. As budgets shrink, it is more difficult to find ways to better manage this mix of uses and users. Clearly, a new land ethnic will demand that people share these resources, with each respectful of other uses and users while practicing good land stewardship themselves.

5. Even as the world's population and resource needs increase and other nations are expecting to share a greater proportion of the world's natural resources, the United States is becoming more dependent on foreign sources of natural resources, ranging from oil to timber products to a wide variety of food and fiber needs. In virtually all cases, the environmental safeguards are

much lower than in the United States, and thus the environmental consequences [are greater]. Although everyone would support a level of world trade based on both capability and competitive advantage, the long-term consequences to the United States of resource exploitation from developing countries are significant, and in many cases the level of resource use is not sustainable. The Forest Service can and should be of substantial help to such countries as they develop sustainable strategies to provide both economic and environmental benefit to their people.

6. An increasing number of the U.S. population lives in urban or suburban areas with little experience or understanding of natural resource management. Many years ago Aldo Leopold could see that time coming, when he said we needed to be particularly concerned when people thought heat came from the stove and milk from the milkman. A particularly significant challenge is to involve our young people as well as adults in meaningful activities which teach them to care for and help sustain our natural resources. This involves as much as possible some hands-on activities to gain some real life experience in the care and use of natural resource. The need to conserve our natural resources for this and future generations is increasing while our capability to provide educational assistance and hands-on experience is decreasing. That is one of our largest challenges, and new ways will be necessary to be successful in reaching new generations.

7. New technology developed through research is even more necessary as we try to find ways to do more with less, including how we use and reuse natural resources. Forest Service Research and its cooperative programs with states as well as International Forestry provide a unique opportunity to help meet needs here and abroad. Unfortunately, it is a particular challenge to invest in such programs in a time of budget and personnel reductions.

8. Finally, after twenty-five years of relative calm, Mount St. Helens has recently been making noises again, just to remind us that we are not really in control of many events. Humility is still a virtue when it comes to dealing with natural events.

As I left the Chief's job on February 2, 1987, I noted in the Friday newsletter that "There comes a time when it is both timely and appropriate to turn over the reins to a new Chief. In doing so, I take this opportunity to thank you for your generous and very much appreciated support during the last 7 ½ years that I have been Chief." That feeling of gratitude to the many men and women of the Forest Service who go about their work each day dedicated to the goal of caring for the land and serving people remains just as strong today as it did almost eighteen years ago.

I had then and still have great confidence in the dedication, conservation leadership, professionalism, and integrity of Forest Service people who in cooperation with the states and other organizations and individuals can do great things.

I hope these few reflections have been interesting to you. Fortunately, the Forest History Society book *The Chiefs Remember* has just been published and, with the new Centennial Congress movie, will provide greater insight to the last hundred years and hopefully provide some lessons learned that will be helpful as the Forest Service begins its next hundred years. As stewards of these bountiful resources, we each have a sacred responsibility to use them carefully and to remember our obligation to those yet unborn.

A FORESTRY AGENDA
Goals of the Forest Service, USDA
to Help Meet Increasing Natural Resource Demands
July 1979

1. Implement RARE II, including Congressional action, on recommended wilderness areas, and prompt management of non-wilderness areas.

2. Acceptance and use by the Administration and Congress of the RPA process and long-term program as the basis for making short-term decisions on forestry programs.

3. Strengthen internal management to get work done within stringent dollar and ceiling constraints.

4. Make affirmative action and equal opportunity a fact, not just a goal in the Forest Service.

5. Achieve broad consensus (including Congress, Administration, Forestry community, and others) on what's needed to bring privately owned forest lands to the optimum level of management.

6. Improve coordination of assessments and long-range planning processes and decisions among natural resource agencies.

7. Examine the impact of federal programs and policies on forest landholdings and industry structure as part of the USDA's structures review.

8. Increase NFS land productivity for all purposes through better analysis of investment opportunities, better utilization of available wood fiber, and application of latest research.

9. Represent USDA as a major natural resource management department, especially within the Administration.

10. Expedite desirable land exchanges among Federal land management agencies.

11. Develop and apply new technology to increase and extend natural resource goods and services from public and private lands.

12. Continue Forest Service leadership in international forestry and renewable resource management.

13. Strengthen Forest Service ties with the publics not traditionally involved with our activities, such as urban minority interests, while maintaining effective communication with grass roots and other traditional publics.

14. Accelerate our energy-related activities to contribute to a solution of the Nation's energy crisis. Reduce our energy consumption.

F. Dale Robertson
Twelfth Chief, USDA Forest Service (1987–1993)

The change in Chiefs from Max to me in 1987 was a rather smooth transition. I had been Max's associate chief for over four years, and we had worked closely together. In large part, my first few years as Chief were a continuation of the many good things that Max had set in motion.

National Forest Land Management Plans

I think one of the major Forest Service accomplishments during my tenure was the completion of national forest land management plans. It was the most comprehensive planning effort ever undertaken by the Forest Service to get local people involved with local Forest Service professionals in determining how best to manage each national forest over the next ten to fifteen years. We even dealt with the future management of each individual roadless area, as required by the release language negotiated by Max with Congress on statewide wilderness bills.

As controversial as the forest planning effort was, with many appeals and some lawsuits, the Forest Service nevertheless worked its way through the process, and decisions were made. However, it wasn't long before the implementation of forest plans got badly disrupted with broad cross-cutting issues like the spotted owl, which I will talk more about later.

Partnerships in Recreation, Fishery, and Wildlife

When I was appointed Chief, one of my top priorities was to promote partnerships. Before this, the Forest Service used words like "cooperators," "permittees," "volunteers," and "interest groups," implying a more standoffish relationship. There was a concern that working with people as partners might compromise our objectivity and skew our priorities.

This was one of the times that I used the power of the Chief's office to personally shape the partnership philosophy of the Forest Service. The philosophy was pretty straightforward. The Forest Service would seek out partnerships with any group that had a common interest and was willing to work together and provide resources to get a job done. We worked with the Office of Management and Budget and with Congress to get challenge cost-share money to finance partnerships. I even did the unthinkable for a federal bureaucrat: I told OMB and Congress that I would return to the federal Treasury any money that I couldn't get matched at least fifty-fifty from partners. The response was tremendous, and I was especially proud of the recreation, fishery, and wildlife communities for stepping up to the plate and working in partnership with the Forest Service to achieve our common objectives.

Legal Entanglements That Drastically Reduced the Timber Sale Program
And finally, no history of my tenure as Chief would be complete without talking about the legal entanglements over the active management of the national forests. One set of laws, like the Multiple Use-Sustained Yield Act, directs the Forest Service to actively manage the national forests in a way that best meets the needs of the American people. What that meant in any one particular year was hammered out with Congress in rather specific terms of output targets and associated finances in the annual appropriations bill. A set of environmental laws, like the Endangered Species Act, told the Forest Service to be very, very careful and don't do anything that might adversely affect the environment very much as you go about managing the forests. Then there was another set of laws, like the National Environmental Policy Act and the National Forest Management Act, that were planning or process and procedure oriented that told the Forest Service how to go about making decisions and resolving any conflict among the various laws as they are applied to on-the-ground management. The clash of values, as represented by these various laws, came to a head during the latter part of my tenure. Through lawsuits, the conflicts got referred to the federal judges across the country to resolve. One judge in Oregon once commented that it was all enough to drive a person to drink! By and large, the federal judges, as forest managers, came down on the side of a rather strict interpretation of the environmental laws.

Active management gave way to environmental protection or, as viewed by some, "minimum or nonmanagement" of the forests. For example, ever since the 1950s the Forest Service had been a major supplier of timber to meet the nation's need for lumber and plywood. The average production of timber from the national forests from 1960 to 1990 was 10.5 billion board feet. Today, it is about 2 bbf, a reduction of about eighty percent. That's where the Forest Service sits today with the current legal interpretation of the laws, and it isn't likely to change much without Congress stepping in to clarify the purposes for which the national forests are to be managed.

There was this little owl that burst onto the national and international scene called the northern spotted owl. I remember in June 1990, I was in Israel on a trip with the Jewish National Fund. I visited the Hadassah Hospital in Jerusalem. When I was met by the chief medical officer, he shook my hand, and his first words were, "Tell me all about the spotted owl." So I couldn't even get away from the spotted owl by going to Jerusalem!

The spotted owl's favorite habitat just happened to be the old-growth forests in Northern California and the Pacific Northwest, which produced about fifty percent of the timber sale program. The spotted owl controversy brought into sharp focus the conflicts between multiple use management, as practiced by the Forest Service, and the requirements of ESA. I recruited my most talented and experienced wildlife biologist, Jack Ward Thomas, to help me figure out what I should do about the spotted owl. Well, before Jack and I could resolve the controversy, I was gone and Jack was in charge of the whole shootin' match, and he can tell you his own story. As the result, there was a sharp falloff in timber production. The money appropriated by Congress was spent without the timber sales to show for it. Up until then, the Forest Service had a reputation of being a can-do outfit that always rose to the occasion and got the job done regardless of the difficulty. I was the first Chief to have failed to meet that expectation and had a lot of explaining to do to my political bosses and the Congress.

Let me just summarize by saying that multiple use management, as practiced by the Forest Service since the 1960s, rather quickly hit the wall during the latter part of my tenure as Chief. I think the management of the national forests had been benefiting the "greatest number of people," but the Forest Service had a basic problem of some ecological values, like endangered species, not being sustained over the "long run." So the Forest Service had to do a lot of rethinking and move quickly to change the management of the national forests.

The policy outcome was that the national forests would be managed in the future as healthy and productive ecosystems and that clearcutting would be used only on an exceptional basis, rather than being a standard timber harvest practice. That policy decision was announced by President [George H. W.] Bush in June 1992 at the United Nations Earth Summit conference in Rio de Janeiro. I followed up with a letter on June 22, 1992, directing the regional foresters to implement ecosystem management on the national forests.

I was gone eighteen months later and left most of the hard work up to Jack to figure out how to implement ecosystem management.

Jack Ward Thomas

Thirteenth Chief, USDA Forest Service (1993–1996)

An Unusual Path to the Top Job

I came to the position of Chief directly from being the chief research wildlife biologist at a Forest Service laboratory in La Grande, Oregon. I was a senior research scientist in the agency and a twenty-seven-year Forest Service employee, but I was not a member of the Senior Executive Service. Therefore, my appointment was a Schedule C (political) designation. I was promised that the appointment would be quickly converted to one in the Senior Executive Service, which was a matter of considerable concern to me and to most Forest Service professionals. That promise, made in the enthusiasm of hubris typical of a new administration, proved impossible to fulfill.

The circumstances of Chief Robertson's and Associate Chief George Leonard's departure—summary dismissal—had left an atmosphere of unease and uncertainty in the ranks that required my immediate attention. Therefore, my first decision, which was not particularly appreciated above my pay grade, was that there were to be no immediate changes in leadership positions. Dave Unger, who was acting chief upon my arrival, was made associate chief.

Steady on Course

Chief Robertson had embarked upon three courses of action which I fully supported and which I vigorously pursued. First, the day of primary focus on the timber program based on even-aged management with clearcutting as the harvesting technique was over. Second, ecosystem management was to continue to be emphasized as the guiding principle for the national forests. Third, fair and equitable treatment of women and minorities was to continue to be vigorously pursued.

The plethora of environmental legislation from the environmental era of the late 1960s and 1970s finally arrived during Chief Robertson's tenure and continued to accelerate in effect. The three-legged stool that supported national forest management operations—the Multiple Use-Sustained Yield Act (which broadened the mission), the National Forest Management Act (which instituted forest-by-forest planning), and Forest and Rangeland Renewable Resources Planning Act (which prescribed assessment of natural resources) strained under the accumulated weight of environmental-era legislation—primarily the National Environmental Policy Act and the Endangered Species Act.

Dealing with the Spotted Owl: Ecosystem Management

At Chief Robertson's direction, I had participated in three teams (and led two) to develop plans for the federal lands in the Pacific Northwest relative to threatened and endangered species—primarily spotted owls and anadromous fish. These teams included the Interagency Scientific Committee to Address the Conservation of the Northern Spotted Owl; the scientific assessment team formed to answer Judge William Dwyer's questions relative to Bureau of Land Management Director Cyrus Jamison's decision to withdraw from the proposed ISC strategy; the "Gang of Four" assigned by the House Agriculture Committee to provide an array of management alternatives; and finally, the Forest Ecosystem Management Assessment Team, chartered by President Clinton. These efforts dramatically increased the scale of planning operations from individual national forests to all federal lands and ecoregions. The management alternative ("Option 9") selected by President Clinton morphed during the preparation of the environmental impact statement, the standards and guidelines, and the record of decision into the Northwest Forest Plan. This plan, which Judge Dwyer ruled "minimally met" the requirement of applicable laws, reduced the timber yields in affected national forests and BLM districts by eighty percent, with associated social and economic disruptions—and political backlash.

Similar declines in timber harvests occurred elsewhere across the National Forest System. These declines were not a reflection of who held political power. The decline in timber outputs continued from the presidency of George H. W. Bush, through that of William Clinton, to the present under George W. Bush. Some elected officials from impacted areas lashed out in their frustrations at the Forest Service. But without changes in law, those reductions were inevitable.

The Northwest Forest Plan was put into action during my tenure. The plan did a good job of protecting species associated with late-successional forests but failed, so far, to produce projected timber yields due to overzealous application of the "precautionary principle," typified by the addition of such appendices as "survey and manage" by teams assigned to prepare the final plan to enhance probabilities that Judge Dwyer would find the plan in full compliance with applicable laws. Regardless of the rationale, what was designed by

FEMAT as a dynamic management plan trended, in application over time, toward static management—that is, maintenance of the status quo.

This same trend toward management inactions spread across the National Forest System with increasing involvement of the courts. What was to be entitled "analysis paralysis" spread through the National Forest System.

The Columbia Basin: The Chore That Almost Never Ended

Mike Dombeck, then BLM director, and I convinced our bosses to extend the processes of "ecosystem management" pioneered in the Pacific Northwest to planning and assessment activities in the Interior Columbia Basin. In response to criticism of the "closed nature" of the development of the Northwest Forest Plan, this effort was overseen by a team of land management and regulatory agency administrators. Elected officials at all levels of government watched closely.

The effort drug on for years as more and more and more assessment was demanded. The results of multiagency oversight resembled a square dance without a caller. Elected officials discovered that as long as the process continued, there was no legal compulsion to act on the basis of that information, so the effort drug on and on and on. However, the information base produced during that effort is without parallel in terms of both its quantity and quality. At some future point, land management agencies will have to consider and then act on the information developed during that effort. Ecosystem management continued to prove politically difficult to institute—but it won't go away.

Storm King Mountain: Change in the Wind

In 1994, a wildfire in Colorado resulted in the deaths of fourteen firefighters at Storm King Mountain. Before the end of that summer, twenty more fatalities occurred. I felt, and assumed, responsibility and with Mike Dombeck instituted intensive reviews and remodeling of firefighting-management efforts, with considerable personal involvement. In 1995, new policies and innovative approaches to firefighting and firefighter safety were adopted.

The Salvage Rider: No Way to Run a Railroad

The "Salvage Rider" to the Appropriations Act in 1995 was overwhelmingly passed by Congress and signed by President Clinton, despite reservations on the part of the Forest Service. The Forest Service was told, emphatically and repeatedly, to meet the targets for timber salvage. I reported, in biweekly meetings, to the director of the Council on Environmental Quality as to progress in that regard. The Forest Service was excused from consultation with regulatory agencies, but we consulted anyway. Then, the environmental community, who had the rapt attention of the administration, seized the issue, and confusion increased as sale after sale was questioned. Several sales were cancelled by direct calls from appointed officials thousands of miles from the scene of action, with no consultation with agency leadership. Though the targets were met in the end, it was a confusing, embarrassing, acrimonious, and contentious episode that left few reputations unscathed—and lasting tensions. Tours of contested salvage operations were arranged for political overseers, but in the end, I was unaccompanied on the reviews.

Ecosystem Management

In 1995, the Forest Service convened a fourteen-day workshop in Tucson, Arizona, to put a foundation under the concept of ecosystem management. Support from other agencies was lukewarm, but the right people showed up. The result was the three-volume *Ecological Stewardship: A Common Reference for Ecosystem Management* that emerged after my departure to considerable worldwide praise but with little attention in federal agencies. So the infant that was ecosystem management continued to struggle in its crib.

Law Enforcement: The "Stovepipe"

Law enforcement had been "stovepiped" directly to the Chief's office via reorganization during Chief Robertson's tenure. The Timber Theft Investigations Branch was established in the Pacific Northwest at that time. This semiautonomous group had made one significant case. The director of Law Enforcement, and numerous others, brought it to my attention that this group was operating essentially without oversight. I decided to bring the group into extant law enforcement structure. Members of the group asked to meet with me to hear their views and concerns. I met with several involved officers and promised to put any action on hold until I had reviewed the situation. I kept that promise—in spades. The Office of the Inspector General was asked to review the situation. They recommended that I proceed with plans to disband the group. To assure no interference with ongoing investigations, the pending cases, along with all officers and resources requested, were turned over to the FBI. After sometime, the FBI closed the cases in question and returned the involved officers to the Forest Service. They were absorbed into the law enforcement structure. That decision is still on appeal after ten years.

Who's in Charge?

My tenure was marked by considerable confusion as to who, on a day-to-day basis, was in charge of the Forest Service, particularly the National Forest System. Players that exercised power, from time to time, included the secretaries of Agriculture and Interior, the director of the Council on Environmental Quality, "the White House" (which was always something of a mystery), the under secretary of Agriculture (whose power waxed and waned), and other "mystery players" who could not be clearly identified without a program—with which we never provided. Such was conducive neither to good order nor to sustenance of high morale.

Congressional Hearings as Theater

The Republicans took over both the House and the Senate in 1994. The Democrats on the committees with which the Forest Service dealt simply dropped out of the game and effective participation. The seemingly endless hearings produced some wonderful sound bites for those on both sides of the issues, but little of real substance emerged. The hearings, in their totality, did demonstrate clearly that the Forest Service was caught squarely in the middle of a divided government produced by a divided electorate and a confused mishmash of laws and court rulings that deprived the Forest Service of a clear mission and clear direction.

Time to Fade into the Sunset

By December 1996, a disagreement between the secretary and me relative to staffing reached impasse. Health issues, which were corrected after retirement, were depleting my stamina—and temperament. Attractive offers relative to a postretirement career were on the table and looking more and more attractive. It became clear that it was time for me to move on to something less emotionally draining and to allow appointment of a new Chief more trusted by and more in tune with the style and objectives of the administration.

I left proud of the Forest Service, of my thirty years with "the outfit," and honored to have served as Chief. I handed the secretary a list of colleagues that, in my opinion, "packed the gear" to provide strong professional leadership to the world's best conservation agency. I was off to Montana to become the Boone and Crockett Professor of Wildlife Conservation at the University of Montana. The secretary picked a topnotch professional with a Forest Service background as my successor. Now, it was Mike Dombeck's turn.

Mike Dombeck
Fourteenth Chief, USDA Forest Service (1997–2001)

During Chief Thomas's tenure, I was at the helm of the Bureau of Land Management. It seemed I always followed Jack at the podium and never could match his oratory skill. Now, even in retirement, some things never change.

Chief Thomas described the climate swirling around the Forest Service during our respective transitions, which were very different from the smooth transitions described by Chiefs Peterson and Robertson. I will only add that four days before I moved into the Chief's job, a Jack Anderson column ran in newspapers all over the country highlighting Forest Service problems and saying that the Forest Service couldn't be reinvented. It seemed like there were broken or strained relationships almost everywhere. It was clear that the status quo in Washington wasn't working and that changes were needed. Some of the changes I made worked, some were popular, and some were not. But almost everybody agreed that the agency needed to do things differently, mend some fences, and capture at least some of the high ground during the last four years of the Clinton administration.

Chiefs Robertson and Thomas had laid the foundation for ecosystem management and civil rights. We moved forward with the large-scale ecosystem plans like the Northwest Forest Plan, Sierra Nevada, Columbia Basin, southern Appalachian, and Southwest. I remain proud of the diversity we brought to leadership positions and throughout the agency.

The nearly completed Tongass National Forest Plan was in my lap even before I got the Chief's chair warmed up. The new challenge on the table was financial management and accountability. I believe I had more congressional hearings on financial management and accountability than all of my predecessors combined. I'm pleased that the continued focus on financial management by Chief Bosworth has yielded not just one but three consecutive clean financial audits. I know this hasn't been easy, but it is absolutely essential.

I was proud of the innovative approach of the Enterprise teams. The agency-wide adoption of competitive, private sector-like business practices can save the Forest Service tens of millions of dollars, which can then be invested in the land and the surrounding communities. Don't settle for the status quo just because it's what you're used to or because it is supported by the old systems already in place. Push the envelope of innovation.

Fire

With the exception of the 1988 Yellowstone fire, Jack and I seemed to usher in the resurgence of big fire years in the 1990s, starting with the tragic 1994 fire season. We ordered exhaustive reviews of policies and safety procedures in the public land management agencies. I believe lives and property have been saved, but continued vigilance is imperative.

The National Fire Plan that followed President Clinton's 2001 tour of the Burgdorf Junction fire set the stage for our biggest budget increase in history. The increases in the fire budget have continued into the current administration. Much heavy lifting remains to be done as we struggle with forest health, sprawl, the unknowns of climate change, and social attitudes toward wildfire.

The Natural Resources Agenda

Several months into the Chief's job, I was visiting with the secretary's chief of staff after a subcabinet meeting. I was lamenting that all we were doing was going to hearings and getting beat up and playing defense. We lacked a comprehensive strategy to deal with some of the tough issues and were proposing almost nothing. Secretary Glickman walked in about then. He listened for a bit and then suggested we develop a strategy that we could go with. That fall, at a National Leadership Team meeting in St. Paul, the Natural Resources Agenda emerged with a focus on (1) watershed health and restoration, (2) sustainable forest ecosystem management, (3) recreation, and (4) roads. The issues were not new. Our goal was to set the agenda, elevate the visibility of the challenges, and reinvigorate the bully pulpit of the Forest Service.

To connect an increasingly urban populace to the land and increase awareness for forest management, I personally set out to talk about watershed health and restoration and the importance of forests as our largest producer of water in the country.

I'm happy that Chief Bosworth's "Four Threats to National Forests" continues this focus. This is real demonstration that even when an administration with a different land ethic and emphasis takes over, there is still significant continuity.

Roadless

As we four retired Chiefs prepared for this panel, we decided that the roadless issue deserved more than just a few words about events during our respective tenures. So I will mention a few highlights that preceded my tenure. It's important to keep in mind that roadless, roads, Wilderness (with a capital W), old-growth, and wildlands are all inextricably intertwined. Few conservation issues have dominated the Forest Service more over the past one hundred years than struggling over where and how much of the national forests should remain roadless.

In 1913, Aldo Leopold began discussing the idea of wilderness. In 1921, he wrote an article for the *Journal of Forestry* suggesting wilderness of five hundred thousand acres in each of the eleven western states. In the early 1920s, controversy over roading the Boundary Waters of the Superior National Forest boiled over, and the Forest Service conducted the first roadless area inventory in 1926.

With the passage of the 1964 Wilderness Act, the Forest Service conducted its first Roadless Area Review and Evaluation (RARE) in 1967. In response to an unfavorable 1972 court decision, Chief McGuire ordered a second evaluation, dubbed RARE II, which was completed in 1979. During Chief Peterson's tenure, the agency focused on passage of state-by-state wilderness bills with release language, which resolved the especially intense controversy in Oregon and Washington but not the wilderness and roadless issues of Idaho and Montana.

In 1995, Chief Thomas directed the removal of all roadless areas from the suitable timber base—or commence plans for their harvest.

In 1997, it was my turn at this roadless issue. The Forest Service roads budget had been in steady decline due to the reductions in timber harvest. It had also been the subject of both House and Senate floor fights for more than a decade. An amendment in the House reducing the Forest Service budget by another eighty percent escaped passage by only one vote while we were settling on an $8 billion road maintenance backlog. The status quo not only wasn't working, it was leading us further into the hole.

Initially, the approach was to adopt an eighteen-month suspension of road building in roadless areas. Next was the development of a transportation system policy headed by then-Regional Forester Dale Bosworth.

The response to the suspension of road building in roadless areas captured the interest of the White House and President, who in 1999 directed us to develop a rule to permanently prohibit road building in roadless areas, which I encouraged. Like the Northwest Forest Plan, the agency completed the rule-making in record time, demonstrating that the bureaucracy can respond when the White House wants something done. With a record number of public comments, the roadless rule was signed by Secretary Glickman.

Less than two weeks later, President Bush was inaugurated, and it was back to the drawing board for roadless, leaving the issue unresolved for yet the next Chief to deal with. With a new administration and the pendulum swinging in the opposite direction, it was time for me to move on. I did so in as diplomatic a manner as I knew how, for the good of the Forest Service.

Conservation Leadership

I have always believed that wealth and quality of life ultimately come from the land. Gifford Pinchot focused on the "greatest good," and Aldo Leopold so eloquently wrote about the land ethic and an ecological conscience.

In closing, here is my advice to you: Always remember why you went to work for the Forest Service and into this business to begin with. Treat the land with humility and gratitude for sustaining us. Carry the torch of conservation leadership and maintain the health of the land for the next one hundred years and beyond. I wish you well.

■ ■ ■

In the Q&A session, Associate Chief Sally Collins asked what single act as Chief gave me the most satisfaction. I'd like to mention two.

First: The completion of the roadless rule, which was actually a lot more than a single act.

Second: My role in the establishment of the fifty-three-acre San Patricio Urban Forest Reserve in San Juan, Puerto Rico, one of the most densely populated large urban areas in the world. It is my belief that, in large part, the Forest Service culture has forgotten how to use the clout of the Chief. That was not the case with Dr. Ariel Lugo. I was visiting Puerto Rico in 1998, and he took me to San Patricio, a fifty-three-acre former military installation that was being overtaken by trees and vegetation in the middle of San Juan. Developers were after this last remaining space to build high-rise housing. We had a picnic and meeting with the local residents, a press conference, meetings with the governor and the leader of the senate. San Patricio is now a fifty-three-acre urban forest improving the environment and quality of life in San Juan, one of the most densely populated cities in the world.

Sally Collins: I'd like to start the questions with one from the audience. Numerous changes in the world are already influencing the daily operations of the Forest Service. How will larger global trends like international markets for forest products, global trade, and information technology affect the future of the agency?

Max Peterson: I'll start it. I think that it's going to affect us in ways that we can't fully envision because as we get more and more population around the world, we're simply not going to be able to import all the things that we've imported from other parts of the world because they want those resources for their own use. I think that as we become more interdependent as countries, we're going to find that many people will want to come to this country to experience the wide open spaces and so on. We just have a little glimmer of just how that's all going to work. I want to sum up by saying that as more and more people compete for resources, we have to learn how to share those resources better. More of us have to able to share those lands with other people and be respectful of those people.

Sally Collins: Any one wish to add anything?

Dale Robertson: I might add that Gifford Pinchot and Teddy Roosevelt had this philosophy of using the forest for the benefit of the people and still preserving the forest. I don't think in today's world we have that quite right. Some adjustments need to be made. As Max said, right now we're willing to make the economic sacrifice to import our natural resource needs, and yet we have some of the most productive forest lands for all resources in the world. I think it just behooves us Americans to figure out how to strike that balance again that Gifford Pinchot and Teddy Roosevelt talked about in the beginning. The current generation of Forest Service people has their work cut out for them.

Sally Collins: Jack, I have a question for you. Would you share with us what was your most difficult moment was as Chief?

Jack Ward Thomas: That's not very hard because it's very sad. The phone went off in the middle of the night, around two o'clock in the morning. It was Deputy Chief for Administration Lamar Beasley, and he said, "Chief, we think we may have lost forty firefighters at Storm King." It turned out it wasn't forty, but that's what we thought then. Mike [Dombeck, then acting director of the

Bureau of Land Management] and I were talking and decided that we should get there as quickly as we possibly could. And we did.

We walked in and the survivors were there. I pulled out my credit card, and Mike pulled his out, too, and we began to buy beer. It helped to loosen things —a little. They had the Hotshot crew there, and they were in shock. Their leader said, "They're going to hang me." I said, "For what?" He said, "I don't know. But it was my responsibility." Mike and I told him that, no, it was as much our responsibility as it was his and that we would find out what happened, and that we would do what we could to correct it. But that wasn't the end of it. Before the end of that season, thirty-four firefighters died. It was very obvious that we had some problems, and that was the most difficult, difficult moment. Perhaps the next most difficult moment was when the Occupational Safety and Health Administration report came out and reported that we had made mistakes. I don't think Mike or I resented that. But that report intimated that we didn't care. I'm not too proud of this, but I called the guy from OSHA about nine kinds of a son of a bitch and left it at that. That was the most difficult moment and is still the most difficult moment.

Dale Robertson: Can I tell you something about this guy? When we were in the spotted owl controversy, we were both receiving a lot of death threats. I talked to Jack, and he said they would call him at night, at like two or three in the morning, and threaten his life over the spotted owl. Jack said that he told this one caller at two in the morning that I only take death threat calls between nine A.M. and five P.M. at the office. [Laughter]

Jack Ward Thomas: There's more to that story. Then I gave him my phone number real slowly. And I could hear him repeating the numbers. The guy was obviously whacked out of his mind. But he was writing the number down so he could call me the next day. [Laughter]

Sally Collins: Mike, what would you say was your most rewarding moment as Chief was?

Mike Dombeck: Over all, visiting with employees was always the way to recharge the batteries when tough things were going on. It's interesting that when you're in the hot seat and then you have a few years for things to settle down—and they may not have settled down for any of us yet—how grateful I am for having had the opportunity to have done something that I never could have dreamed of. I remember walking into District Ranger Bob Miley's office on my first day of work and seeing [former Chief] John McGuire's picture hanging on the wall above his desk. I didn't have a clue who he was or why it was there, and I didn't ask. I always tell students now that the most important thing now is not to close any doors. So, it's really tough. I can't put my finger on one specific rewarding thing, but working with the tremendous professionals not only with in the Forest Service but in all of the agencies was one.

Dale Robertson: I'll tell you a story about Mike, too. I was Chief and the Bush administration came in, and BLM did not have the technical expertise that the Forest Service had. Cy Jamison, director of the BLM, talked to me and said that he'd like for Mike to come over and give him some scientific background, reputation, and technical expertise in the BLM. I remember Mike coming into my office and he said, "Chief, they want me to come to BLM. What's your advice?" I said, "The BLM needs you worse than the Forest Service, but I'll make a commitment to you. If things don't work out, you can come back to the Forest Service."

Mike Dombeck: I just want to add to that. In Dale's letter, he didn't specify the grade. [Laughter]

Max Peterson: Sally, as long as Dale is telling stories on people, I'm going to tell one on him. When he became Chief, I told him that he'd be a lot smarter after he walked down this hall and walked into the Chief's office, because when I became Chief in 1979 and I walked down that hall, that was the easiest transfer I ever made. The reason I know this is because as I walked down that hall, people paid a lot more attention to what I said right after that. You'll be a lot smarter after you do that. [Laughter] I asked him, "Are you fully prepared for this?" He said, "I feel ready." I said, "Well, you might notice that your shoes are different—one's black and the other's brown." That's a true story! [Laughter]

Dale Robertson: Never in my life have I put on mismatched shoes till that day. So, Max announced his retirement, and the secretary announced me as the new Chief. The press started calling in, and Max suggested we have a press conference with the old Chief and the new Chief. We had the press conference in the Chief's office. Let me tell you, trying to hide your feet from a room full of reporters—that was my number one problem.

Max Peterson: Well, you started out on the right foot anyway. [Laughter]

Sally Collins: One day, Chief Bosworth told me that he should tell me what Max Peterson told him one time, about what is the most important trait or characteristic you have to have for being Chief of the Forest Service. It's something that I'd like for each of you to answer from your perspective.

Dale Robertson: I'll start. I think entrepreneurship. You know, this federal government is not designed to get things done. Unless you've got entrepreneurship, innovation, creativity, and have an agenda and push it and do things, Washington, D.C., will just grind the Forest Service—or any other agency—

down to mediocre or even worse. Unless you've got the entrepreneurship and creativity, and start doing things that are going to raise eyebrows and get the Forest Service out of the mediocre performance that has ground them down by the D.C. environment, the Forest Service is just not going to be very successful. I would just say, "Go for it." Go to work every day as if you were willing to be fired.

Mike Dombeck: I'd add adaptability to that, since I was one all my life who hated controversy. In between the time that it was announced I'd become Chief and I moved into the chair, Dale called me and said, "Mike, you're going to be the most popular your first day on the job." And I have some advice that I added for Dale Bosworth, and that is, the second day is the day that you leave. [Laughter]

Max Peterson: I would say two words: hope and humility. You can't lead an organization unless that organization has hope that they're going to be successful—and I've seen that over and over—unless that organization feels that they can be successful through hope. The second is humility. If the Chief gets the idea that he is the know-it-all, be-it-all, that is the first step in his downfall. Someone asked me one time if I felt the weight of the Forest Service on my shoulders with all these people depending on me. I was kind of surprised and said no. And they asked why not. I said because there are forty thousand other people out there carrying the load. And if the Chief thinks that he's carrying the load, that's a mistake.

Jack Ward Thomas: I wouldn't dispute those things, but I think the thing that I saw—I didn't get to practice to be Chief…

Max Peterson: Oh! You practiced *after* you became Chief? [Laughter]

Jack Ward Thomas: …the thing that I quickly caught on to was how much of an icon the Chief was to the employees. If you gave somebody two things: —one, that I care about you personally, and two, I trust you personally—those are the things that I quickly caught onto. And when you showed up and told them those two things—that I trust you and I'm going to back you and I care about you personally, which I think was true of all the Chiefs, and—I think that's what I saw and learned very quickly. Not to say that these other things are not also true.

Sally Collins: Mike, you talked a lot about watersheds, and you continue to talk about watersheds in your new position about watersheds. What is that about?

Mike Dombeck: One of the frustrating things about being Chief is you look at all the wonderful things the agency is doing, and yet you are literally consumed by about ten percent of all the controversial issues that are literally white hot, whether it's the Tongass National Forest or roadless areas or old-growth or things like that. You struggle with, "What is it that we can carry to the American public that will reconnect them with nature and begin to get them to care?" which I think is still our biggest challenge in an increasingly urbanized society. Yes, some people still care about grazing but most don't, and, yes, some people still care about timber harvests but most don't, and about mining and other interests. I quickly decided that water was the issue to get on the bully pulpit with to try to connect people with why forests are important because forests remain our largest supplier of water in the country. If we're going to have a problem in this century worldwide, it's going to be water. Forest managers ought to be taking a bow for what they do for the world population to ensure a water supply.

Sally Collins: I know that some of you continue to speak, to give talks, and appear at events. What kind of advice would you give to an outgoing Chief in terms of how to represent yourself and your position as a retired Chief?

Max Peterson: I didn't know we had an outgoing Chief, Sally. [Laughter]

Sally Collins: We have no outgoing Chief! Thank you, Max.

Max Peterson: Since I've known Dale since he was eight years old, I figure I can give him some advice not as outgoing Chief but as a Chief for several more years. As others have said here, probably the greatest challenge of the future is to somehow connect young people to the land. Even Aldo Leopold said in some of his writings that we're going to be in a lot of trouble when we think that heat comes from the stove, and milk comes from the milkman. My wife and I have a dozen grandchildren, and you look at these youngsters and they're all in urban areas. They have very little association with natural resources; they have very little understanding of it other than what little we're able to do with them. And I've become concerned that they live in a cyber world. They don't relate to the land or where things come from. If it's in the grocery store or the hardware store, it's okay with them. And that's a real question, in the whole idea of how we train young people in conservation, because at the time Gifford Pinchot talked, ninety percent of the people in the United States were living on the land, and they understood natural resources and how they related to them. I think that's our greatest challenge of this century—to somehow connect the next generations to conservation.

Dale Robertson: Did your question deal with outgoing Chiefs?

Sally Collins: Yes.

Dale Robertson: It kind of depends on the individual. There are four of us here, but I'm the only one who is fully retired. The other three are working at least part time. I'm having a wonderful time. When I retired, I moved to Sedona, Arizona—the "new age" capital of the world. I know all this new age philosophy now and am loving that people think I'm brilliant when I can interject that into forestry. But it all depends on what you as an individual want to achieve in life. I never did really care for D.C. and the grind, as my friend Jack Ward Thomas would agree with me. It's great to retire. I live in the middle of the Coconino National Forest and I'm enjoying it—every day of my life I put my foot on the Coconino National Forest when I'm home. My advice is, if you're the retiring type, is to just enjoy life, and to do the things that makes you happy and the things that you want to do, rather than trying to work, which in my case just didn't work.

Jack Ward Thomas: My advice is, as Sally will attest since I'm still active, is that about the time that I feel compelled to pontificate, I'll send in whatever I've written in and ask if this is going to cause a problem. The one thing that you have to remember when you walk out that door is that, in one sense, you are always "Chief," but we don't need but one Chief at a time, and we've got a damn good one. I try to check and make sure that when I am pontificating that I'm not going to get in the way.

Sally Collins: The trailer last night for the film *The Greatest Good* alluded to what is the greatest good. What does that mean and what does that mean for us in the next century? Any thoughts, Mike?

Mike Dombeck: Water and education.

Jack Ward Thomas: I think I'd harken back to what Pinchot said, which is that it's going to change. We're always going to need water, and some things are forever. Historians give credit to his wife for swatting him upside the head and reminding him that he was not speaking for all time. We have that land, and that's always the trust. And we have that research responsibility, and that's always the trust. But that's always going to be changing. Pinchot made another observation, and it's in the film: the best local decisions are made on local grounds. Somehow or another, the laws and court cases have just sucked that up and sucked that up until we're not making those decisions as close to the ground as we ought to. If I had one thing as Chief that was a failure, it was that I was constantly trying to push things down in the decision-making process, and people over me were elevating them up, which was probably my most frustrating moment. Still, I think that is still the advice—that things are going to change, and that the people that who are going to change it are going to be the ones close to the ground—and that that's where the decisions ought to be made, and we should make them there if at all possible.

Dale Robertson: I agree with Jack. We've just gotten a lot of stickiness in the process. Judicial decisions have just kind of got things stuck. We don't have that kind of flexibility that Jack talked about. In a democracy—I have great faith in the people, and—we shouldn't be so arrogant as to think that we know what the next generations will want from their national forests. But there is this sustainability principle that goes across the generations. As long as we stick with that, then let the people in the future decide. And it will change, as Jack says.

Max Peterson: I think that that's still a pretty good statement in that it indicates that we're looking for benefits widely distributed, and that we're also looking at the long run. Now, during my tenure we came up with the phrase, "Caring for the land and serving people." I think that those two principles are a shorter statement of it because you need to do more than care for the land. If you only care for the land and don't serve people, eventually you won't have the land to care for because the people will rebel against land if they can't get some level of benefits from it, whether it's outdoor recreation, whether it's hunting and fishing, or other benefits, whether they're tangible or intangible. There has to be a balance between caring for the land and serving the people. That's going to be the challenge of the next century because we're going to be serving more people with the same land base.

Sally Collins: We have only just a few more minutes. If you imagine us sitting around a hundred years from now—assuming that we still have a Forest Service that is managing the forests and grasslands and is taking care of them and being stewards of them—what would be your hope for the reflections that would be going on one hundred years from now?

Jack Ward Thomas: Probably the same reflections that are going on here now, except—barring that there's no catastrophe—there's going to be more people, there's going to be more demand on the resources. I would assume over that one-hundred-year period that we're also going to know a lot more both from our research base, from our experience base—what's worked and what hasn't worked—and about what those reflections are. Assuming one hundred years from now that we are still living in a vibrant democracy, I would assume that those things are very much the way that they are today—provided that we have done a good enough job and our successors have done a good enough job that that land is there intact and functioning and available for use.

Max Peterson: I think that we'll all accept the invitation to come back here a hundred years from now and join Pinchot to look back from the other side.

[Laughter] On a more serious note, I think that we can't really imagine that because of the number of people that we'll have, and we just hope, that as Mike and others have said, that the concern for our water, the concerns for our health care, the concern for the wellbeing of our citizens will just unfold in ways that we just can't even imagine. I can't imagine what's going to happen next year, let alone what's going to happen a hundred years from now. We would hope that people would prize the resources and be willing to sustain them over time for the next generations.

Dale Robertson: I at least hope that the people sitting up here a hundred years from now won't be talking about roadless areas! [Laughter] You know, some issues get settled over time, and if you think about them over a hundred years' period of time, a lot of issues get resolved over that time, but there is a sustainability of issues. So as you solve one, another one pops up. I can remember reading the state-of-the-union speeches of the Forest Service Chiefs and every year was the most challenging year we've ever had.

Max Peterson: That's right. And the next one's going to be more challenging.

Dale Robertson: So I served as Chief during the seven most challenging years of the Forest Service, and I'm sure Dale Bosworth is serving the year that's the most challenging year of the Forest Service. Issues are going to come and go, but I think if you think of it in terms of one hundred years, things like roadless areas won't continually be debated. And there will be a whole new set of issues, as Max talks about, that we haven't conceptualized yet.

Sally Collins: I know that we're out of time, and I would like to remind everybody that we've got a book-signing ceremony at noon at the Forest History Society booth. For those of you who acknowledge that this is really a historic moment to have these four with us and that you are privileged to be a part of it, I would just like you to join me in thanking them all. [Applause.]

Outside Perspectives on the Forest Service:
Social, Economic, and Environmental Benefits

January 4, 2005
11:05 am

Jo Ellen Force *(Moderator)*
Mavis C. Hill
Debra Shore
Robert Model
John Shelk *(no paper available)*
Todd Davidson *(no paper available)*

january 3-6
2005
washington dc

US Forest Service

Centennial Congress

A Collective Commitment to Conservation

Mavis C. Hill

Executive Director, Tyrrell County [North Carolina] Community Development Corporation

What's Expected of the Forest Service
in the Twenty-First Century

What are the Forest Service's greatest conservation accomplishments of the last century?

In Forest Service eyes: As an outsider looking in, it is clear there have been many accomplishments for the Forest Service over the past century:

- We have a broad-based system of national forests that are integral components of the "green infrastructure" needed to protect the nation's watersheds, ecosystems, and air quality. These forests are accessible to all U.S. citizens and visitors, and they also contribute economically to communities, regions, and the country.
- The Service is engaged in important forestry research efforts that are helping natural resource agencies, landowners, industry leaders, and communities be more effective in understanding and managing sustainable forests.
- The Forest Service, sometimes in response to dramatic challenges, is working more closely with communities, in partnerships that probably could not have been imagined a hundred years ago, on addressing a wide range of environmental, economic, and social issues.
- The agency is more diverse today, with women, people of color, and other special populations increasingly in positions of leadership, and bringing those more diverse perspectives to the table in shaping policies and programs for the Forest Service.

In the public's eyes: Broadly, public support for natural resource protection is reflected in the more than fifty thousand environmental regulations on the books, more than ten thousand environmental nonprofits, and more than twelve hundred land trusts across the country, and in the more than $25 billion in environmental referenda that voters have approved in the last twenty-five years.

There are many specific measures of the USDA Forest Service's success nationally, including the health of forests and watersheds, the acres of publicly held forestlands being sustainably managed for generations to come, the timber and nontimber forest products that are the backbone of many rural communities, the recreation usage and visitation numbers, and the partnerships with communities and landowners.

Our partnership with the USDA Forest Service in Tyrrell County is an excellent example of extraordinary accomplishments that are turning around the economy in one of the poorest and least-populated counties in North Carolina. Located in the northeastern coastal plain between the Albemarle and Pamlico Sounds, Tyrrell County's peat wetlands and riverine swamp forests provide critical habitat for a range of endangered bird and animal species, including the red wolf, bald eagle, American alligator, peregrine falcon, and red-cockaded woodpecker. The Albemarle-Pamlico estuary, almost one-third of North Carolina's land base, is one of the largest and most ecologically significant in the country, surpassed only by the Chesapeake ecosystem.

The ecological riches in Tyrrell County exist side by side with some of the more economically depressed conditions in the South. Tyrrell is the least-populated county in North Carolina, with a population of just over four thousand, or nine residents per square mile. It has the lowest median family income in the state, at $23,400, and a per capita income of $7,884, compared with the state average of $12,880. The per capita income for African Americans is substantially lower, at $5,124, than their white counterparts'. Winter unemployment rates can reach 25 percent, with a year-round average rate of 11 percent, compared with the state average of 4.8 percent or urban rates as low as 1 percent. The poverty rate is 25 percent, almost twice the state average of 13 percent. More than 42 percent of Tyrrell's people of color live in poverty, compared with 15 percent of white residents.

In 1989, our county undertook a strategic planning process that identified tourism as an economic development strategy—right behind the plans for a hazardous waste incinerator that was defeated by one vote by a county commission that was desperate for anything that would create jobs. The county government is the largest employer in Tyrrell County, which creates many social and economic challenges, particularly for people of color who—at the time—had never really been invited to participate in a meaningful way in local decision making.

When The Conservation Fund purchased 110,000 acres and created Pocosin Lakes National Wildlife Refuge, government and grassroots leaders came together to work on an intensive community planning process that identified two critical needs: (1) jobs for adults, to replace more than five hundred jobs that were lost when First Colony Farms went bankrupt, and (2) job training for our young people, who were leaving the county because of the lack of jobs and employment opportunities. During the community meetings, residents made it clear they did not want to create a theme park or look like Myrtle Beach, and asked why we could not attract tourists through our *natural assets*— the forests, wetlands, sounds, streams, and lakes—and our *human assets*, the people who had been stewards of the natural resources for hundreds of years.

Enter the USDA Forest Service, with the Rural Community Assistance programs that were designed to support natural resource–based economic development. With a small $5,000 planning grant, we partnered with the University of North Carolina at Chapel Hill and The Conservation Fund to explore the feasibility of implementing ecotourism as an economic strategy. Community leaders worked with graduate students who confirmed that it was, in fact, a sustainable economic development strategy and helped us think through the steps that would be needed to implement ecotourism.

Fast-forward to 2005 and see the results. That $5,000 Rural Community Assistance grant has helped leverage real change in our community:

- The Tyrrell County Community Development Corporation was established in 1992 and continues to provide community leadership in sustainable development efforts. Our small business incubator currently serves thirty-six minority-owned small businesses, and six to ten new businesses are added each year. Many of these enterprises are part of our ecotourism efforts: tour guide services, hunting and fishing guides, signmakers, craftspeople, family-owned restaurants and catering, insurance providers, accountants, and more.

- The Tyrrell County Youth Conservation Corps has provided natural resource-based job skills and educational training to over 125 young people. One-third of our Youth Corps graduates have gone on to college, and the rest have been placed in full-time employment. The Youth Corps has worked on reforestation of red-cockaded woodpecker habitat, propagated native plant and tree species for wetland restoration projects, and built over two hundred miles of trails, boardwalks, duck boxes, and interpretive signage for federal and state conservation agencies and local governments or nonprofit organizations. Forest Service funds supported our Youth Corps' initial construction project of a half-mile-long interpretive boardwalk that has made our Tyrrell County visitors' center the second most-visited Department of Transportation rest area in the state.

- Our Sustainable Careers Internship Program has provided opportunities for Youth Corps graduates to work in conservation career-oriented internships with federal agencies. The SCIP interns have accomplished important work for the refuges, parks, forests, and fish hatcheries and have won awards for leadership and service to their agency. At the same time, agency leaders have seen first-hand that long-time residents have an innate understanding of how our natural systems work, and that our cultural ties to the land can be an important addition to the scientific basis for natural resource management. The program has also encouraged our interns to explore natural resource management careers, which will likewise help diversify the workforce in natural resource agencies for the long term. Forest Service funds have supported this program as well.

- We helped establish the Partnership for the Sounds, a nonprofit organization that is promoting ecotourism and environmental education as a regional economic strategy. The Partnership has leveraged over $10 million in state and federal funding for environmental education centers, boardwalks, and trails that are providing ecotourism infrastructure in five of North Carolina's poorest counties.

- In 1999, The Conservation Fund partnered with the North Carolina Department of Transportation to purchase ten thousand acres of red-cockaded woodpecker habitat in Tyrrell County. The Palmetto-Peartree Preserve is being managed as an endangered species mitigation bank, while also being sustainably harvested for timber and developed as an ecotourism destination. Jobs are being created for loggers trained in shovel logging techniques; and we are working with The Conservation Fund to ensure that the community will be involved in forest management and ecotourism over the long term.

- The preserve is serving as the "green infrastructure" for ecotourism development, with boardwalks, trails, canoe and kayak launches, boating access points, wildlife viewing areas, and interpretive signage. Local residents are being employed in managing the forest, harvesting the timber, maintaining the roads, and developing the ecotourism infrastructure. The Community Development Corporation recently helped secure a special grant that is providing natural resource-based entrepreneurship training in five counties; and we are working with Elizabeth City State University, a historically black college-university on formalizing the natural resource-based entrepreneurship training for minority students. Again, Forest Service funds are supporting us in providing technical assistance to entrepreneurs in starting, financing, and successfully managing natural resource-based businesses.

- Throughout all of these efforts, the USDA Forest Service has provided support, technical assistance, and partnership. That $5,000 grant twelve years ago has helped to leverage well over $30 million in public and private investment, has created over two hundred jobs and small businesses, and has helped our citizens build long-term capacity for being involved in managing the natural resources. Perhaps more importantly, the young people who have completed the Youth Corps program are the future leaders of our community, and we anticipate strong and informed support for natural resource management issues from these future decision makers.

What are the three most vital issues that confront the agency in this new century?

As we move into the second century of operation for the US Forest Service, I'm reminded of that automobile commercial from a few years ago: "It ain't your daddy's Forest Service anymore." The Forest Service has come a long way since 1905 and has worked to adjust to the increasingly fast changes in the world around us. In the twenty-first century, we can only assume that the rate of change will increase dramatically, increasing the pressures to be flexible and the need to work in ways we might not be able to imagine right now.

From the perspective of rural communities, it will be important for Forest Service leaders to keep in mind that the most vital issues confronting the agency in this century are connected—to people and communities; across social, economic, and environmental lines; and across geopolitical boundaries. The good news is that rural folks have always been good at what used to be called survival but today is known as multitasking—and because forestry has been a part of our lives and our economy for generations, we want to partner with the Forest Service so we can continue to grow our economies and our communities, along with our forestlands.

Socially. The Forest Service successes in Tyrrell County are a good example of what could happen across the country if social issues are fully integrated into natural resource management efforts. In North Carolina, throughout the South, and across the country, there is a direct geographic correlation between forest cover, persistent poverty, and communities of color. In the South, often the people who actively managed the natural resources were the Native Americans and slaves who were brought from Africa because of their expertise in cultivating the land. The fact that our ancestors also brought over strong cultural commitments and expertise in being stewards of the land was an added bonus. Historically, though, people of color have not been seen as the face of the conservation movement.

In the twenty-first century, it will be important for the USDA Forest Service to acknowledge the changing demographics in rural communities, understand and celebrate the cultural and social ties to the land, and work with communities to involve residents in cooperatively managing the whole systems that include national forests and rural communities. With growing numbers of urbanites, we think of rural residents as an endangered species—and a keystone species that can be a formidable ally in managing our resources holistically. This means that we all need to work together, to understand the different issues and diverse perspectives, and to appreciate the expertise and knowledge that each of us brings to the table.

What can the Forest Service do? In rural communities such as Tyrrell County, this means that local people could be hired to work in natural resource management, or helped to start up natural resource–based businesses. There could be "cross training," where the Forest Service helps local residents understand the science behind management issues, and local residents help the Forest Service learn folklore on the natural systems and traditional uses of the resources that have been passed down through the generations. It means working with us as partners, helping us understand the operating and management mandates and constraints of the agency, while we help you understand the challenges we face and the assets we bring to the table.

The community planning processes that have been accomplished through the Rural Community Assistance programs have helped communities better understand their assets and focus their efforts so that economic development supports natural resource management objectives. They have helped people come together, develop a shared vision for their communities' sustainability, and bridge the divides, not just between communities and the Forest Service but also across race, class and political boundaries. It's a win-win for everyone and should be continued and expanded throughout our forest-based communities.

Environmentally. With ever-increasing demands on our natural resources and dwindling resources with which to manage those systems, it will be vitally important for us to work in partnership to manage resources for the nation as a whole. Water supply and quality will, without a doubt, be perhaps *the* most pervasive natural resource issues we face in this century. The Forest Service's focus on watershed management needs to be continued and expanded if we are to effectively manage our national forests for the ecological goods and services that are provided—clean air, clean water, healthy forests, and more.

It goes without saying that the Forest Service should continue to manage the resources for a sustainable system of national forests, and to provide leadership in the research initiatives that will help us manage our forestlands for the environment, the economy, and communities in the twenty-first century. Environmental protection is an inclusive process, so it will be vitally important to cross those boundaries and include diverse individuals and communities in management activities, keeping in mind that it is important to go beyond the "input" stage and ensure that diverse populations are fully engaged in decision making and implementation.

Economically. Those of us in the South have been hard hit by global economic shifts, particularly in agriculture, manufacturing, and forestry. Over the past ten or twenty years we have seen huge shifts in forestland ownership, in New England in the 1990s, and now in the South. The Southern Forest Resource Assessment projects that thirty million acres—fifteen percent of the forestlands in the South—will change ownership by the year 2020. Again, when we look at the interconnectedness of economic, environmental, and social priorities, we see a direct geographic overlap of forestlands, persistently poor counties, and communities of color. Given that many of the forestlands are being purchased for seasonal or second-home development, it is reasonable to presume that significant changes are likely to happen in some of our most distressed communities.

In the South, the "Black Belt" and Southern Appalachian regions are home to eighty-three percent of the persistently poor counties in the entire country, yet less than ten percent of the Rural Community Assistance program funding has been invested in the region. Investing now in helping these communities develop and implement natural resource–based economic development initiatives will help to promote forest health, as well as sustainable communities.

There are also public and private partners, including strong foundation interests, and networks of nonprofit organizations that have struggled with effective models for alleviating poverty, building community, and protecting resources. Through partners like the Tyrrell County Community Development Corporation, the Forest Service can access strong networks of leaders who would bring energy, people, and resources to the table to help further our shared objectives. You will find many individuals who understand and care for the land and will welcome the opportunity to "make money off the natural resources without messin' them up."

How can the Forest Service better serve the public while caring for the land in the twenty-first century?

We are seeing a shift from regulation, litigation, and legislation to an "era of sustainability" that will focus on environmental protection and economic return. I would suggest that the Forest Service will need to continue growing the Rural Community Assistance programs that are already helping to address these shifts. There are four main drivers at work:

The shift from federal action to local action. Devolution is a reality and will continue in the coming years; in order to make it work effectively for all of us, though, we need to be sure there is sufficient capacity at the local level to manage the mandates for the long term. Community forestry, which has been successful in many developing or Third World countries, shows great promise as a strategy for strengthening economies, engaging citizens and landowners, and protecting the natural systems. However, there is typically a need for investment in creating organizational or institutional capacity, or in broadening the mission of an existing organization if the work is to be sustained for the long term. We have seen in Tyrrell County how strategic investments can leverage much larger investments and generate strong public support, and I urge you to continue and to expand those investments.

A shift from public action to private action, with a focus on private lands and working landscapes. It is very important to have forestlands be managed for broad public benefit; however, it is equally important to have privately held forestlands be managed for the ecological goods and services they provide for the public, as well as the private benefits to their owners. Programs like the Forest Legacy Program are helping to ensure that private lands are an important part of the "patchwork quilt" of forests that benefit all of us, so it will be important to continue Forest Legacy and the technical assistance the agency provides to private landowners.

A shift from regulatory to nonregulatory action, with an emphasis on incentives and education. Programs such as our Youth Conservation Corps have done more to raise awareness and generate support for environmental protection than any government mandate might have done. In one of our early community meetings, for example, one African American minister was asked whether he would support a chemical plant coming into Tyrrell County if he knew it would dump toxins into the rivers and wetlands that pervade the community. His response was an unequivocal "yes" because it would create jobs. However, when our young people were building boardwalks into the wetlands and were physically working in that same river, he realized that there could be very real—and damaging—consequences if the river were full of toxins, and he asked what we could do to clean up the river. Yes, you can achieve natural resource protection without rules and regulations.

A shift from piecemeal conservation to whole-systems conservation. Natural resource protection is a very complex and connected process. It includes—but is not limited to—natural science, social science, research, analysis, economic alternatives, community engagement, and partnership building. It will be vitally important for the Forest Service to ensure that people are part of the picture and to place a value on rural communities as well as natural communities.

In Summary…

The USDA Forest Service must be relevant to the communities in which they work. Addressing economic and social issues will go a very long way toward managing and protecting our forest resources.

The Forest Service and communities must work to create strategic partnerships across sectors. Again, networks of community development corporations, arts organizations, faith-based groups, education entities, and other special interests should be involved in protecting the forest resources while growing new economies, revitalizing old economies, and promoting social improvement.

Community consensus-building will require an understanding of and sensitivity to economic issues and a willingness to listen to and engage local residents, leaders, and landowners. This has been the hallmark of the Rural Community Assistance programs and should be continued and expanded into the future. It is also the most effective strategy for achieving *results*: jobs created, businesses started up, forests managed and harvested, and more.

Leadership development is critical in conservation, economic development, civic engagement, and other sectors that affect the environment. Be sure to look beyond the traditional leadership to ensure that diverse populations and perspectives are involved in decision making.

Creativity will be vitally important to successful natural resource protection. In this time of budget shortfalls and economic downturns, we need to get multiple benefits out of conservation dollars. As in the example of the Palmetto-Peartree Preserve, you can protect the environment, grow the economy, and engage the citizenry simultaneously.

Debra Shore
Director of Development, Chicago Wilderness

Chicago Wilderness: Can the Forest Service of the Twenty-First Century Be Relevant to Cities and Suburbs?

In the Chicago Wilderness, for the first time in history, millions of people will live in and around a living wilderness that depends utterly on the action, restraint and wisdom of their deliberate stewardship of biodiversity. Unlike the Native peoples who managed the land with fire for attracting game or gaining advantage in warfare, we will be thinking of genes for agriculture and industry. We will also be reaping the aesthetic, economic and recreational benefits and scientific knowledge and a re-established connection with the natural world. There will be many differences between the Chicago Wilderness of the 21st century and the Che-ca-gou of the Potawatomi. But there will be a continuity for thousands of species of plants and animals who will continue this journey with us.

    —from a January 1995 strategic document for Chicago Wilderness

Surprising as it may seem, the Chicago region is home to the greatest concentration of threatened and endangered plant and animal species in the entire state of Illinois. The nation's third-largest metropolitan area—not the surrounding farmland—harbors the world's best remaining assemblages of our original midwestern landscape: the tallgrass prairies, oak savannas, marshes, and woodlands.

In a crescent stretching from southeastern Wisconsin through northeastern Illinois to the Indiana Dunes lie approximately three hundred thousand acres of protected natural lands—forest preserves, state and national parks, other federal lands, and private holdings—that provide habitat for native plant and animal communities of global biological significance. We call these natural communities Chicago Wilderness.

But Chicago Wilderness is also people. The crescent around the southern tip of Lake Michigan is home to nearly nine million people, including the tenth-fastest-growing county in the country, Kendall County, in northeastern Illinois.

By the early 1990s, conservationists and scientists in the region recognized that if the rare natural communities here were to survive and thrive, conservation planning, land acquisition, research, and monitoring needed to be done on a regional scale. Ecosystems transcend political and institutional boundaries. Animals migrate, water flows, fire moves across the landscape (where it is permitted to do so). Thus a concern for ecosystems—their survival and the health of the myriad creatures they harbor—compelled the conservationists in the region similarly to transcend political and institutional boundaries in thinking about how to create a framework in which people and organizations might work together on behalf of ecosystem health for the benefit of all.

Their answer was to establish a new regional collaboration known as Chicago Wilderness, an effort to share resources and expertise among public and private agencies in order to protect the precious natural ecosystems of the Chicago region for the benefit of all.

Formally launched in April 1996 with significant support from two federal agencies—the USDA Forest Service and the USDI Fish and Wildlife Service—the fledgling consortium included the leading conservation groups in the region, public agencies at the city, county, state, and federal level, scientific and research institutions, and small nonprofits.

A statement released by Chicago Wilderness participants in April 1996 reads:

"We have hopes that the Chicago Wilderness initiative will become a model both for citizen participation and for inter-agency cooperation in conservation. This effort has been described as having the elements of a new environmental ethic, one, which recognizes human beings in a metropolitan area as important and necessary components of a thriving natural system. We envision the work in Chicago moving like a prairie fire, igniting the spirits of people in other places and inviting others to take, like sacred fire, this idea home to their own communities."

In the eight years since its inception, Chicago Wilderness has grown to 178 public and private member organizations and has formed a corporate council, now including twenty-two corporations from Wisconsin, Illinois and Indiana.

The goals of Chicago Wilderness are these:

- to educate the public about the natural resources of the Chicago region so that citizens might be encouraged (1) to restore degraded habitat, (2) to participate in scientific monitoring, and (3) to become advocates for conservation in the region;

- to assess the health of the various natural communities here and to prepare a comprehensive recovery plan for the ecosystems and the rare species that they harbor;
- to pursue and promote best practices in habitat restoration and land management;
- to collaborate with other regional initiatives to ensure that a healthy and sustainable economy for the region is based on a healthy and sustainable ecology.

Chicago Wilderness has received additional federal funds from the Environmental Protection Agency and NASA, state funds (such as C2000) supporting projects of ecosystem partnerships, and private funds from several foundations. Substantial contributions have been made by member organizations through a new dues program, the dedication of staff, office space, and other in-kind support that have matched and exceeded the federal contributions.

Since April 1996, Chicago Wilderness has undertaken a variety of initiatives emphasizing scientific research, public participation, restoration activities, and education and outreach.

Notable achievements are:

- The Chicago Wilderness Biodiversity Recovery Plan, a 190-plus-page document resulting from three years' work by the leading scientists, land managers, educators, and communicators in the region, and other private and public stakeholders, to describe the natural communities of the Chicago region, assess their health, identify threats to their survival, and make recommendations for their conservation in the future.
- Publication of *Chicago Wilderness, An Atlas of Biodiversity*, a sixty-four-page, full-color explanation of the natural heritage and natural resources of the Chicago region. Forty thousand copies have been distributed to teachers, students, families, planners, environmental educators, and others.
- Development of a *Conservation Design Resource Manual* and a set of sustainable design principles for use by local governments interested in modifying local comprehensive plans, zoning and subdivision ordinances, and other ordinances to accommodate the principles and practices of conservation design.
- Establishment of regional Teacher Training Hubs to help educators infuse information about regional ecology into their curricula.

- Development of a Burn Training Course and Burn Communication Tools to prepare more professionals and volunteers to conduct controlled burns in natural areas and to assist land management agencies in communicating about this vital technique.
- Pilot projects in four urban communities—Waukegan, Gary (Indiana), Matteson, and Chicago—of Asset Based Community Development, working with residents of each area to identify the natural assets in their communities and to create plans and events to care for them.

Currently, Chicago Wilderness is preparing a State of the Region Report Card, seeking to develop baseline information on the health of various natural and human communities, report on our collective progress in achieving the goals of the Biodiversity Recovery Plan, and identify trends. Chicago Wilderness is also developing a regional monitoring protocol and database to share information and provide data that can inform land managers' decisions.

The Forest Service in the Twenty-First Century

From an urban perspective, the challenges to the Forest Service as it moves into the Twenty-First century are these: socially, *to be relevant*; economically, *to conduct essential research*; and ecologically, *to be responsible* as a land manager and policy maker.

First, let's consider relevance. The U.S. population is increasingly clustered in cities and their suburbs. At the same time, more and more people lack a basic understanding of natural processes and are estranged from wild places and wild creatures. How can the Forest Service demonstrate its relevance to the lives of people who live far from wild nature and who may never have an opportunity to visit a national forest or other federal lands? How can the Forest Service provide support for those organizations and programs that do work in cities and seek to reconnect people with natural communities?

Chicago Wilderness organizations, for example, have developed and expanded a variety of innovative and effective programs. One is called Mighty Acorns, which introduces young people in the Chicago metropolitan area to nature through stewardship and exploration in a way that fosters a personal connection to natural areas. Mighty Acorns brings fourth- through sixth-graders, mostly from urban schools, on three seasonal field trips to "adopted" local natural areas, such as nature oases within city parks and nearby forest preserves.

Led by trained volunteers and accompanied by teachers and staff from the landowner, small groups of five or six students explore nature and practice stewardship by collecting seeds of native plants, removing invasive weeds, and cutting brush. Returning to see the results of their work and their developing relationship as stewards of the natural area strengthens the students' connection with nature. Teachers and volunteers are trained to facilitate the students' spontaneous exploration and discovery and focus their learning with informal activities.

Staff and volunteers from the Field Museum, The Nature Conservancy, partner organizations, and schools collaborate with teachers to connect stewardship experiences with classroom lessons. Midewin National Tallgrass Prairie in Will County, Illinois, for instance, part of the National Forest System administered by the U.S. Forest Service in cooperation with the Illinois Department of Natural Resources, is a major provider of Mighty Acorns programs. The partnership Mighty Acorns creates with schools allows teachers to explore the use of natural areas for curricular projects, service projects, and the social development of children in their classes.

Mighty Acorns is a wonderful program, but funding remains a challenge, and many more schools wish to participate than current funds can support.

The Forest Service in Cities

Over the years, the Forest Service has struggled to find ways to support the work of Chicago Wilderness. At the outset, Chicago Wilderness benefited from the generous support of Congressman Sid Yates, who in the mid-1990s chaired the Interior subcommittee of the House Appropriations Committee and worked to increase the entire budget for urban and community forestry. In the intervening years, funding for Chicago Wilderness has come primarily because Congress, through congressional earmarks, has directed the Forest Service to do so. This is not a desirable situation from any point of view. It prevents the Forest Service from "owning" the highly successful work by Chicago Wilderness organizations, such as the Mighty Acorns program, to name but one, and from declaring victory for highly successful urban initiatives.

"While we *say* we want to find innovative approaches to work in inner cities," said one respected agency executive, "we seem at a loss to provide in-house support. The Forest Service just doesn't know how to support organizations that are different—collaborations and networks, such as Chicago Wilderness."

As a result, the Forest Service does not take credit for the achievements of organizations or projects it has supported, nor does it tell the many success stories that emerge from these projects. Finally, the system of support from earmarks prevents many worthy programs and organizations from planning effectively and using federal support to leverage far more in private investment.

Moreover, Chicago Wilderness has become a model of collaborative conservation work through public-private partnerships for many other urban areas, both nationally and internationally. Houston; Portland, Oregon; Kansas City; Oahu; even Curitiba, Brazil—all have adopted or adapted aspects of Chicago Wilderness to engage a diverse constituency in addressing local conservation problems.

What if the Forest Service saw the way to get its work done in urban communities was through supporting innovative collaborations—[such] that these became the public face of the Service in cities and suburbs? The Forest Service could easily have a huge presence in cities if it championed the work of broad collaborations such as Chicago Wilderness and found ways to support similar collaborations in other urban centers. This could go a long way toward demonstrating the Service's relevance in an increasingly urbanized society, but it will require a new agency culture and mindset. By raising its profile in cities, by demonstrating its relevance through education, outreach, restoration, and research, the Service is building a constituency that could be mobilized to support its mission overall. Collaborations become the delivery vehicle for local programs—but they can also mobilize members and others to support the special values of public lands around the country.

The Forest Service of the twenty-first century should be on the cutting edge of research, both in the economic arena and in communications.
Chicago Wilderness strives to help the Chicago region meet some of the social and economic challenges faced by urban areas around the nation. Studies have demonstrated that access to and enjoyment of natural areas contributes to urban residents' sense of satisfaction with their communities, and building a strong quality of life for people who live in an urban area is crucial to attracting the high-quality workforce needed for a thriving, modern economic base.

We need to know more—and to make the case compellingly—about the value of ecosystem services to urban and suburban residents. All people need and deserve clean air and clean water, for instance, but urban residents frequently lack knowledge about the processes that produce and contribute to these vital elements. Do woodlands with a flourishing herbaceous understory do a better job of retaining stormwater runoff—and thus a better job of preventing or reducing flooding—than a woodland choked by invasive buckthorn? Does a grassland of native prairie plants sequester as much carbon as a woodland? What is the effect of controlled burns on air quality in an urban area? What are the benefits—ecologically and economically—of using native plants in landscaping? How can we craft messages that address people's values so that the protection of nature becomes woven into the fabric of our culture?

Invasive species are a substantial threat to the health of the natural lands and waters in our metropolitan region: Asian carp, garlic mustard, purple loosestrife, zebra mussels, European buckthorn, reed canary grass, Asian long-horned beetle, gypsy moths, emerald ash borer, and even the nefarious snakehead. Can we develop early warning systems to provide first alerts and prevent the spread of new invasives? How do invasives affect the regional economy and people's attitudes about nature?

Finally, let's consider the Forest Service's challenge, in the twenty-first century, to be a responsible—and responsive—environmental steward. Undoubtedly the Service possesses a broad view of the landscape, nationally and regionally, with considerable expertise in land management. Indeed, how the Service manages public lands, how it embraces and fulfills its role as steward of natural resources, often sets a precedent for management by other agencies. So it is especially important that the Service set a good example, making decisions informed by sound science, demonstrating sensitivity to regional and local needs.

In Chicago Wilderness, where even the highest-quality natural areas exist as fragments in the landscape, we have a number of remnant-dependent species, including federally endangered orchids, butterflies, and dragonflies.

Given this, can the Forest Service, with experience at managing ecosystems on a much larger scale, adapt its policies to the constraints of remnant natural communities? Should the Forest Service's own land management practices be applied to small, fragmented habitats? Can the Service be responsive to ecological challenges that vary from region to region, even from county to county? And can the Service play an increasingly vital role as an information clearinghouse, sharing information gathered by citizen scientists and techniques developed by land managers in one part of the country with eager stewards in another? Is this facilitative function—the ability to foster partnerships and share best practices—not one of the most valuable roles the Service can fulfill as we move forward?

Take fire, for example, perhaps one of the biggest challenges facing the Forest Service, in terms of both land management and communications. The native ecosystems of Chicago Wilderness are nearly all fire-dependent communities, and fire suppression has been one of the biggest causes of biodiversity loss and habitat degradation. With the Forest Service's help and support, Chicago Wilderness has developed a burn training manual and protocol devoted specifically to the needs and conditions prevalent here, in an urban-suburban-wildland matrix. We will not have the crown fires of a ponderosa forest, but we do need to manage smoke when conducting controlled burns in a region filled with drivers using cell phones!

Still, in our region, as elsewhere, the use of fire to recover and sustain ecosystem health remains counterintuitive. Here, as in many parts of our country, few people understand fire as a necessary ecosystem process, but we live in the nation's third-largest media market. With the Forest Service's help, we can research how to communicate about fire and get the word out to our nine million residents, who otherwise are too remote from the national forest discussions to benefit from them.

One final thought about how the Forest Service can link with urban areas relates to governance. Urban areas are politically complex places for anyone to do business. Any single entity—be it a nonprofit organization, a corporation, or a government agency—has a huge challenge in making a difference on its own. Coalitions like Chicago Wilderness provide a governance structure that federal agencies can simply plug into. Instead of the old federal top-down management model, which federal agencies are working to get away from, Chicago Wilderness horizontally integrates government agencies in support of locally driven efforts. There is ample opportunity for federal partners to influence priorities in the process, but they critically need the delivery mechanism that urban coalitions like Chicago Wilderness provide.

As the Forest Service shapes its vision for the future and defines its role for the twenty-first century, ask this: How can the Service harness the tremendous energy, creativity, and diversity found in metropolitan regions? For whatever our racial, religious, political, ethnic, sexual identities, and beliefs, whatever sports teams we cheer (Go Cubbies!), whatever music we love and food we relish, we all depend for our survival on healthy nature. Can the Forest Service of the twenty-first century become the leader of this noble enterprise, weaving a conservation ethic across the land? I think so. For us, here in Chicago Wilderness, living a land ethic starts at home.

Robert Model

President, Boone and Crockett Club

What's Expected of the Forest Service in the Twenty-First Century

Partners since the Beginning—and for the Future

The Boone and Crockett Club, founded in 1887 by Theodore Roosevelt, has a long and proud relationship with the U.S. Forest Service. The Club gave strong support—both as a club and through individual members, such as Theodore Roosevelt, Gifford Pinchot, George Bird Grinnell, Arnold Hague, John Lacy, and others—to the establishment of the Forest Reserves. The Club was there at the beginning—and since—in support of the transfer of the Forest Reserves from the Department of Interior to the Department of Agriculture with the associated establishment of the Forest Service.[1] Many of the Forest Service's Chiefs have been members of the Boone and Crockett Club, including Edward Cliff, Gifford Pinchot, Henry Graves, John McGuire, Max Peterson, Jack Ward Thomas, and Dale Bosworth.[2]

As a result of that long association with the Forest Service, the Club has both a great interest and a stake in the answer to the question, What's expected of the Forest Service in the twenty-first century? The answer, of course, depends upon who is providing the answer. The answers that will pour forth from a variety of individuals and well-organized interest groups will, I suspect, be characterized by only a single factor: significant disagreement. But that, of course, is nothing new in the history of the Forest Service.

Changes in the Forest Service over Time

Too many respondents, dreaming of a past that no longer exists, will assume that the Forest Service itself can, and should, provide the answer. And, it is further assumed, the Forest Service should proceed to act upon that authoritative response. The makeup of the Forest Service has changed dramatically over the second fifty years of its existence. For its first fifty years the agency was dominated by white male foresters with a very clear mission stated in the Organic Administration Act of 1897: (1) improve and protect the forest within the boundaries, (2) secure favorable conditions of water flows, and (3) furnish a continuous supply of timber for the use and necessities of the citizens of the United States. This primary mission was not altered significantly in legislation until the late 1950s.[3] The 1906 Use Book listed the two chief duties of Forest Service personnel as follows: (1) protect the reserves against fire, and (2) assist people in the use of the reserves.[4]

This simple fifty-year-old mission changed beginning in the 1950s with the Clean Air Act of 1955, Multiple Use–Sustained Yield Act of 1960, the Wilderness Act of 1964, the Wild and Scenic Rivers Act of 1968, the National Environmental Policy Act of 1970, the Federal Advisory Committee Act of 1972, the Endangered Species Act of 1973, the Forest and Rangeland Renewable Resources Planning Act of 1974, the Federal Land Policy and Management Act of 1976, the National Forest Management Act of 1976, and many others.[5]

The requirements of these laws and attention to civil rights brought about dramatic changes in the Forest Service's workforce, both in terms of technical specialties and in terms of gender and ethnic origin. Today's Forest Service employs large numbers of biologists and ecologists of various types, engineers, social scientists, hydrologists, soils scientists, economists, biometricians, computer specialists, analysts, and many other specialists, who collectively now significantly outnumber foresters and engineers. Women now commonly occupy professional positions, including such managerial positions as associate chief, deputy chief, regional forester, research station director, forest supervisor, district ranger, and research project leader. The last five Chiefs included an engineer, two foresters, a wildlife biologist, and a fisheries biologist.

As a result, today it is much less likely that there is a clear internal "Forest Service view" about any natural resources issue beyond a basic adherence to the general dedication to the agency's motto, "Caring for the Land and Serving People."

The Forest Service Cannot Control Its Own Destiny—and Shouldn't

I suggest that we begin our search for an answer to the question with a clear understanding that the Forest Service cannot, and should not, define its conservation mission or its expectations of performance in this new century, beyond assurance of a dedicated, efficient, and effective pursuit of its assigned mission. Once upon a time, and to a large degree, such a mission could be dramatically influenced through the agency's ability to influence legislation, write rules and regulations, sway public opinion, and thereby strongly influence budgets put forth by Presidents and the Congress.

That is, simply, no longer true. And furthermore, it is time to recognize that those "good old days" are gone forever. It is time to replace residual myth with a strong dose of reality. The Progressive Era that spawned the Forest Service and influenced its actions and influence now lies far in the past. The idea that a "professional" agency employing the "best and the brightest" and carrying out its tasks—largely self-defined—in the most efficient manner so as to produce, in the words of the agency's first Chief, "the greatest good for greatest number in the long run" is no longer realistic.

Active Management Is Grinding toward a Halt

The Forest Service desperately needs a crystal-clear conservation mission established in law. That is the responsibility of the Congress. And Congress has, over the past one hundred years, certainly passed a plethora of laws doing just that. Unfortunately, the current state of those laws is that there are so many laws that are so overlapping, so contradictory, so confounding, and so variously interpreted by the courts as to have produced a state of affairs wherein active management of the national forests, for any purpose, continues to grind slowly toward a halt. At the same time, an excess of mandated interwoven processes to arrive at any management action has produced a circumstance where it is unlikely that any significant land management action can produce a result where the benefit exceeds the cost.

The interactions of this plethora of law and regulations, and associated required processes, have resulted from Congress laying down broad guidelines in laws and deferring to the courts to determine if the Forest Service and other management agencies are operating within those parameters. As a result, the specter of the "tragedy of the commons" (wherein lands owned in common by the people were doomed to abuse and overuse) has evolved into a quite different tragedy—a "tragedy of little or no use" related to production of wood products.[5]

In the Beginning: Simple Promises

The promises of the Forest Service's first Chief, Gifford Pinchot, were basically two in number. Both were both simple and straightforward. The first was that the national forests were "for use" in such a way that the "greatest good for the greatest number in the long run" would be realized. The second was that "local decisions would be made on local grounds".[6] That second promise, too, has faded as the combination of growing numbers of poorly coordinated laws, with an associated cascade of court decisions, has tended to increasingly concentrate key decisions once made at local levels at higher levels—many above the Forest Service. Failure to adhere to those promises has produced consternation in rural areas in proximity to the national forests, particularly in western states containing the majority of the national forests.

Courts Increasingly Call the Shots

As one federal judge put it,

> when a society puts these kinds of issues into a single branch of government designed not to be responsive to the electorate—the judicial branch—you may well have seriously weakened the fabric of a republican form of government in a democratic society, that being representatives chosen by the people themselves. Every subtraction from the power of the legislative and executive branches in areas where it ought not to be weakens your democracy and your republic. You didn't elect me and you can't get rid of me…I do believe that at the federal level the Congress has lodged far too much power in the judicial branch. But I do not think that it is realistic to expect any substantial or large-scale change.[7]

I hope that Judge James M. Burns is wrong, given the consternation that has built with the continued flood of judicial decisions since he made that statement seventeen years ago.

And the courts are ever-more challenged, and inclined, to judge the adequacy of agency responses to various laws and regulations. The legal precedents set by the rapid accumulation of such judicial decisions are increasingly voluminous and confused when considered in their totality. Sometimes, situations emerging from judicial decisions vary between judicial districts when they are, intentionally, not appealed to a higher court for clarification. Legal challenges to governmental actions have been facilitated by the Equal Access to Justice Act, which allows plaintiffs to be paid for their costs when they prevail against the government and to be excused from responsibility for the consequences of their actions if they lose.

Lack of Consensus Equals Increasing Paralysis

Consensus is lacking among the citizenry—at least among those who care deeply about the public lands—as to the appropriate management focus for those lands. That situation is reflected in the Congress. Clearly, the emphasis of how, and for whom, and for what the national forests should be managed now varies markedly, depending upon who holds power in the Congress and who occupies the office of the President. Contrast the differing emphases given by Presidents Clinton and George W. Bush to that management—and the backgrounds of those they appointed to cabinet and subcabinet positions in the Departments of Interior and Agriculture and the Council on Environmental Quality.

Elevations in Decision Making above the Level of the Forest Service

Decisions once solely within the purview of the Forest Service are now made at the political level of the under secretary of Agriculture, or elsewhere in the hierarchy of political appointees. Regulations issued pursuant to legislation, originally conceived of as maximally flexible, have, over time, become cast in concrete due to political sensitivities.

The Endangered Species Act Produces "Comanagers" for the Forest Service

With every listing of a threatened or endangered species, the Forest Service picks up a comanager from the Fish and Wildlife Service or the National Marine Fisheries Service. As each agency guards its own powers and responds to different authorities and different constituencies, full coordination and cooperation between agencies are often less than they should be but become manifest in land management—or the lack thereof.

Court Games: "Sue and Settle"

Recent administrations of both major political parties have learned to manipulate the judicial system through the relative recent ploy of "sue and settle." In this game, arrangements are made to bring a legal challenge before a federal judge considered likely to render the desired decision (referred to as "judge shopping"). The government, having lost the case, then chooses not to appeal the decision and proclaims that "the judge made us do it." This is certainly clever. But it would be vastly better if Congress redeemed its responsibility to make such decisions. And public trust and confidence in government is likely to be degraded in the process.

Congress: Time to Step Up

Clearly, a significant number of the members of Congress and governors of the states—particularly those in the West, where most of the public lands exist—do not agree with the current state of national forest management. But these officials have demonstrated neither the will nor the power to significantly change operative laws. Current efforts to modify the Endangered Species Act may prove to be an exception. We will see.

So, many of such elected officials use a strategy of placating various user groups who have suffered from declines in timber production, mining, grazing, and other commercial uses of national forests by castigation of Forest Service officials, publicly and in hearings before congressional committees. And amazingly, it seems to have worked for well over a decade. The ploy seems to be wearing thin because the Forest Service's ability to carry out land management activities at reasonable cost has not proven to be significantly related to which party controls the executive branch—indicating that the problem is not the agency's willingness to proceed with active management.

Ties That Bind: The Forest Service's Gordian Knot

The Forest Service's present status can be likened to that of Gulliver in the fairy tale: a once (and potentially once again) powerful giant increasingly restrained by a thousand threads of law, regulations, confounding court decisions, shifting political power, and a divided electorate. These threads meshed over time and have now become woven into a Gordian knot that preludes consistent land management activities, and cannot be undone by the agency itself.

The proverbial Gordian knot was a puzzle designed to identify the rightful ruler of Asia, who, alone, would be able to undo the knot. All who tried to pick apart the knot and thereby attain the prize of Asia failed until Alexander the Great drew his sword and simply sliced it in two. Only the Congress holds the sword that can sever the knot that binds the Forest Service.

Solution Is Probably Not within the Purview of the Administrative Branch

I repeat, the Forest Service, acting alone, cannot—and probably should not— spend time or resources in attempts to reinvent itself, or its mission, for the twenty-first century. The agency has struggled mightily over several decades to accomplish that result and failed. That failure is not one of will or of competence or a lack diligent effort.

Clearly, a change in administrations, even administrations as dramatically different as those of President William Clinton and President George W. Bush, has not significantly loosened the Gordian knot. Significant change will take more than a dramatic political change in power in the executive branch. Only Congress holds the key, that key being an overhaul of the laws and regulations governing the management of the national forests. The executive can only propose; the Congress must dispose. More patches applied over the top of patches of the past will not solve the current stalemate and even has potential to make matters worse. A continued failure of the Congress to wield their sword condemns our national forests—and the Forest Service—to a status quo that increasingly satisfies no one.

It is obvious that the system of governance for the national forests is broken. It needs fixing. And only Congress can do that job. If and when Congress gets around to that job, it would be well that "multiple use" be addressed through land-use zoning. That pattern has become well established with designation, in compliance with legislation, of wilderness areas, wild and scenic rivers, recreation areas, municipal watersheds, national monuments, etc. In addition, the overriding de facto objective for the management of the remainder of national forest land has evolved to become the preservation of biodiversity. This results from the application of the so-called diversity clause in the agency's planning regulations, which requires that "viable populations of native and desirable non-native species" will be maintained "well-distributed" within planning areas. That regulation, coupled with the evolved policy of absorbing the responsibility of meeting the requirements of the Endangered Species Act on federal lands to the extent possible, reinforces that mandate. Experience reveals that this overriding de facto mission—with a stiff dose (some would say an overdose) of the "precautionary principle" thrown in—leaves little room for timber or grazing programs or manipulation of habitats to favor wildlife species for purposes of hunting or fishing. Unless some lands are zoned wherein those objectives receive paramount attention, their future is bleak.

The Forest Service–Boone and Crockett Club Connection: A Tie That Binds
The U.S. Forest Service has had, and has, no bigger or better fan club than the Boone and Crockett Club—even if and when there are minor disagreements. We believe that the national forests and the dedicated people of the Forest Service people, both past and present, stand out as true national treasures. We believe that the Forest Service has demonstrated, during a century of service to the nation, what a well-led and dedicated agency can and should be.

And we pledge our help in getting the Forest Service an answer, a clear and unambiguous answer, from Congress, to the question, "What's expected of the Forest Service in the twenty-first century?"

But in the meantime, hang tough, do the best you can, and keep the faith. You are of the "long green line" that has pointed the way, for our nation as the world, for a full century as to how, with dedication, pride, and honor, to "care for the land and serve the people." Don't forget who you are, where you came from, and where you are going as you provide world leadership in conservation efforts for another century. Keep the faith!

Literature Cited

[1] Trefethen, J.B. 1975. *An American crusade for wildlife*. Boone and Crockett Club, Alexandria, Virginia.

[2] Boone and Crockett Club. 2004. Boone and Crockett Club's 2004 Membership Directory. Missoula, Montana.

[3] USDA Forest Service. 1993. *The principal laws relating to Forest Service activities*. Government Printing Office, Washington, D.C.

[4] USDA Forest Service. 1906. *The use book: Regulations and instructions for the use of the national forest reserves.* Government Printing Office, Washington, D.C.

[5] Thomas, J.W. 2004. The "tragedy of the commons" revisited. *Journal of Forestry* 102(2): 60.

[6] Burns, J.M. 1988. The role of the courts in resolving land use questions. Lecture. November 17, College of Forestry, Oregon State University.

The Chiefs Remember Book Signing

January 4, 2005
12:15 pm

january 3-6
2005
washington dc

US Forest Service

Centennial
Congress

A Collective Commitment to Conservation

The Chiefs Remember Book Signing

During the lunch break on Tuesday, January 4, 2006, the Forest History Society hosted a book signing for its publication, *The Chiefs Remember: The Forest Service, 1952–2001*, edited by Harold K. Steen.

The Chiefs Remember presents excerpts from interviews with Forest Service chiefs whose tenures spanned fifty years: Richard E. McArdle, 1952–62; Edward P. Cliff, 1962–72; John R. McGuire, 1972–79; R. Max Peterson, 1979–87; F. Dale Robertson, 1987–93; Jack Ward Thomas, 1993–97; and Michael P. Dombeck, 1997–2001.

In the book, the former chiefs look back at the issues they faced during their administrations and allow readers to glimpse the inner workings of the Forest Service. Sometimes caught unawares by the forces of change, sometimes prescient, by turns humble and defiant but always candid, the chiefs reflect on their efforts to carry out the agency's mission in a time of turbulence.

The four past living chiefs participated in a book signing for *The Chiefs Remember*. Shown are Jack Ward Thomas (left) and R. Max Peterson.

Public Policy Panel:
The Multiple Use Challenge

January 4, 2005
1:30 pm

Patricia Limerick *(Moderator)*
William H. Meadows
Paul Hansen
John Heissenbuttel
Butch Blazer *(no paper available)*
Robert E. Douglas
Lyle Laverty *(no paper available)*

US Forest Service
Centennial
Congress
A Collective Commitment to Conservation

William H. Meadows
President, The Wilderness Society

The Multiple Use Challenge

It is an honor to be here and to be part of this celebration. I am also flattered to be on a panel with such a distinguished group of colleagues.

This week is a celebration of a rich one-hundred-year history for the U.S. Forest Service. It could have been marked by a series of self-congratulatory speeches and presentations, but instead, in its wisdom, the Forest Service determined that the best way to mark its hundred-year history was to pause—to check the pulse: How are we doing? What is needed in the future?

Let me admit, I am not a forester. I am a citizen advocate, vitally interested and somewhat knowledgeable about our national forests. From that seat for over thirty years, I see an inherent tension within the Forest Service—between conservation values and commercial values. The Wilderness Society, founded by foresters who believed strongly in conversation values, believes that there are some places—wilderness and character—where management should not be encouraged. We believe we should manage people, but the landscape should evolve naturally.

Yesterday was the thirtieth anniversary of the Eastern Wilderness Areas Act; we should be celebrating that, too. This legislation gave voice to the power of nature, the power to regenerate—to restore the landscape—something I believe to be absolutely critical to our conservation future.

Work on that legislation, as a volunteer in Tennessee, was my first significant involvement in national conservation policy and conservation politics. Over the last thirty years, I must admit to a schizophrenic view about the U.S. Forest Service. On the one hand, it is revered as a conservation organization. My personal experiences, with many of you in this room, affirm that reverence. But if one has been involved in conservation policy and politics for thirty years, one cannot forget the intense conflicts around specific policies and places. We cannot forget the ancient forest debate coming at a time when eleven billion, twelve billion board feet were being cut on our national forests—thousands and thousands of road miles being added each year. Thank God we are through that—at least for the most part. But within our community, the conservation advocacy community, we are still not quite sure.

We continue to see efforts to log the last remaining big trees in the Tongass and efforts to give governors responsibility to determine whether roadless areas in our "national" forests will be protected. Is this truly the greatest good for the greatest number over the longest time? There continues to be debate over economics and ecological values of salvage sales, especially the Biscuit Salvage in the Siskiyou National Forest.

And just thirteen days ago—during the Christmas holidays—the Forest Service released the final National Forest Management Act regulations that govern land use and resource management planning on the national forests. There has been much written about the regulations, but the unanimous view, from the conservation community, is that the regulations remove key environmental safeguards for national forests that have been in place for more than twenty years.

So, we are still not quite sure. Can we trust the U.S. Forest Service? When I ask that question of Dale [Bosworth], Sally [Collins], Fred [Norbury], and others, I get reasonable answers, good responses, good reasons, but the analysis and the regulations, from our perspective, demonstrate that they are weaker.

I would like to say a word about trust. When I speak with Dale Bosworth—and I believe Dale and I have a sincere friendship—I am impressed by what he says and what he believes. At the centennial forum in Boise, only six weeks ago, Dale spoke about a new period for the Forest Service, a period of ecological restoration and outdoor recreation. He said, "Maybe more than ever, we focus on delivering values and services like clean air and water, scenic beauty, habitat for wildlife, and opportunities for outdoor recreation. These are the main things people today want from their public lands. We know that from our surveys and from talking to our partners and to people in our communities." In all fairness, he goes on to say: "We also deliver opportunities to harvest timber, graze livestock, and extract minerals. With goods like these come important values like jobs and community stability. We know that Americans want these values, too." And finally, Dale said: "To deliver all these goods, services, and values, we have got to manage the land for the long-term ecosystem health while meaningfully engaging the public in our decision making. We believe that what we leave on the land is more important than what we take away." I could not agree more. This section of Dale's speech could have been written by The Wilderness Society. I, too, agree that in making decisions about our national forests, we must consider economic, social, and cultural values as well as ecological values. We must find ways in which human communities can thrive within natural communities. In my view, there is no better organization to lead in that challenge than the Forest Service. The Wilderness Society will help.

So, I believe. I trust Dale. Then we get into these policy disputes because our community wants legal safeguards. Unfortunately, that has to do with trust. It has to do with our perception of what is happening on the ground, in the Tongass, in the Siskiyou.

So let us look at how we can build trust. I believe it comes through open, honest, and frequent conversations and a commitment to work together. And ultimately, it comes from results—conservation results—on the ground.

Today's panel discussion is entitled "The Multiple Use Challenge." Rather than think about the multiple uses that are derived from our national forests, I prefer to think about the multiple needs, the various constituencies that depend on them. It is The Wilderness Society's belief that our national forests should be managed according the needs of the diverse community of life that depends on these lands—managing for fish, wildlife, and water. We should be protecting the ecological integrity of old-growth and roadless forests, managing for recreational use, clean water, and viable wildlife habitats.

There are three components to a strategy that would meet the needs of the broad community of life that depend on our national forests. Each of these components speaks to the social, environmental, and economic issues that confront the Forest Service.

The first component is restoration. We can talk more about the specifics, but at the heart of any restoration effort, there must be a focus on renewing watersheds.

Not surprisingly from The Wilderness Society, the second component is wilderness designation and the protection of roadless and old-growth forest. Wilderness designation is mentioned in the Multiple Use Act. It is necessary—but not sufficient—for conserving our last public lands. From a social perspective, The Wilderness Society believes that it is in the nation's best interest to ensure that wilderness endures and that Americans for generations to come will be able to enjoy all that these wildlands have to offer. We also believe that protecting our last remaining roadless areas from new development is crucial for preserving wildlife habitat and recreational opportunity. Given the fact that currently have a $10 billion road maintenance backlog on our national forests, now is not the time to build new roads.

The third component of a strategy to address the diverse needs of all life that depends on our national forests is effective management of outdoor recreation. Chief Bosworth has highlighted unmanaged use of off-road vehicles as one the four threats facing our national forests. We applaud him for recognizing the problem, and we look forward to working with the Forest Service to strengthen the ORV rules. However, I look at effective management of recreation as including the full spectrum of recreational activities—finding designated routes for ORVs, but also ensuring that there are still places where families can go to camp, hike, hunt, fish, and canoe.

I am pleased to be here representing The Wilderness Society at this centennial celebration. The Wilderness Society's roots are tied to the Forest Service. Many of our founders and early leaders—for example, Bob Marshall and Aldo Leopold, two of our principal founders—were your colleagues. They would love to be here talking about a future for the Forest Service that is built on restoration, recreation, and the management of our national forests so that the needs of this diverse community of life can be met.

Paul W. Hansen

Executive Director, Izaak Walton League of America

The Multiple Use Challenge

For eighty-three years, the Izaak Walton League of America has been the voice of thousands of Americans on conservation of our nation's "soil, air, woods, waters and wildlife," as stated in our motto. League policies are set by our members, who are politically diverse in their views—almost evenly divided between Republicans, Democrats, and Independents—but united in their desire to see responsible care, stewardship, and management of our nation's forests, natural resources, environment, and landscape. We have been alternately described as the nation's greenest hunters, or its most well-armed environmental group.

These citizen conservationists bring a profoundly commonsense and practical perspective to these issues. They are committed and experienced outdoors users who have an intimate knowledge of the natural world and wildlife. Most hunt and fish. Some prefer hiking, wildlife observation, whitewater activities, or simply being outdoors. I appreciate the opportunity to share the League's perspective on a few of the major issues facing the U.S. Forest Service on the occasion of its centennial.

From my position as executive director of the League, for the past ten years I have been extremely privileged to spend a great deal of time with groups of colleagues that are as diverse as the League's membership. We are part of the "green group," the forum of the leaders of the major national environmental groups, which I chaired in 2000. We are also part of the American Wildlife Conservation Partners, the forum of the leaders of the major national hunting-conservation groups, which we helped start in 2000. For six years, I was honored to interact with a broad group of forestry leaders as a member of the Sustainable Forestry Initiative's External Review Panel, which I chaired for three years. For the past six years, it has been my pleasure to be a director on the board of the Louisiana Pacific Corporation, a remarkable building products company that has undergone a tremendous improvement in all aspects of its environmental performance. From my contacts with these diverse groups, I see the same strong desire for responsible care, stewardship, and management that I see from the Izaak Walton League's diverse membership.

During the next one hundred years, our national forests will become infinitely more valuable to the American people, especially as population and land values soar. Recreational demand and the need for clean water are increasing, as is the need for wood products. Our generation has an awesome responsibility to get it right. My comments are a plea for a fresh start to move on to the common ground that exists for most of us on so many of these issues.

I hope that this Centennial Forest Congress will follow the example of Roosevelt and Pinchot by using this time to look forward to ways to provide for, in Pinchot's words, "the greatest good, to the greatest number, for the longest time." My comments represent only the position of the Izaak Walton League.

In more than eight decades of defending the public interest, League members have adopted hundreds of position statements concerning lands administered by the Bureau of Land Management and the U.S. Forest Service. The basic issues have changed little throughout the years: some commercial interests seeking undue preference in management decisions or even outright title to the public's lands; appropriations insufficient for the needs of professional resource management; restrictions on the public's access to its own lands; pressure for short-term management for special interests; and balancing the competing demands of user groups.

From our perspective, we see partisan politics, language, cultural differences, miscommunication, and mistrust getting in the way of our attaining the level of care, stewardship, and management that we all desire. We hear some partisan voices on both sides of the political fence that seem more interested in preserving political issues for rallying their base of supporters than in implementing practical solutions that most Americans would support. We seem to forget that all change is incremental—sometimes painfully so.

In recent years, some environmentalists have made the perfect enemy of the good on too many issues, causing gridlock and stopping progress. A few months ago, I attended the September 19 gala celebration of the fortieth anniversary of the passage of the Wilderness Act. I remember looking around the room full of friends and wondering, "If the act were before us today, would any of the celebrants in the room support it?" The act was far from perfect. It provided limited protection to only nine million acres. It did, however, set up a logical, inclusive, and consultative process for protecting more acres. Under this process, every president over the last forty years has signed legislation that added land to the wilderness preservation system.

Similarly, I wonder why some of my friends and colleagues in the forest products industry oppose efforts to limit new road construction in the remaining

U.S. forest roadless areas. For the most part, there are very few significant timber resources in these areas. There are far more and far better trees in other parts of the national forests that have relatively less value for wildlife, watersheds, and recreation. The lands that environmentalists care about the most are the same ones that industry cares about the least, and vice versa. Isn't this a great opportunity for a deal that would protect much of the roadless forests while allowing for more timber harvest in second-growth areas that already have roads?

At the Izaak Walton League, we are keenly aware of the fact that our nation has become as dependent on foreign sources of fiber as we are on foreign sources of petroleum. At a time when less than one cubic foot of fiber is harvested per acre of national forest, our nation imports nearly two-thirds of its forest products from other countries. Most of these countries have environmental and forestry standards that are much lower than ours. In America, we have a lot of guilty producers and innocent consumers.

The League believes that there are areas in our national forests where timber management can be practiced responsibly—reducing fire risk, improving wildlife habitat, creating jobs at home, and taking pressure off critical habitat abroad. We believe that old-growth forests and inventoried roadless areas are the last places where these activities need to occur.

Roadless Areas and Wilderness

The League has promoted the concept of designated wilderness since well before passage of the Wilderness Act in 1964. We supported the act and the inclusive and deliberative process it set up for adding to the wilderness system. We oppose unilateral actions to end the wilderness study process in any state or on any unit of public federal lands. We do not think that decisions on wilderness or roadless area protection should be dumped on the states or made contingent on state approval. Our wilderness areas and roadless areas are among the best places on earth to fish, to hunt, or to just be. These lands belong to all Americans.

Every year, I spend more time in the Bridger-Teton National Forest and Gros Ventre Wilderness, and leave more money in the local economy, enjoying the place, than all but a few of the individuals who live within a hundred miles of the forest. Should I have less of a voice in its management just because I am not fortunate enough to live there all year? Local and other interests should receive due consideration in the administration of public lands, but the overall public interest must be paramount. Frequently, the people who live closest to the forest are not the ones who use the forest most or know it best.

Working for three years with a diverse coalition of stakeholders calling itself the Forest Road Working Group, we submitted recommendations to the Forest Service regarding the management and conservation of Inventoried Roadless Areas of the National Forest System. These recommendations were based on nearly two years of deliberations by the working group and a third year soliciting the views of everyone from conservationists and timber companies to ranchers and recreationists. The key recommendations are:

- The existing Roadless Area Conservation Rule provides an acceptable basis for national management of inventoried roadless areas and should continue to be implemented.
- After several years of gaining experience through implementation of the rule, exceptions to the rule's prohibitions could be considered, as necessary, for legitimate forest health maintenance activities.
- Recreational vehicle use should be better managed to reduce impacts to inventoried roadless areas.
- The Forest Service should establish a formal advisory group and deliberative process in order to consider guidance for implementation of—and if necessary, improvements to—the Roadless Area Conservation Rule.

The Forest Road Working Group believes these recommendations provide a sensible and logical way to protect roadless areas and the exceptional fish, wildlife, and water values they represent. They also provide certainty and stability in the management of roadless areas. We believe that local interests should be given significant consideration, but we do not believe that decisions on management of national forest roadless areas should be made by state governors.

Fire and "Healthy Forests"

In many ways, it seems to us that the need for forest management to help reduce conditions conducive to uncontrollable wildfires is an issue where agreement may be broadest. Ironically, it is an issue that has been among the most controversial in the past four years.

We remember that after the severe fire season in 2000, the western governors and the Clinton administration agreed to a multiyear plan to thin and otherwise manage overly dense, even-age stands of timber. We noticed that consensus on this issue was broad and deep. Notably, the environmental community did not object to this plan.

Given the highly unusual, and hopeful, degree of agreement on this issue, we were surprised to see the legislative polarization that ensued. This was a forest management issue on which there was almost unprecedented agreement. In 2000, getting the job done required the appropriation of dollars to do the work on the ground. In 2005, it still does. Almost five years later, only a tiny fraction of the work needed has been done.

Recreation and Off-Highway Vehicles

Recently, we witnessed an example of political courage when U.S. Forest Service Chief Dale Bosworth announced a rulemaking to control the growing abuse of off-highway vehicles on Forest Service lands. At the 2003 Izaak Walton League convention, Chief Bosworth called OHV abuse the fourth-greatest threat to our national forests. He told us, "Each year, the national forests and grasslands get hundreds of miles of unauthorized roads and trails due to repeated cross-country use. We're seeing more and more erosion, water degradation, and habitat destruction."

Make no mistake: OHVs are great tools and great toys. They can be very useful and a lot of fun. However, every form of recreation has its miscreants. Not all people who participate should be blamed for the bad behavior of a few. With thirty-six million Americans now owning or using OHVs, even a tiny percentage of bad actors means hundreds of thousands or even millions of people are off-trail, destroying wildlife habitat, disrupting hunts, polluting the air and water, or leaving permanent scars on the landscape.

We anticipate the designation of many miles of legal OHV trails and roads. This rule should, however, ban cross-country travel for whoever gets a notion to tear across a wetland, a soft meadow, or a streambank. We think that people of good faith and integrity can come together to help Chief Bosworth find a common-ground set of regulations that the majority of us can agree to. Americans can continue to enjoy OHV use on our national forests, but in a way that does not destroy as much wildlife habitat in these forests—or the ability of others to enjoy them. The Izaak Walton League of America will be there to support the Chief in this important undertaking.

We know that these issues are difficult, and "the devil is in the detail." We are not trying to oversimplify these issues, but we appreciate the honor of being able to offer a few examples of the common ground we see on a few key issues, by way of a plea for a fresh start and a renewed effort by all on this historic occasion.

Other Principles

[There are] other issue areas where the Izaak Walton League sees a great deal of common sense and common ground. Included here is a review of the management principles for the national forests articulated by our members as they have set League policy over the past eighty-three years.

In particular, given the League's long history with recreational fishing, we were delighted to see the Forest Service conduct a review of its recreational fishing program. The review team made some important recommendations, and we hope the Service will move quickly in implementing those recommendations.

1. Public lands are a perpetual trust to be administered for the long-range benefit of all people. Local and other special interests should receive due consideration in the administration of public lands, but the overall public interest must be paramount, and special interests must not be allowed to exploit public lands or to gain vested rights to the public's resources.

2. Any individual or group that is granted the privilege of special use of the public lands should pay a reasonable fee for that privilege, based on fair market values, and should be held accountable for any abuse.

3. There should be no mass transfer of public lands to private ownership, or of federal lands to the states.

4. The public lands should be managed so as to protect or enhance the resource base.

5. Under the concepts of sustained yield and multiple use, the public lands should be managed for a mix of purposes, including watershed protection, soil and forest conservation, wildlife habitat improvement, wilderness, and outdoor recreation—as well as for the production of timber, livestock, minerals, and other commodities. The public interest requires continued availability of renewable resources of the highest quality.

6. Public lands should be classified into management units, with each unit managed according to a comprehensive, multiple use land management plan. Management plans should be prepared by interdisciplinary teams of natural resource professionals, with ample public participation and in full compliance with the National Environmental Policy Act.

7. To realize long-term productivity potentials of public lands, mechanisms should be established to promote long-range management planning and to ensure commitment of funds for the long run.

8. To permit efficient administration and management of all public land resources, action should be taken to eliminate undesirable private inholdings, dispose of small, isolated tracts not useful to the public, block out boundaries, and otherwise consolidate public land holdings through exchange, purchase, sale, or other means.

9. User advisory boards should be truly advisory—not administrative in nature—and should equitably represent all land user interests, including outdoor recreation and wildlife.

10. The League rejects the concept of dominant use proposed by the Public Land Law Review Commission and opposes any measure that would give timber production, livestock grazing, or mineral extraction philosophical or legal precedence over other multiple use objectives for public lands.

11. Public land resources should be managed by professional managers, without political intervention in the analysis, evaluation, and display of management options. Choices among options may be made properly on political or economic grounds.

12. Publicly owned conservation areas should not be used as waste disposal sites.

13. The public forests should be managed to serve a broad spectrum of public purposes and uses, recognizing that the bulk of the nation's long-term timber potential is on lands owned by industry, farmers, and other private parties. Commodity uses of public forests must not be overemphasized at the expense of public values, such as fish and wildlife, outdoor recreation, water quality, scenic beauty, wilderness, and natural ecosystems.

14. The League supports the sustained-yield concept of forest management but recognizes that sustained timber yields should not necessarily be taken from lands that are valuable primarily for noncommodity purposes and where sustained-yield harvest would be incompatible with those purposes.

15. Management of timber on federal forestlands should be according to standards that

- are consistent with the nondeclining, even-flow, sustained-yield concept;
- analyze each proposal for the culture and harvesting of forest products and related construction activities in terms of impacts on water quality standards, fish and wildlife habitat, old-growth values, protective buffer strips, endangered species, aesthetic values, silvicultural practices, and forest type;

- permit individual forests to set their own goals through the forest-planning process, even if those goals do not meet national output targets;
- provide for public participation in planning;
- identify areas where harvesting of forest products is prohibited or subordinate to other uses;
- require reforestation of inadequately stocked forestland and generally prohibit timber sales in the absence of techniques and funding to assure restocking with desirable species within five years;
- base allowable cut on actual standing timber, not on theoretical gains from intensive forestry practices;
- provide for the full utilization of any timber cut or killed;
- ensure that rotations are sufficiently long in duration to serve wildlife, recreation, and other public purposes and are fully compatible with multiple use management;
- prohibit conversion of existing stands to other forest types solely to maximize commodity outputs;
- ensure that management practices minimize damage to the environment and that unavoidable damage is promptly mitigated;
- encourage uneven-age management, especially in the eastern hardwoods;
- limit the size and visual impact of clearcuts where even-age management is used;
- implement an environmentally safe gypsy moth management program; and
- are conducted in strict compliance with all environmental laws.

16. In general, the next generation of forest plans should place greater emphasis on fisheries, aquatic resources, remote habitats, watersheds, and wildlife; deemphasize timber harvest relative to other resource values; and scale back excessive road building.

17. When properly planned, controlled burning offers a valuable tool for scientific forest management.

18. Exportation of raw logs from federal and state lands should be restricted to ease demands on federal forests and protect domestic wood products jobs. Importation of foreign timber products that have not been treated for pests should be banned.

19. Federal old-growth forests in the Pacific Northwest should be protected from logging wherever old-growth values are incompatible with timber harvest. The League urges Congress to protect the biologically significant rem-

nants of remaining ancient forests. Other old-growth areas should be managed to maintain existing old-growth attributes and dependent plant and animal communities, to minimize fragmentation of stands, and to preserve migration corridors. Harvests of old-growth forests at nonsustainable levels should not be mandated by law, nor should Congress limit judicial review of federal forest management.

20. The national forest road system includes some three hundred eighty thousand miles of roads, many of which are in poor condition and causing environmental damage. Approximately one-third of national forest lands are still roadless and provide many ecological benefits for wildlife and the environment. The U.S. Forest Service has established policies that would protect these areas from future road building and restore roads that are causing associated damage. The League supports:

- Forest Service efforts to delineate and protect the inventoried roadless areas from permanent road building;
- elimination or repair of existing roads that are causing environmental damage;
- adequate Forest Service appropriations by Congress to accomplish these goals;
- exclusion of all off-highway vehicles within the designated roadless areas, except on officially designated trails; and
- active management, when deemed necessary, by stewardship contracting rather than commercial logging contracts.

John Heissenbuttel

Vice President, American Forest and Paper Association

The Challenge of Keeping U.S. Conservation Competitive Globally

It is an honor and a privilege to represent the U.S. forest products industry at the centennial celebration of the U.S. Forest Service. I would like to cover three areas today. First, reflect on the last one hundred years. Second, pass along a few thoughts on the current situation. And third, identify what I believe is the challenge for the next century.

The Last One Hundred Years

Over the past hundred years the American public has adopted forest conservation as a core value. The Forest Service deserves most of the credit for instilling this core value. Of course, there were important partners, including the state foresters, but the Forest Service was the real leader. Think about it: today the public expects reforestation, protection against forest fires, providing wildlife habitat, and professional forest management. Every man and woman who has ever worked for the Forest Service should be very proud of instilling this forest conservation value in the American public. This brings me to the current situation.

The Current Situation

It is because of this publicly held forest conservation value that we now have abundant forests, and all of the various interest groups on this panel and in the room can argue as to how they should be managed. The good news is that today there is pretty good agreement at the fifty-thousand-foot level by the broad diversity of responsible interest groups. This is significantly different than just ten or fifteen years ago, when those of us on this panel could not have a constructive dialogue.

It is because of this publicly held forest conservation value that we have protected our forest so much and now have 190 million acres of federal lands at risk of catastrophic wildfire. The good news is that the public supports active forest management as a key element to solve this problem.

We also now have numerous interest groups and individuals whose mission it seems is to attack the credibility of the Forest Service. The good news is, and the fact is, that the Forest Service enjoys the highest credibility of any organization with the American public when it comes to issues related to the environment and forests. Poll after poll of public opinion confirms that the Chief of the Forest Service is the most credible spokesperson in America on these issues. The Forest Service should be very proud of this credibility they have earned over the past century. This brings me to my third point.

The Challenge for the Next One Hundred Years

Some indicators of the challenge include:

Land conversion. We are now seeing working forests converted to other uses at the rate of thousands of acres per day nationwide.

Increasing wood imports. We are seeing imports of wood products increase, with much of this increase coming from countries that do not share our forest conservation values.

Decreasing U.S. wood products production. While our forest growth far exceeds our harvest, the U.S. wood products industry is shrinking.

Increasing demands. We seem to demand more—clean water, wildlife, aesthetics, wood fiber, recreation, etc.—from our forests than we ever have, and those demands continue to increase.

It seems we have been successful in instilling the forest conservation value, but we have yet to figure out how to make this forest conservation value competitive in the global marketplace. *We will not continue to enjoy the broad benefits of our U.S. forests if these lands do not retain their value to the landowners. If the benefits of our forests are undercut by foreign competition, then there will likely be a strong incentive to convert forests to other uses with higher values.* This is our biggest challenge over the next century. The Forest Service must leverage all the credibility it has earned with the public over the last century to lead or facilitate the U.S. forestry community and public to figure out how to make our country's forest conservation commitment competitive. State and federal agencies, industry, private landowners, conservation groups, and local communities need to be part of responding to this challenge.

Just a few thoughts on strategies or tactics: I believe I would start with thinking beyond the Forest Service as just national forests. The Forest Service includes Research and State and Private Forestry. Forest Service research can help increase forest productivity, which will increase the global competitiveness of U.S. working forests. At the same time, research can help us figure out how to do this in a way that protects, provides, and increases all the values we expect from the forest.

Many speakers today have mentioned the need for outreach to the public and urban areas. This is where Forest Service State and Private Forestry is so important. Forest Service State and Private Forestry programs, together with their state forester partners, are critical to reaching these people. At the same time we can't forget about the largest landowner segment in the United States—the family forest. We must find a means to create some economic incentive for private landowners to extract some financial value for producing public benefits—for meeting the expectations of the American forest conservation value.

Now that I have thrown out some thoughts, let me summarize.

First, the Forest Service should be proud of instilling a core forest conservation value in the American public and in the process earning enormous credibility.

Second, the Forest Service should use this credibility to help the American people find a way to make our commitment to forest conservation globally competitive.

I am optimistic that we can make our commitment to forest conservation globally competitive. I am optimistic because I see evidence that many of the leaders of the various interest groups are more willing to find solutions. I am optimistic because making our commitment to forest conservation globally competitive is the right thing to do, and despite our differences, Americans have always figured out how to do the right thing. I am confident that at the bicentennial, the Forest Service will reflect proudly on the previous century.

Robert E. Douglas
President, National Forest Counties and Schools Coalition

Multiple Use Management as the Foundation for National Forest and Community Sustainability

It is a distinct honor to be here representing the almost eight hundred forest counties and over four thousand forest communities of America. As counties and communities that are in and adjacent to our national forests, we currently have—and historically have had—a deep and abiding interest in the health and management of our national forests. After all, these forests are where we have chosen to live, work, and raise our families. Over the course of the last one hundred years, our communities have been active partners with the U.S. Forest Service in the management of our forest reserves and national forests. In the early 1890s, there was great concern in the forest counties of the West when Congress granted to the President the power to set aside U.S. forest reserves by proclamation. In a sixteen-year period from 1891 through 1907, almost 148 million acres (153 national forests) were set aside as forest reserves. These lands were set aside, removed from settlement and economic development, but without guidance as to their management. As you might imagine, emotions and viewpoints were intense. In 1897, when the Black Hills Forest Reserve was formed, thirty thousand people gathered in a demonstration in Rapid City, South Dakota, condemning the reserve as disastrous to the economy of the Black Hills. Part of the problem was that we as a people had not decided what we wanted to accomplish with these new reserves. By the end of 1897, the level of concern had grown sufficiently strong that Congress acted to begin to define the purposes for how our national forest reserves would be managed. They defined these purposes to be

- to improve and protect the forest within each reservation;
- to secure favorable conditions of water flows; and
- to furnish a continuous supply of timber for the use and necessities of citizens of the United States.

From 1897 through 1908 this multiple use concept was further refined and focused and the relationship between forest communities and the national forest was defined. The general mood of the country can be summarized by a quote from the assistant commissioner of the General Land Office in 1905:

"The general policy of the Forestry Bureau and our office, so far as these reserves are concerned, is to utilize them to the largest degree possible, consistent with good administration. It is necessary to the successful policy and administration of the forestry work, to allow the largest use possible of the reserves consistent with proper protection."

During that same period the differences between national parks and national forests were defined. Those intended differences were reflected in the following quote from the report of the Chief Forester in 1913: "The National Forests are set aside specifically for the protection of water resources and the protection of timber. The aim of the administration is essentially different from that of a National Park, in which the economic use of material resources comes second to reservation of the natural conditions on aesthetic grounds."

Thus, from the beginning, our national forests were established for the dual purposes of protecting the resource and for the utilitarian purpose of the people. In his 1907 book entitled *The Use of the National Forests*, Gifford Pinchot stated, "The National Forests are for use by all of the people. Their resources are now used in such a commonsense way that instead of being used up they keep coming. They are for the present use, for use a few years ahead, and for use a long time ahead." He clearly envisioned sustained multiple use of our national forests in perpetuity.

To finally address the concerns of forest counties regarding the economic impacts of establishing these reserves, the Congress acted in 1906 to share ten percent of all national forest revenues with forest counties for the maintenance of public schools and public roads. Two years later, in 1908, in response to a continuing outcry from the West, the revenue share was increased to twenty-five percent. So by 1908, the forest counties of America had become active partners with the U.S. Forest Service in the management of our national forests. The management philosophy of sustained yield, multiple use management was the very foundation of this 1908 compact with the forest counties and communities of America. Clearly, the intent of the compact was to actively manage these lands in a multiple use manner in perpetuity, and to share the revenues derived from their management with local forest counties and the U.S. Treasury. In return, forest counties agreed to provide the essential infrastructures of public schools and roads in communities in and adjacent to the reserves.

From the perspective of our forest counties, this compact worked marvelously well from 1908 until the mid-1980s. Forest counties developed and prospered as a result of natural resource–based economies founded upon sustained yield, multiple use management of our national forests. However, during the last twenty years we have strayed away from our founding philosophy and vision of our national forests. Commonsense conservationism has been overpowered by the political and legal pressure of active environmentalism. Our laws, regulations, and courts have systematically transformed the dual mission of our national forests—to improve and protect forest resources while simultaneously using these resources to benefit the people of the United States, including those who live in and adjacent to our national forests. Over the last two decades, the mission has been dramatically shifted from a vision of improving and protecting our forests to an interpretation that our new mission is one of hands-off preservation, at the expense of (1) forest health, (2) the economic and social stability of forest communities, and (3) a reduced return on investment to the taxpayers of America. Our forests were originally established for a well-thought-out dual purpose, and the forest counties of America remain steadfastly committed to maintaining these purposes. We believe a thoughtful and purposeful return to our foundation philosophy is desperately needed and overdue. We also believe that long-term sustained yield management of our national forests is both economically and ecologically possible, given modern forest science.

It is ironic that the conditions and concerns when our national forests were created in 1905 are remarkably similar in many ways to the conditions and concerns that exist today, although the reasons for those concerns are quite different.

1905

For instance, in 1905, we were experiencing the rise of conservationism in response to public concerns about uncontrolled wildfires and reckless timber harvesting. In 1905, the conservation movement was approximately thirty-five years old.

The prevailing public interest was in protecting our forests for future generations.

From a business, industry, and consumer viewpoint, our national forest founders were equally concerned with providing forest materials and abundant water for a growing nation.

2005

One hundred years later, in 2005, we see definite parallels.

We are experiencing a rise in environmentalism as our population becomes more concentrated in urban and suburban centers and less connected to the land. The modern environmental movement is about thirty-five years old.

We have intense public concern about conflagration-level wildfires as a result of overstocked timber stands and accumulated fuel loads. (We are reaping the benefits of a hundred years of highly effective fire prevention efforts.)

Our most unique modern concern about the protection of our forests centers on their health; specifically, we have serious concerns about overstocked and dangerous forests due to escalating fuel loads, epidemic insect infestations, and uncontrolled competition from nonnative invasive plant and animal species. Today our forests are not being victimized by reckless harvesting, but are instead in danger of demise from the side effects of inactive management.

Finally, from a business, industry, and consumer viewpoint, we continue to be concerned about the need for forest materials and abundant and reliable water supplies for a continually growing population.

In 2005, the United States is the largest consumer of wood products worldwide, and our appetite for forest products is growing each year.

In the last twenty years, timber production and harvesting on national forest lands have declined by over eighty-five percent and are continuing to decline on most forests.

Unfortunately, we are displacing our growing appetite for wood products on selected undeveloped areas of the world, many with less stringent environmental protections. In 2005, we need to be concerned about the stewardship of the world's forests as well as our own.

The Future

Our challenges in the coming century lie in the following areas:

- restoring our national forests to pre-European structures and a condition of long-term sustainability;
- providing fiber, materials, and clean water for a continually expanding nation;
- meeting the recreation needs of an expanding American population;
- creating new and better systems for managing the wildland-urban interface as our population surrounds our public lands; and
- creating a new nation of commonsense conservationists that truly understand the science and vision of sustained, multiple use management.

These challenges are not mutually exclusive but are deeply interrelated and interdependent. In our view, we must return to the active multiple use management of our national forests in order to simultaneously achieve all of these goals:

- We must build upon the excellent start outlined in the Healthy Forests Restoration Act. We must improve, treat, and restore the health of our national forests on a landscape scale. They are deteriorating and being destroyed on a landscape scale and nothing less will stand the test of the challenge before us.

- We must acknowledge that it is once again appropriate and desirable to provide materials from our national forests to supply new and emerging industries in our forest communities and the nation. By doing so, we restore long-term economic and social stability to these communities, protect their vitally needed industrial infrastructures, and generate federal revenues for reinvestment in forest restoration. We must no longer apologize for harnessing the free-enterprise system to utilize, in a sustained manner, marketable forest assets owned by the American people as a means of ensuring that our forests are improved and restored for future generations.

- We must recognize that economic and ecological sustainability in a modern era are interrelated and interdependent. We need to provide U.S.-grown forest products for our expanding population's demand for wood products on a long-term sustainable basis. Reducing both our trade deficit and our reliance on foreign natural resources is an essential step in strengthening our economic well-being. Simultaneously, we need to become more responsible consumers of global forest products and become more reliant upon our own resources instead of exploiting the less-protected forests in other parts of the world. The U.S. Forest Service should be the leaders in promoting responsible stewardship of the world's forests by exporting research, technology, and silviculture while simultaneously managing our own national forest resources in such a way that we reduce U.S. reliance on foreign forests to the extent possible. Congress must maintain trade policies that place incentives on the use of U.S.-grown forest products in order to facilitate achieving an appropriate balance between domestic and foreign reliance.

- We must maintain our commitment to forest science inquiry. In our view, the long-term health and vitality of our forests and our communities are also directly tied to U.S. Forest Service research efforts in the Forest Products Laboratory, experimental forests, and forest research stations. Robust support must be maintained for these efforts. The foundation for emerging industries and technologies and the future health of global forest ecosystems hinge upon the success of these endeavors.

- We must find more and better ways to assist and engage the American public in using and improving the health and vitality of our national forests. Gateway communities and communities within the national forests are now more important than ever. Maintaining infrastructure, such as roads, schools, hospitals, and law enforcement, is essential. With increasing user pressures, protecting the economic well-being of these communities is a primary ingredient in ensuring that there is a well-trained workforce to manage the public lands, and businesses and services to provide for those who use these lands. In our view, the key to expanding the national forest experience for a growing American population lies in strengthening the U.S. Forest Service partnership with forest counties and communities. In addition to providing services, local communities must be more engaged in defining public land management practices. We must defeat adversarial gridlock, one community at a time. Current cooperative partnerships, such as the seventy resource advisory committees that have been established in the last four years under the Secure Rural Schools and Communities Act of 2000, the community-based forestry projects growing across the country, and the budding stewardship projects all point to a stronger, more proactive partnership between local communities and the Forest Service, with multiple benefits for all, including the American public and their forests.
- Finally, educating the American public about the philosophy and science of sustained, multiple use management of our national forests must occupy a central place in the twenty-first-century mission of the U.S. Forest Service. As a society that is increasingly centered in urban and suburban communities, we face mounting public policy challenges. Never before have so many been so far removed from the land that sustains their lives. The impact of agricultural and natural resource illiteracy on America's economic, ecological, and social future may prove to be staggering. We must be committed to creating a scientifically literate population that can inform future public policy as a new generation of "scientifically grounded commonsense conservationists." This needs to be a national effort combining the powerful resources of our nation's public school system, our national textbook publishers, our state and federal natural resource management agencies, conservation organizations, and our forest communities. In a democracy, the most effective public policy is created when there exists an enlightened electorate. This will protect our national forests from succumbing to the politics of extremism on either side of the forest

management debate. The U.S. Forest Service should take the lead in launching a new, nationwide initiative to create an enlightened American populace regarding the philosophy and science underlying sustained, multiple use management of our national forests and rangelands. Replanting and nurturing scientifically grounded commonsense conservationism in America needs to be a central part of our work together over the next century.

We have many of the same concerns that we did in 1905, but in most cases for different reasons. Over the last one hundred years, we have made great strides in our understanding of forests and their ecosystems, and as a nation we have learned much about our bold experiment with public lands. We have made mistakes and have learned from them. Our greatest hope lies in harnessing the human resources living in forest communities and cities across this land. Together, as concerned citizens and stewards of the forests for our next generation, we can and will find collaborative solutions to the challenges that lie ahead. We must strive to positively revise our laws, regulations, and legal interpretations in a manner that places incentives on the sustained multiple use of our nations natural resources. If we are successful, then we can expect the U.S. Forest Service during its next one hundred years to contribute to the health and vitality of our forests, our communities, and our nation. We deserve nothing less.

Premier Screening of *The Greatest Good:*
A Forest Service Centennial Film

January 4, 2005
3:15 pm

Char Miller
Steven Dunsky

january 3-6
2005
washington dc

US Forest Service
Centennial
Congress
A Collective Commitment to Conservation

Char Miller

History Professor, Trinity University

The Greatest Good: A People's History of a Public Agency

The Forest Service was born in controversy—and has yet to escape its birthright. That's a good thing. No public agency, regardless of its age and mission, should be free from public scrutiny, released from public accountability, or able to finesse public critique.

Gifford Pinchot, the agency's founding chief, knew this stricture full well. Arguing in 1907 that the national forests "exist today because the people want them," he declared that the citizenry must assume the primary responsibility for determining their political context and environmental management: "To make them accomplish the most good the people themselves must make clear how they want them run." The public's manifold concerns would not always be in concert, but the social tensions that would result were an essential part of democratic life. Only by acknowledging that controversy is the norm would the Forest Service long endure. That's why Pinchot's most famous maxim was predicated on discord: "and where conflicting interests must be reconciled the question will always be decided from the standpoint of the greatest good of the greatest number in the long run."

The central place of controversy in the history of the Forest Service forms the leitmotiv of *The Greatest Good*, a compelling two-hour documentary of the agency's first one hundred years. Structured in four parts, the film explores in "The Fight for Conservation (1864–1910)" the complex set of forces that brought the agency into being in the late nineteenth and early twentieth century; evaluates, in "Building the System (1911–1940)," how the agency developed the national forests, and the bureaucracy that managed them, paying particular attention to the natural catastrophes and human pressures that challenged its management; "Boom! (1941–1970)" depicts the mid-twentieth-century transformation of the Forest Service from a custodial agency to a timber-producing organization, whose wood products helped build modern suburbs and the consumer culture of the late twentieth century, and gave birth to a series of escalating conflicts that battered the agency's reputation; and "The Greatest Good?" (1971–2005) bears witness to the nation's struggle to come to terms with its demands for new resources on and uses of the public lands, which often clashed with postwar timber production—conflict that challenged and redefined the Forest Service's mission.

As *The Greatest Good* probes this complicated history, it asks tough questions about organizational behavior and cultural discord. How do we explain the source of the long-standing arguments over the Forest Service's actions? The film makes a good case that this has been the result of the agency's origins. Its creation, after all, was a radical experiment in American political history. When in the late nineteenth century the first federal forest reserves were set aside, it marked a sharp break with past practices. Until then, the General Land Office in the Department of the Interior had one key function—to dispose of the public domain. With the creation of the forest reserves in 1891, their enlargement later that decade, and consolidation and rapid expansion as national forests beginning in the early years of the twentieth century, a new form of public lands management was established that was tied to the emergence of a more powerful nation-state. In creating an agency that would in time control more than 190 million acres, Gifford Pinchot and President Theodore Roosevelt were also extending the clout of the executive branch, shaping the lives and livelihoods of a largely western citizenry. Ever since, we have been fighting over the Forest Service, its existence and regulations.

Capturing those struggles, and reflecting the agency's influence on political life and popular culture, has led the filmmakers—Steve Dunsky, Ann Dunsky, and Dave Steinke—to dig deeply into archives and repositories around the country. They unearthed an estimated sixty thousand still images and have pored over reams of official correspondence, public relations releases, and memoranda. In addition to viewing innumerable home movies, television shows (think *Lassie!*), commercials, and agency filmstrips, they conducted upwards of sixty interviews with scholars, activists, agency leaders, field scientists, and office staff, totaling upwards of six hundred hours of raw footage. That they were able to reduce this massive amount of material into an action-packed, two-hour documentary is a testament to their skills as filmmakers and storytellers. Out of their love of the organization for which they work, and their fascination with its rich, flawed, and provocative legacy, has emerged a documentary of delicate balance, precise detail, great energy, and palpable compassion.

Yet for all the film's success on the screen, its creators' exhaustive (and exhausting) research has led to another, more bibliographical triumph. As they worked in the National Archives, the National Agricultural Library, and the Denver Public Library, among other repositories, the team scanned and digitized thousands of images and records. Part of their commitment to preserving the past they were uncovering was to give copies of their research to the libraries where they located them; each now has a high-resolution, digitized, and easily referenced resource that will benefit all subsequent users.

Although Steve, Ann, and Dave may not have known it, their commitment to enhance public access to the history of conservation parallels a decision one of their principal subjects made about his vast trove of documents, records, and correspondence. Gifford Pinchot's will stipulated that all his papers were to be donated to the people of the United States and housed in their archive, the Library of Congress; they form the single largest private collection in its holdings. Wanting nothing to do with a "Pinchot Library," in which his literary remains would be embalmed, he wanted his records to be fully accessible, placing no stipulations on who might read them or how they might be analyzed and interpreted. Because he lived his life in public and served at the people's pleasure, his words and deeds were by rights theirs. A similar conception shaped the decision of the filmmakers of *The Greatest Good* to upgrade substantially the documentary collections they were privileged to work with. In so doing, they share Pinchot's deepest conviction: that the greatest good is the public good.

Steven Dunsky
Audiovisual Manager, USDA Forest Service

Production of *The Greatest Good* Centennial Film

On Tuesday afternoon, January 4, The Greatest Good: A Forest Service Centennial Film *had its world premiere at the Forest Service Centennial Congress. The Congress organizers provided a large ballroom in the Grand Hyatt that easily seated the more than six hundred delegates and invitees. The moviegoers were greeted with a red carpet, large Oscarlike statues at the main entrance, and plenty of popcorn, candy, and soft drinks. The mood was festive and anticipatory as Dr. Char Miller made his introductory remarks. Showing the program to a large audience for the first time, we, the filmmakers, had few clues as to how it would be received. This was the culmination of a four-year effort which bordered on the obsessive. Too nervous to sit, I paced the back of the room as the lights dimmed and the opening quotation appeared on the big screen.*

The idea for a documentary on the history of the Forest Service germinated in a hotel lobby in Rapid City, South Dakota. In March 2001, Dave Steinke and I had just finished shooting a short video introducing the new Chief of the Forest Service. We were already exhausted from chasing Dale Bosworth around the country with a camera for two weeks. Nevertheless, we talked until four A.M. about this big potential project. We knew that no one had ever done a comprehensive film about the agency and its important legacy. We also knew that a successful project would require a deep understanding of the history, support from all levels of the organization, access to thousands of official records, and a great deal of trust from agency leadership. We believed that we were the ones that needed to make the film.

After sleeping for an hour or so, I caught a six A.M. flight back to San Francisco. Dave drove home to Denver, planning to catch some sleep at a rest area along the highway. Instead, he was called to a fire in Oregon and spent the next two weeks sleeping on the ground and working as an incident information officer. That might have been a warning sign; we did not stop running for the next four years.

This was 2001, and we proposed that the project would be completed for the 2005 Forest Service centennial. In fact, the centennial would be prime reason for getting the program approved. We figured that the Forest Service would want a history video but would probably ask for it at the last minute, resulting in a mediocre product. A definitive program would require several years of planning, research, shooting, and editing.

Our first step was to invite a group of colleagues—filmmakers and historians—to a one-day meeting at Grey Towers, the national historic site managed by the Forest Service in Milford, Pennsylvania. Our conference would become a significant milestone in the project (for several reasons; more on that in a moment), as it generated the ideas and the overall outline for the script treatment.

Over the next several months, our proposal filtered up through the Washington Office with support from a newly created program called New Century of Service. This nationwide team of employees, headed by Linda Feldman, was already generating ideas to propel the agency into its next hundred years.

Linda brought the idea to Dale Bosworth and his staff, where it was quickly adopted. Deputy Chief Tom Thompson took the lead role as adviser to the project and liaison to the Chief's office. We soon added Steven Anderson, president of the Forest History Society, and Jeffrey Stine, historian at the Smithsonian National Museum of American History. This small team of reviewers provided invaluable insights at critical junctures throughout the entire production process.

And it turned out that the Forest Service, from the Chief on down, was very supportive of the project. We were given the great privilege and great responsibility of telling this story.

Our group flew into Newark Airport on Sunday, September 9. We picked up a large van and drove across New Jersey to Grey Towers in Milford, Pennsylvania, just across the Delaware River Gap. This chateau-style mansion was once the Pinchot family's summer home. Several of our audiovisual colleagues joined us for a one-day meeting with historians, including Char Miller, biographer of Gifford Pinchot, and Gerald Williams, Forest Service national historian at Grey Towers.

On Tuesday morning we began our meeting, starting to outline the shape and scope of the project. A short while into our meeting, Ed Brannon, the director of Grey Towers (also in the film), came into the room and told me that we should know that a plane had hit the World Trade Center. He did not want to disrupt the meeting, but when we heard about the second plane, our plans for the day's agenda changed quickly. Needless to say, we were all in a state of shock. We had planned to visit New York City later in the week, and we had seen the Twin Towers while flying into Newark two days earlier and even thought we might go sightseeing there.

Moreover, Flight 93 was the same one on which Ann and I were scheduled to return to San Francisco later in the week. That plane crashed in a field not too far away, in western Pennsylvania.

Despite the great tragedy, September 11 turned out to be a strangely auspicious start to the project. We were all stranded in this wonderful historic mansion and in this quaint town of Milford, which is also important to the story. We were able to pick the brains of these respected historians. We had the biographer of Gifford Pinchot, Char Miller, at our disposal. And we were all trying to find some distraction from the events that were unfolding in the outside world.

We decided that we should focus on the project since we were clearly not going anywhere for several days. And so we got to work on the film. Early in the process, we settled on a couple of key points that made it all the way through and into the final show. We wanted to find a "core problematic" for the program. Char Miller suggested a great one, which is that "conflict is inherent to the management of public lands in a democracy." This gave us the key to the film in several ways: it allowed us to talk about the conflicts that have been with the Forest Service since the beginning, and do it in a way that embraced the controversy. In other words, conflict is a good thing; it shows that our system is working, as Char Miller says late in the film. Also, from a filmmaker's standpoint, this is a great theme, because as we all know, conflict is essential to dramatic storytelling.

The other thing we decided on early, and never changed, was the main title, "The Greatest Good." It comes from a letter that Gifford Pinchot wrote to himself as the Chief Forester of this new agency that he and Teddy Roosevelt created in 1905. The letter spells out the mission of the Forest Service, and one phrase, and one that appears at the beginning of the film, states: "where conflicting interests must be reconciled, the question shall always be decided from the standpoint of the greatest good of the greatest number in the long run." It is a concept that Pinchot is borrowing from the nineteenth-century philosophy of utilitarianism. It sums up the idea that natural resources are to be used, and not overused, for the benefit of all people in a sustainable way. Because these resources are limited, we must have some principle for resolving the conflicts over use.

Now, the questions of what that greatest good is and who gets to decide it are, in hindsight, quite troublesome questions. Pinchot and the other Progressives believed that those questions, particularly with regard to public lands, should be decided by professionals—scientific foresters, such as him. Bill Cronon says at one point in the film that Pinchot's foresters believed they were doing the right thing, and in the face of the massive forest and range degradation that they faced at the time, it is hard to argue with them. But, Cronon adds, their missionary zeal will sometimes get them into trouble. As we will see in the film, our ideas about the greatest good change over time, and as we reach the later years of the twentieth century, our ability to reach any consensus on a common greatest good breaks down, along with our trust in scientific "experts" and government agencies. One of the challenges we face in the next hundred years is finding that common ground that allows us work together to solve very real problems.

An important subtheme of the film, around which many of the stories revolve, is the idea of "use," and in particular the tension that has existed throughout the history of the conservation movement between use and preservation. Since perhaps the 1950s, the outdoor recreating public, particularly people from urban and suburban areas, have lost the distinction between the ideas of conservation and preservation, and in doing so, they often confuse national forests with national parks. This has led to a lot of misunderstanding about the mission of the Forest Service, and it is one that we try to clarify in the film.

One thing that did change in the process of making the film was the subtitle. We went from calling it "*The* History of the Forest Service" to "*A* History of the Forest Service" to "A Forest Service Centennial Film." This reflected our increasing awareness that we would only be able to tell a small part of the story. There is just too much complexity in the organization and across the country for us to tell a complete history in two hours. And so, by necessity and with regret, we left out a lot of information that is critically important to understanding the Forest Service. The two criticisms that we get, sometimes in one breath, are that the film is too long and why did you leave out…(fill in the blank). We do, however, have James Lewis's book *The Forest Service and the Greatest Good*, which serves as a wonderful companion text. And we included five additional hours of video material on a three-disk DVD set. These fill in many of the gaps in the movie.

The making of the film itself was a three-year process that involved an enormous amount of research. In order to develop the treatment, I read shelves of material. We worked closely with our advisers from Forest History Society and the Smithsonian. We delved deeply into the audiovisual records of the National Archives, looking at hundreds of old Forest Service films, going back to 1918. We looked at thousands of old photos there, and at the Denver Public Library, and lots of other university, library, and Forest Service collections. We even asked Forest Service retirees for their old home movies.

We decided to shoot it in HD, at a time when it was just getting started as a production format—a steep learning curve. We shot footage around the nation and even a bit in France and Germany (on our vacation). We wanted the film to reflect the many perspectives that have shaped the Forest Service and national forests for the past century. And so we interviewed over seventy people around the country—historians; people from industry, the political arena, and environmental community; as well Forest Service retirees, including all the living Chiefs of the Forest Service. We used about forty of the seventy interviews in the program, but we learned from all of them.

In all, we had over six hundred hours of material with which to work, in addition to several thousand photos. The unenviable task of pulling all this into a coherent program fell to the editor—my wife, Ann. She worked nonstop for the last six months of postproduction and did an amazing job of pulling it all together. Fortunately, digital technologies, using high-resolution scans and file transfers and low-cost animation software, allowed us to work collaboratively with people in Seattle, San Francisco, Denver, Atlanta, and Washington, D.C.

We were influenced by many factors, some of which were other films. A documentary called *The Kid Stays in the Picture* provided some ideas for treating still photographs, and I have always admired an older film called *The World of Tomorrow* (about the 1939 New York World's Fair) for its treatment of old films and photos not just as illustrations of a time, but as cultural products of their time.

We see this type of film as an iterative process, whereby we learn about the subject as we make the film. We tried hard to avoid preconceptions and to give all sides a fair hearing. Most of all, we did not want it to be, in Ed Brannon's phrase, "a glorious rendition of a flawless past." We did not want to make a puff piece about the Forest Service. We deliberately chose not to cover the events after about 1990. They are too recent for a reasonable historical analysis and too much a part of the current political debate. The film does provide some context for this debate, however, and shows us that these conflicts are not new. We also wanted the ending of the film to be open-ended. The centennial is not at the end of anything here; we are in the middle of a very important process in which we all need to be engaged. We would like to hear your thoughts on what is the greatest good.

To return briefly out our 9/11 experience, I should mention that we decided to drive back across the country. Seven Forest Service audiovisual specialists boarded our rental van in eastern Pennsylvania, and we stopped in various states to drop off people in different Forest Service offices. Ann and I drove all the way back to California.

After our three years of production, The Greatest Good *premiered at the Forest Service Centennial Congress on January 4. It was a long road from Rapid City to Washington, D.C., but the positive response from the audience overwhelmed us with a mixture of joy and relief. We thank the Forest Service, our advisers, and our families for all the support we had received during the making of the film. We feel extremely privileged to be given the opportunity to tell this wonderful history and then to show it at this historic event.*

Congressional Views on the Nation's Forests and Rangelands

January 5, 2005
8:00 am

Mark Rey *(Moderator)*
Greg Walden
Larry Craig
Pete Domenici *(did not attend)*
Mark Udall
Norm Dicks *(did not attend)*

january 3-6
2005
washington dc

US Forest Service
Centennial
Congress
A Collective Commitment to Conservation

Greg Walden

U.S. Representative (R-Oregon)

Remarks on the Occasion of the Centennial of the U.S. Forest Service

It is an honor and pleasure to join you for this historic event to celebrate this agency's century of service to our country and its forests and grasslands; and to ponder its next one hundred years.

It is especially nice to be with Under Secretary Mark Rey and Chief Dale Bosworth and their staff. President Bush has assembled a team that I believe will go down in history as one of the best the Service has seen—one that is willing to tackle tough problems and develop balanced solutions that are based on the input and support of local citizens. Thank you for your leadership.

This morning, I will briefly focus on the history of the forest reserves, the management problems that we've encountered along the way, and how best to solve those problems.

Though it's always difficult to predict the future, one thing we know is that whatever road the agency takes, it is going to be a rough one, with plenty of ruts, bumps, washouts, and detours. The best we can hope is that we have a strong rig, a veteran driver, a good map, and plenty of fuel. We have a long way to go, and much to accomplish.

Other speakers at this conference have no doubt discussed those great visionaries of a century ago who saw the need to protect lands, especially in the West, for future generations. The creators of the great forest reserves, parks, and grasslands understood the importance of these resources both for wildlife and for the country's future development.

In a speech he delivered in Salt Lake City one hundred years ago, President Theodore Roosevelt spoke of the purpose of the forest reserves and the need for local support to ensure this new federal policy would work. Let me share with you his words from that day:

> *Almost every industry depends in some more or less vital way upon the preservation of the forests; and while citizens die, the government and the nation do not die, and we are bound in dealing with the forests to exercise the foresight necessary to use them now, but to use them in such a way as will also keep them for those who are to come after us.*

The first great object of the forest reserves is, of course, the first great object of the whole land policy of the United States—the creation of homes, the favoring of the home-maker. That is why we wish to provide for the home-makers of the present and the future the steady and continuous supply of timber, grass and above all, of water. That is the object of the forest reserves, and that is why I bespeak your cordial cooperation in their preservation.

Remember, you must realize what I thoroughly realize, that however wise a policy may be it can be enforced only if the people of the States believe in it. We can enforce the provisions of the forest reserve law or of any other law only so far as the best sentiment of the community or the State will permit that enforcement. Therefore it lies primarily not with the people of Washington, but with you, yourselves, to see that such polices are supported as will redound to the benefit of the home-makers and therefore the sure and stated building up of the State as a whole.

In these words and actions of President Theodore Roosevelt we can still hear the echo of balance and multiple use—of providing for the needs of that day, and for the needs of the future.

Theodore Roosevelt was many things, but principal among them, he was a man of action. And if he were to join us today, I hardly believe he would be happy knowing that 190 million acres of the federal forest reserves are subject to catastrophic wildfire, disease, and bug infestation. This Rough Rider of a President would throw a fit if he knew we were losing more than forty-five hundred acres a day to the spread of noxious weeds. The man who charged up San Juan Hill would never stand for the gridlock that has overtaken the ability of the trained professionals in the Forest Service to effectively manage the forests. And neither should we.

Gridlock, litigation, divisiveness, process predicament, polarization: these are words and phrases that describe national forest issues today.

Let us not defend a system that allows a symphony of fiddlers to tie us up in court for years while bugs devour our forests and fires ravage our communities.

Let us not defend a system that is so complicated that it takes three times longer to remove a burned, dead tree than to rebuild the Pentagon.

And let us not believe that we lack the power to change things. Not only do we have the power to affect change, but also we have the solemn responsibility to identify what is wrong, engage the public in finding solutions, and then take the action necessary to bring about a better policy.

Too often my colleagues in Congress blame agencies and the courts for what we see as wrong. And yet, we are the writers of the laws. We are the ones empowered to solve problems. And the time has come for us to do the heavy lifting.

There are many factors that have contributed to create this state of affairs, such as

- an inconsistent and often contradictory "crazy quilt" of laws and regulations, as Jack Thomas aptly put it;
- an increasingly urban population that in the East is far removed from forest realities;
- a well-funded environmental political industry that aggressively opposes active forest management; and
- and an indecisive if not bipolar Congress.

These and a number of other factors have created a situation that has proved calamitous to forests and forest communities.

A few years ago these circumstances would have seemed insurmountable, but the recent passage of the Healthy Forests Restoration Act with such resounding bipartisan support leads me to believe that a new consensus is emerging that will provide the Forest Service with the mandate and support it needs to move towards the sustainable management of our national forests.

While the passage of this act is important and precedent setting, it is hardly grounds for euphoria, especially given that there are approximately 190 million acres of federal land still at a high risk of catastrophic fire, and the act's provisions are limited to just 10 ½ percent of that area. But at least we have turned the corner, and this is cause for hope.

Now other words and phrases are beginning to illustrate national forest issues: community wildfire protection plans…resource advisory committees… collaborative stewardship…partnerships…desired forest conditions…light-touch forestry…

As Chief Bosworth says, we must focus less on what we take *from* our forests and more on what we *leave* behind.

This is a dialogue that can only effectively happen close to the forests themselves. Conflicting values at the national level, propagated by special-interest name-calling and sloganeering, have not and will not produce lasting solutions.

It's often said that all politics is local; this is even truer for forestry. While national guidelines and sideboards are necessary, it is at the individual forest level where decisions best incorporate the uniqueness of each ecosystem— local climate, flora, fauna, soils, communities, economies, knowledge, and the many other factors that vary from place to place. Handwringing rancor inside the Beltway does little for a bark beetle epidemic in the Sierras or hurricane blowdown on the Apalachicola.

The future of the Forest Service and the health of our national forests will be tied directly to our ability to successfully maintain this trend of moving dialogue and decisions closer to the ground, where issues are tangible and decisions have their greatest impact. This is the very concept declared fundamental by President Roosevelt in speeches a century ago.

While much has changed since President Roosevelt made his remarks, his warning that local communities and states must believe in and be a part of national forest policies for them to be successful continues to ring true. A policy of benign neglect that allows our forests to continue to become tinderboxes may appease a small segment of the population in the short term, but in the long term it will certainly spell disaster for the necessary support and ultimate health of our forest reserves.

As chairman of the Subcommittee on Forests and Forest Health, I plan to pursue an aggressive agenda of problem solving and action in the 109th Congress. I want to know how the Healthy Forests Restoration Act is working, and if there are problems, I want to hear about them and fix them. Further, I intend to hold the agency accountable to using these new tools to aggressively bring about healthier forests, watersheds, and habitat, while making our communities safer.

I want to get a better understanding of the backlog of reforestation. How far behind are we in planting new trees for the next generation? I want to untie the knots of postcatastrophe restoration. Why does it take three years to cut burned, dead trees after a fire? Why do the courts rule the forests while bugs devour, multiply, and take flight into healthy stands? Why do we let the value slip away when we lack funds for restoration?

What is the status of our national trails system? As a hiker and backpacker, I've seen some spectacular trails and sights, and I've seen the danger of neglect.

And we will continue our work to make sure our firefighters have the tools and funding to match the courage and ability we've seen time and again.

The United States Forest Service is an organization that has a proud past and can still have a bright future. There is a wonderful camaraderie among Forest Service employees that is enviable for any large organization, let alone a government agency. The future of the Forest Service rests on the shoulders of this spirit and provides hope for the many of us that want to see it thrive and succeed in its mission of caring for the land and serving people.

Together we have the knowledge and ability to help federal land managers become the best stewards on the face of the planet. We in the Congress owe no less to those in the Service and to current and future generations.

I look forward to working with all of you as we attempt to keep Roosevelt's vision intact on the bumpy road of the Forest Service's second century.

Larry Craig

U.S. Senator (R-Idaho)

Good morning everyone. Thank you, Mark [Rey], for that interesting introduction. I say so because I think he puts me in that interesting category of those who might have not been quite so excited about some of his agenda items as others were during the 108th Congress. I will suggest that the 108th Congress was in large part a Congress of change for the U.S. Forest Service and for the public forested lands of this nation. We did accomplish some things after nearly two decades of stagnation as it relates to legislation that in some way directed activities toward the management of our public lands. A congressman who had for some time been in opposition to what we trying to do with the Healthy Forests legislation was seated beside me down at the White House for the signing of the legislation, and I elbowed him. I had served with him in the House in a previous occasion. I asked him, "Why did you finally support this most important piece of legislation?" He looked at me and smiled and said, "Smoke got in my eyes and improved my vision."

I would hope that the smoke that has gotten into our eyes over the last eight to ten years does improve our vision. I think that it has here, in the Congress, as it relates to a need to make some changes in public land and in U.S. Forest Service public land policies that reflect the dynamics of the interests, the involvement, and the use of our public lands today, and I think that we're making some headway in that area. But the struggle that Mark has not mentioned, called Fee Demo [Recreation Fee Demonstration Program], is clearly the need to build a financial base for the U.S. Forest Service that it currently does not enjoy. Its financial situations have changed over the last two decades especially, and the last decade in particular—from an agency that once produced phenomenal revenues for the national Treasury, and therefore had plenty of money to fund all of its interests and all of its programs, to one today that must come to the U.S. Congress and ask for money from the general fund and not put substantial money into the general fund. As a result, it has changed the dynamics, and it has caused us, as I've challenged Mark and Chief Bosworth, to have to find a solution to our funding problems, because we cannot beg from one program and steal from another during critical times of fire and not replace those moneys in a timely fashion for the ongoing programs that we think now are extremely valuable—whether they be stewardship, or whether they are complementary to or intricately involved in the Healthy Forests Initiative, or whether they be recreation or trail maintenance—all of that large agenda out there that the public now expects of us all as we deal with our public land management. So those are our challenges.

I would suggest that, whether it was 1905 or the year 2005, the passion and the interests in our public forested lands are every bit as great. That hasn't changed; attitudes about it have changed. Clearly, perspectives of how we manage these lands have changed over that one hundred years. But the passion is still there, whether it's in my state of Idaho, or in Colorado or Oregon or anywhere else across this nation, where our public enjoys access to our forested public lands. There is without question deep passion for these public lands and all that they provide for us.

I'll suggest just one other area that I find absolutely fascinating, and we've spent some time on it, and we will challenge ourselves to spend even more time on it over the course of the next decade. I've just returned from Buenos Aires, where I led the congressional delegation for the United States to the United Nations Climate Change Convention, or COP-10 [tenth Conference of Parties]. Our scientists today in this country, because of the pooling of science and the building of a new scientific format directed by this administration and the National Oceanic and Atmospheric Administration, are bringing together all of those who had different views about what climate change was all about into a scientific pool that is now beginning to yield a base of knowledge and understanding that I think is going to be extremely valuable for all of us.

Let me conclude with a couple of items.

First of all, this old globe of ours is warming. It may be warming faster than it should, and if greenhouse gases are a contributing factor to that warming, there is no way possible to contain those gases through science and technology alone. They have to be sequestered. And the greatest form to sequester those is vibrant, alive, young, growing forested lands of the globe. All greenness, as you know. That's the reality of what we're just going to have to adjust to.

We're going to be writing a farm bill in a couple of years. My guess is that there will be a significantly larger component in it for American agriculture that deals with that item alone, and we will place a value on it. I was among those who met with about twelve different countries in Buenos Aires and with all the nongovernmental organizations, and they're all a bit unhappy with us at this moment because we didn't accept the Kyoto Treaty. What they are not unhappy about, though, is that we as a nation are investing nearly $6 million a year now in the science and technologies of greenhouse gases and climate change, and that's more than the rest of the world combined, by a factor of two times. And it's going to be our science and our technology that help lead the world in these problems.

My guess is that while we've allowed our forests that were in deep health problems to emit large quantities of carbons over the last decade, we must also recognize that there is phenomenal value in disallowing that and [instead] creating the dynamics of a young, vibrant forest, and that there will be a phenomenal value in that asset as this country and this globe age a bit more, and we find out—as our scientists are now concluding—that there is no way to solve the problem alone. But it's a combination of all those things that come together, and one of those is the ability of our forests around the world to sequester this environmental problem that we may be substantial contributors to.

So the challenges are large for the next century—every bit as great as they were in the first century. I concluded after reading a book about William E. Borah, who was a senator from Idaho here at the time of Teddy Roosevelt, and the debates that spiraled around the creation of the Forest Service and the idea of securing these lands and managing these lands for a variety of public goods, that the quest is still as important today as it was one hundred years ago. The public goods or the public attitudes may have changed, but the passion is still there, as it should be. And I thank all of you for holding that passion.

Mark Udall

U.S. Representative (D-Colorado)

It is great to be here with all of you on this very important anniversary. You all have many reasons to be very proud of all the accomplishments that you have made over the last one hundred years. I will try to keep faith with the charge I was given to look at the accomplishments of the Forest Service over the last one hundred years and then look at some of the challenges that face us as we move into the next hundred years.

As I look back, two Forest Service accomplishments in particular stand out: the establishment and protection of a system of national forests and national grasslands; and the development of the Forest Service itself as a mission-focused institution with a respect for and reliance on scientific expertise.

The idea of national forests—forestlands retained in federal ownership, a uniquely American idea—began before there was a Forest Service. But both the system and the Service took their modern form under the leadership of the two Roosevelts: Theodore, who established the Forest Service and aggressively expanded the forest reserves, and Franklin, whose Resettlement Administration began the purchase of cutover lands that became the eastern national forests and the ravaged Dust Bowl lands that became the national grasslands. Ever since, the Forest Service has made it its mission to maintain these lands as a national asset, a legacy for all generations.

The institutional history of the Forest Service is a proud one. It was the very first federal agency with a land-management mission. The National Park Service came along a decade later, and the Fish and Wildlife Service and the Bureau of Land Management much later still. Over the years, the Forest Service has built up a cadre of experienced people with valuable expertise. This is a resource that it can draw on, provided that it is maintained.

The Environmental Issues of Today

I think Chief Bosworth is right in saying that the Forest Service faces major management challenges. These include increasing off-road vehicle use; the buildup of fuels, which increases the risks of catastrophic forest fires; the spread of invasive species; and habitat fragmentation. I will touch on each of those four areas before moving to a broader conclusion about the Forest Service.

Off-road vehicles. The problems related to ORVs are just one aspect of a bigger problem, and that is the increasing pressure on the forests from recreational users. These pressures will only continue to grow as the population increases in the areas closest to the forests. This has many adverse effects, including erosion, damage to wildlife habitat, and disturbance of cultural and archaeological sites. ORV use has been a part of this problem. While there are many responsible ORV users and organizations, we began to understand as a community that something had to be done to rein in some of the problems that were developing.

Last year the Forest Service took an important step to address the ORV problem by proposing several important changes in its rules, including a ban on cross-country motorized recreation and limiting ORV use to roads and routes specifically designated as open.

Many of us thought that was an important series of steps but that the agency should go further, and wrote to urge that the agency strengthen the final rule to more fully address the threats that off-road vehicles present to public lands. In particular, we think there should be a definite deadline for completion of route designations to close the possible loophole in the proposed rule that appears to allow the continued use of unauthorized routes in the meantime.

We also suggested other changes to strengthen protection for public lands and waters and promote balance between off-highway vehicle recreation and the other uses, such as hunting, fishing, and grazing.

Congress also can help. That is why I worked with my colleague, Representative Tom Tancredo, to pass a bill to improve the ability of the land-managing agencies to adequately enforce the rules that apply to uses of the federal lands. In addition to national forest and BLM lands, it also would apply to lands managed by the National Park Service and the refuges managed by the Fish and Wildlife Service. And it addresses the enforcement of all regulations, not just those related to use of vehicles. I regret that the Senate did not act on the bill last year, but Representative Tancredo and I will try again this year, and I hope that action on the legislation can be completed without too much delay.

Even more than new legislation, it seems to me, the land-managing agencies need more resources—more money and more people—if we want them to do a better job. As originally approved by the Resources Committee, the Tancredo-Udall bill would have helped with that, too, by allowing the agencies to use money from fines to help pay for some of the restoration work caused by violations of regulations, as well as for offsetting the administrative costs involved in enforcement of those regulations. Unfortunately, the Judiciary

Committee evidently had some concerns about that part of the legislation, and so the bill as passed by the House did not include those provisions. This is something that I think should be addressed in the future, and I will seek to work with other members to do that.

Fire. I supported the conference report on the Healthy Forests legislation. It has flaws. But if its provisions are properly implemented, it can help reduce the risk of severe wildfire damage that now threatens lives and property in many communities in Colorado and other states—and for me that is the bottom line.

I am convinced we need to act to protect our communities and their water supplies. For that, a variety of things must be done, including working to reduce the built-up fuels that can increase the severity of the wildland fires that will periodically occur nearby.

The new law requires that at least fifty percent of all thinning-project funds be spent in the interface areas. I would have preferred the 2002 Resources Committee bill, which would have required seventy percent of the money to be spent in the interface. That's because I think the highest priority for fuel-reduction work needs to be in the areas where accumulated fuels present the most immediate risks to our communities and to municipal water supplies. Those are the lands in the wildland-urban interface, or the "red zone," as it is called in Colorado.

I think that we are on the right track, and we have an opportunity to build trust at the local community level to engage people in their own communities and ensure their communities have healthy forests around them. These are the places where forest conditions present the greatest risks to people's lives, health, and property, and so they should be where our finite resources—time, money, and people—are concentrated.

I also strongly support increased public involvement during the planning and other initial stages of fuel-reduction projects, and I think the new law's provisions related to community protection plans have great promise in this regard.

I was not enthusiastic about the way the legislation dealt with the question of easing the National Environmental Policy Act requirements for fuel-reduction projects. But the conference report was a compromise between the House and Senate bills. Under the House bill, no alternatives to a proposed action would have to be analyzed; under the Senate bill, at least the "no-action" alternative would have to be analyzed, and so would a third if proposed during scoping. The conference report followed the House bill for projects within the interface but followed the Senate bill for projects outside the interface. I reluctantly accepted that approach and would not want to see further weakening of the standard NEPA requirements for these projects.

Invasive species and habitat fragmentation. The Chief is right to highlight the threats from invasive species and habitat fragmentation. Unfortunately, the Forest Service itself is making it harder to address those threats. Part of the response to these threats needs to be maintaining the integrity of the remaining roadless areas. This was well put in the environmental impact statement for the 2001 roadless rules, which noted that the roadless areas "function as biological strongholds and refuges for many species" and "provide a bulwark against the spread of invasive species."

I am not enthusiastic about the idea of substituting a state-by-state approach for dealing with the roadless areas. Neither invasive species nor wildlife respect state boundaries, and I don't think decisions about management of roadless areas—or other parts of the national forests—should be based on those lines, either.

Responding to invasive species and habitat fragmentation involves more than roadless areas, of course. It is a silent problem, but an enormous one, if you talk to rangers and ranchers on the ground. Weed control efforts are important and need to be supported with adequate resources.

And the same is true for acquiring inholdings, especially in areas where they otherwise would be attractive for development—with accompanying roads and utilities—that would make the problems worse. The Land and Water Conservation Fund Act can and should be an essential tool for accomplishing this, but in recent years it has not been used enough. We all understand the difficult budget situation. But we must remember that the effects of development are long-term and extend beyond the developed sites themselves, and that reversing those effects is likely to be much more expensive than preventing them. Just as the cheapest way to fight fires is by preventing them, the best way to respond to habitat fragmentation is to forestall it.

The Social Issues Facing the Forest Service

The Forest Service faces two main social issues. One is internal—the need for adequate resources to meet the challenges ahead. The other is external—the need to win and retain the respect and trust of the public.

Resources. By resources, I mean more than just money, although that's essential. The Forest Service also needs to have human resources equal to its tasks. That means it needs to hire and retain people of skill and dedication. And it means that it needs to be ready to base its decisions on their best professional judgment and on sound science. The Forest Service must trust itself if it is to deserve the trust of others, and it must respect its employees if it wants the respect of the public.

Public respect and trust. Creation of the Forest Service was an accomplishment of the Progressive Movement of a century ago. A hallmark of that era was an emphasis on the need for government to make decisions on the basis of science and technical expertise. As the Service's first Chief, Gifford Pinchot had to overcome political resistance—both in Washington and in the states with national forests—to the idea of forest management based on those principles.

The Forest Service did overcome those obstacles, and did win a large measure of respect and trust because it was seen as an agency marked by intellectual and institutional integrity. But obviously times have changed. Recent decades have brought changes in public expectations and, above all, in public involvement. The public's priorities have changed, and they expect the Forest Service's decisions to reflect those priorities.

Forest management issues have become more contentious, more litigious, and more political. So more than ever before, public acceptance of forest management decisions depends on public respect for the way the Forest Service makes those decisions. In short, public respect for results depends on public respect for process.

And here again, as a loving critic, I have to say that I am concerned that the Forest Service is making things harder for itself. For example, consider the new planning regulations. I understand that the Forest Service says it has been suffering from too much planning process, that they are spending too much time and money on paperwork. And there may be something to that.

But cutting down on NEPA analysis means cutting down on opportunities for public involvement. And that means an increase in public wariness. So it will be especially important for the Forest Service to demonstrate that it understands that its decisions not only must be scientifically sound, but also that its process is transparent and that its desire for public involvement is sincere.

I am an optimist, so I am hopeful that the Forest Service will meet these challenges. But I am also a realist, so I know that in the end, time and history will be the ultimate judge.

So again, I want to thank you for your tremendous dedication. I want to thank all the stakeholder groups that are here. One hundred years is quite an accomplishment. I'm bullish on the future of the Forest Service and the noble experiment in the ownership of public lands by all of us.

The Forest Service in a Changing World

January 5, 2005
9:30 am

Ross S. Whaley *(Moderator)*
Emilyn Sheffield
Gifford Pinchot III
James Gustave Speth
Sally K. Fairfax

january 3-6
2005
washington dc

US Forest Service
Centennial
Congress
A Collective Commitment to Conservation

Ross S. Whaley
Chairman, Adirondack Park Agency

It is the responsibility of this panel to examine the changing world in which the Forest Service will find itself. The Forest Service's rich and honorable past has resulted in a firm foundation on which to build a future. That's the good news. Unfortunately, the foundation alone, whether of a home or an organization, no matter how well built, does not guarantee that the organization can withstand the huffing and puffing of the winds of change that it will encounter in the future. And no matter how elaborate the models or wise the forecaster, our estimates of change are always at least partially wrong. As one who has spent considerable time looking at the future, I am particularly cautious. In the late 1960s, I, along with many others, wrote of the coming decline in the workweek and a concomitant increase in leisure time due to efficiencies created by cybernetics—I was *wrong*! In the late 1970s and early 1980s, as part of the Resources Planning Act process, I predicted that because of higher energy costs, both spouses working, fewer children per family, houses would be smaller and apartment living would grow—again *wrong*!

Nonetheless, Joe Coates reminds us, while we cannot predict the future precisely in every detail, we can know enough about it to be useful, and just perhaps, we can influence it. That is the role of this panel—to look at some of the changes afoot that will shape the world in which the Forest Service will find itself. In spite of my past failures, I have been asked to set the stage for this exploration of the world to which the Forest Service will have to adapt. I will try my best to adhere to Einstein's admonition to "make everything as simple as possible but not simpler."

Globalization is a trend that all of us have been tracking, so I will only reinforce the notion here. If you think the trend toward globalization might diminish, let me remind you that if you rank the world economies—that is, the United States, Japan, Germany, etc.—by the time you reach number twenty-three you come to General Motors, which is bigger than Denmark. Mitsubishi is bigger than Israel, and Wal-Mart is bigger than Poland. Therefore, economic and political power is not limited to nation-states alone, and it is the interest of the corporate sector to increase global markets and search for the cheapest locations to produce their goods and services. In fact, I'm not sure what "foreign-made" means anymore. My Toyota was assembled in the United States. In fact, this year one-half of the parts of products produced in the United States will come from other countries. The Houston Aeros' and Houston Rockets' home stadium is the Toyota Center. So what is foreign made? Where the assembly plant is, where the parts are manufactured, where the corporate headquarters is located, or where the investors live? Is my Toyota a foreign vehicle? Are the Houston Rockets, with stars like Dikembe Mutombo and Yao Ming, who play in the Toyota Center, a domestic basketball team? As for the Forest Service, what does "greatest good for the greatest number" mean in a global society, and who should pay the bill?

If we have moved to a global economy and the borders between the nations have blurred, then the fact that there will be fifty percent more of us by mid-century cannot be ignored. Of course, the "us" I am talking about is the world "us," not an American "us." In fact, over a third of the population growth will occur in five countries: China, India, Brazil, Indonesia, and Mexico. What does that portend in terms of markets for natural resources or recreation? What will be the demand on public lands in the United States with a world population fifty percent larger than the current one? Whom should we include in the "greatest number"? We simply don't know what pressures on available resources would result from population increases alone. But if you combine changes in population with economic growth, you come closer to an answer. I have updated the numbers in a 1989 quote from one of our panelists, Gus Speth:

> Speth (1989) calculates that it took all of human history to grow the $600 billion global economy of 1900. Today the economy grows this amount every two years. Unchecked, today's $47 trillion[+] global economy may be five times bigger only one generation or so hence.[1]

Can the world even support a population and economic increase of this size? Many have attempted to evaluate the globe's carrying capacity. I'm intrigued that, over time, the number of estimates of the carrying capacity of earth has increased and so has the range of answers. Either we are not getting much smarter or the degree of uncertainty is growing. The estimates range from a low of about four billion (woops! no need for this particular Congress) to the optimistic extreme of twenty-five times that size. In my opinion, the estimate that is best documented and therefore has received the greatest public scrutiny is the "ecological footprint" developed by Bill Reese and refined by Mathis Wackernagel. Their estimates indicate that we began to exceed the earth's long-term carrying capacity by the late 1970s, and that currently it takes about one year and two months for the earth to replenish what we consume in one year. Are they accurate? I don't know. Would I ignore them if I were thinking about the Forest Service of the future? Absolutely not!

Lastly, I would like to comment on a combination of behavior patterns that will influence our demand on natural resources and wild places. While thirty years ago I was incorrectly suggesting a decline in the work week and an increase in leisure time, if one looks at two different books by Juliet Schor, one dealing with leisure patterns and one dealing with consumption behavior, you get a picture of success and status being measured almost wholly by the amount and conspicuousness of our consumption, thus requiring more work to pay for an appetite for things that exceed our ability to afford them. And even leisure in the United States is being crammed into overly planned, full, every-minute-accounted-for four-day or so minivacations. This is in contrast to France, which closes the whole country during the month of August. Therefore, leisure in the form of a casual cup of coffee or a beer in an open-air café shared with a friend is relegated to the notion of "goofing-off," a pejorative term. The impact of our own desires for material goods on available leisure time is exacerbated by firms doing all they can to avoid paying for vacations and other "nonproducing" perquisites. Have we lost any sense of value to the employee or the employer of rest and relaxation? If I am right in this observation and it continues, will the recreationists at our forests and parks be increasingly foreign, and what will be the fiscal conservative's view of tax dollars paying for them?

My allotted time is up without mentioning the future prospects for energy availability, global and domestic water shortages, increasing trends toward "fundamentalism," whether religious or environmental, used to justify socially unacceptable behaviors if the ends are socially acceptable. And even more importantly, I didn't mention the need of successful organizations to deal with the unexpected. So let me pass the ball to our panel of specialists.

Literature Cited

[1] Goodland, R. 1992. The case that the world has reached limits: More precisely that current throughput growth in the global economy cannot be sustained. *Population and Environment* 13(3): 167–82.

[†] This number was updated from Robert Goodland, The case that the world has reached limits, in *Population, technology, and lifestyle: The transition to sustainability*, edited by Robert Goodland, Herman E. Daly, and Salah El Serafy (Washington, DC: Island Press, 1992).

Emilyn Sheffield

Chair, Department of Recreation Administration, California State University, Chico

The Forest Service in a Changing America: New Opportunities to Care for the Land and Serve People

In 1900 Census Bureau staff counted seventy-six million Americans (Hobbs and Stoops 2002). Life expectancy was about forty-five years, the average workweek was sixty hours long, and pay averaged $13 a week (Kingwood College n.d.). Although the physical contours of the United States were largely established, many of the institutional and political decisions that ultimately shaped the national character had not yet emerged. When the Forest Service was established in 1905, for example, civil rights, suffrage, income tax, and the Antiquities Act had not yet entered the American scene.

In its first one hundred years the Forest Service created a land-based system for conservation and sustained yield that established the agency and the United States as an international conservation leader. In the coming hundred years the Forest Service must foster a citizen-based system for conservation if it is to continue to fulfill its mission of "caring for the land and serving people."

Changes in the size, composition, and distribution of the U.S. population will dramatically change the context within which the Forest Service operates. Brief descriptions of several of these changes are followed by a few observations about outdoor recreation and three Forest Service responses that can help to ensure relevance in the coming century.

More people. From a base of 75 million people in 1900, the United States grew to 281 million in 2000 (Hobbs and Stoops 2002). While the United States as a whole has continued to grow, in recent decades the South and West have experienced the greatest amount of growth (Census Bureau 2000c). By 2100, the population is projected to more than double its 2000 level, with midrange Census projections of 571 million people in the United States (Census Bureau 2000a).

Living longer. As health care and nutrition improved throughout the last century, life expectancy also increased. In 1900, average life expectancy was in the mid-forties, lowered, in part, by high infant mortality rates. The average lifespan in 2100, by contrast, is projected to be in the upper eighties for men and low nineties for women (Census Bureau 2000d). A steep increase in the number of people eighty years and older will be the most notable aspect of an aging America over the next thirty to fifty years as the baby boom generation enters retirement (Scommegna 2004). Along with this greater longevity will come age-related health and mobility issues.

More urban and suburban. A recent report from the Census Bureau (Hobbs and Stoops 2002) illustrates the gradual growth of metropolitan America. In the early 1900s, only twenty-eight percent of the U.S. population lived in metropolitan areas. In the twentieth century, aided by transportation improvements and relatively low fuel and vehicle costs, the percentage of people living in suburban areas increased from less than ten percent in 1910 to more than fifty percent in 2000. By 2000, the percentages of rural and urban residents were nearly reversed, with eighty percent of the United States population living in metropolitan or suburban areas (Hobbs and Stoops 2002).

More diverse. Throughout history people have moved in search of a better future. As transportation costs have decreased and global communications have increased, more people from more places are coming to the United States than ever. By midcentury, the United States will have no clear ethnic or racial majority. By 2100, the projected U.S. population will be approximately forty percent white, non-Hispanic; thirty-three percent Hispanic; thirteen percent black, non-Hispanic; and thirteen percent Asian or Pacific Islander. In contrast, in 2000 the United States was more than seventy-one percent white, non-Hispanic (Census Bureau 2000b).

Outdoor Recreation and the Good Life
Changes in the distribution and composition of the United States population have transformed many aspects of the Forest Service. Changes in outdoor recreation patterns and preferences serve to illustrate the magnitude of these changes. Active outdoor adventure sports and activities like mountain biking, paddle sports, climbing, surfing, and scuba diving have joined traditional stalwarts such as sightseeing, camping, hiking, backpacking, hunting, and fishing as the outdoor recreation pursuits of individuals, families, and groups. Millions of people are getting "back to nature," and many are outfitted with a bewildering assortment of gear. Wildlife viewing has grown rapidly. All forms of outdoor recreation transportation (e.g., snowmobiles, all-terrain vehicles, personal watercraft, boats) have increased in popularity as equipment prices have dropped and safety features and sport clubs have become more common. Nature-based tourism and cultural heritage tourism are bringing new enthusiasts to outdoor recreation and public lands in record numbers.

The range and diversity of outdoor recreation activities have increased through the years, but the factors motivating people to engage in outdoor recreation remain similar. Being outdoors in a beautiful setting with friends and family to enjoy a change from daily routines seems to motivate the majority of outdoor recreation participants (American Recreation Coalition 1998; California Department of Parks and Recreation 2003). The advent of adventure sports, active outdoor recreation gear, and recreation transportation has expanded the range of outdoor recreation pursuits, but the essential motivations for outdoor recreation are unchanged.

Caring for the Land and Serving People for the Next Hundred Years

Changes in the demographic profile of the United States and the increasing importance of recreation and leisure in American society provide exciting new opportunities for the Forest Service to fulfill its mission. Americans have a continuing interest in their immediate living environment, in the conservation and preservation of natural places, and in outdoor recreation. These interests are among the most powerful tools available to connect people to the land. From a host of possible actions, three have potential to provide exceptional benefits to the people, to the land, and to the Forest Service.

Every American benefits from the Forest Service. Environmental debate is often emotionally laden and likely to reveal sharp disagreement about the severity of the issues and the best responses to monitored parameters. Lost in the polarized rhetoric is the near-universal value Americans place on clean air and clean water. Forests and forest fires may be synonymous with the Forest Service, but the agency's equally vital role in ensuring clean water and clean air is a story that needs to be told simply, widely, often, and well.

Recreation matters. Recreation, leisure, and tourism have increased in importance to Americans and the U.S. economy. In its first century the Forest Service became one of the premier providers of outdoor recreation and helped to introduce generations of Americans to nature and outdoor recreation. The benefits of outdoor recreation are many and well documented. Three brief examples suffice to illustrate the point: (1) outdoor recreation keeps Americans physically active, (2) outdoor recreation creates nature lovers, and (3) outdoor recreation creates advocates. Both the land and the people need outdoor recreation.

Volunteerism is recreation. The impetus for volunteerism within the Forest Service has been primarily declining budgets. Consequently, some view the volunteer enterprise with skepticism. But there are reasons to encourage volunteerism. Volunteering is the leisure choice of millions. Volunteering has well-documented benefits to the volunteers and to the causes they support. But volunteerism does not happen in a vacuum; rather, it requires leadership and infrastructure. To do otherwise denies Americans and the Forest Service a powerful tool to connect people to the land. If the Forest Service makes a sustained investment in volunteer programs, it will create a legacy of citizen involvement that will ensure that the Forest Service remains relevant and essential throughout the twenty-first century.

A vibrant and vital outdoor recreation program, especially one that incorporates opportunities for volunteerism, can provide benefits to the land and to the people. As the agency enters its second century of service, the Forest Service can provide places for all people—urban, young, old, all races and ethnic groups, immigrants—to connect to the land and to nature and to each other. The Forest Service can provide places to learn about nature through environmental education and interpretation programs, through citizen involvement and citizen stewardship opportunities; places to engage in active recreation; places to engage in quiet reflection; places to discover the vastness of nature. Places to be and to become.

References

American Recreation Coalition. 1998. Outdoor recreation in America 1998. Available on-line from http://www.funoutdoors.com/research.

California Department of Parks and Recreation. 2003. Public attitudes and opinions about outdoor recreation in California.

Census Bureau. 2000a. Annual projections of the total resident population as of July 1: Middle, lowest, highest and zero international migration series 1999–2100. Report NP-T1.

———. 2000b. National population projections: Summary files, total population by race, Hispanic origin, and nativity. Retrieved from http://www.census.gov/population/www/projections/natsum-T5.html.

———. 2000c. The population profile of the United States: 2000. Retrieved on April 15, 2005, from http://www.census.gov/population/www/pop-profile/profile2000.html.

———. 2000d. Projected life expectancy at birth by race and Hispanic origin, 1999–2100. Report NP-T7-B. Retrieved from www.census.gov/population/projections/nation/summary/np-t7-b.pdf.

————. 2000e. Projections of the resident population by race, Hispanic origin and nativity: Middle series, 2075–2100. Report NP-T5-H. Retrieved from www.census.gov/population/projections/nation/summary/np-t5-h.pdf.

Hobbs, F., and N. Stoops. 2002. Census 2000 special reports, series CENSR-4, Demographic trends in the 20th century. Washington, DC: U.S. Government Printing Office. Available on-line at http://www.census.gov/prod/2002pubs/censr-4.pdf.

Kingwood College Library. n.d. American cultural history: 1900–1909. Retrieved on November 1, 2004, from http://kclibrary.nhmccd.edu/decades.html.

Scommegna, P. 2004. U.S. growing bigger, older, more diverse. Population Reference Bureau. Retrieved from http://www.prb.org.

Gifford Pinchot III
President, Bainbridge Graduate Institute, Bainbridge Island, Washington

Yogi Berra said, "I never make predictions, particularly about the future." I'm going to ignore that wise advice because I've been told to speak on the future of technology and its impact on society and business—in eight minutes' time.

We've just learned about how big the effect of global warming is going to be on everything that we care about, and that's pretty big news. Technology is going to be changing at a comparable rate. Ray Kurzweil, who is one of the great technology geniuses of our time, said that the rate of innovation in the twenty-first century is going to be about a thousand times the rate of innovation in the twentieth century. He had some good reasons for believing this. Personal computers will be about as smart as human beings by the year 2020. That's going to change things a little bit, particularly when they begin self-replicating. All of this lies in the future, and some people are really worried about it.

But I don't want to talk about that. I want to talk about a few things that are going to affect the forests. One thing that is going to affect the forests and recreation is virtual reality. I was doing a project about what should go on up on the moon. It turned out that the young people who were part of the research really didn't think the moon was that interesting because video games could be more interesting than anything they could possibly do on the moon. Reality is becoming less and less important. Virtual reality is becoming more important. Why go to the national forests when you can go to a *virtual* national forest, where you can wrestle with bears and dragons and all sorts of things? And you can be absolutely sure that that's going to happen. In fact, you can probably win most of the time, too.

It seems strange, but this world is coming upon us very rapidly. Consequently, we're going to need to think about what the recreational experience on the national forests is going to be like. In this context, I want to say that I did some work a few years ago in Region 5 in California. We concluded at the end of that project, that if you look at what the national forests are producing for the California region, and if timber counts as 1, then recreation counts as 10, and water counts as 100. Have we really got those priorities firmly in mind when we're managing? If recreation is all that important, then it's going to have to be fun. One of my pet peeves is the word "interpretation." When I want to think about a recreational experience and I think about how am I going to make this sound really fun, am I going to call it interpretation? Have we really caught up with Disney yet? I would suggest the word "edutainment" might be a better word for thinking about what we're doing when we're out there doing interpretation. We have to realize that we're in competition. For a whole bunch of reasons, the future of the natural forests depends upon people loving the natural forests, and they're only going to love the natural forests if they go and see them every once in a while. And they're only going to see them if they have a good time while they are there.

That brings up a couple of thoughts. One of them is risk. One of the things that makes life exciting is taking risks. Please take this with a grain of salt because I'm someone who still skis the double black diamonds and still rock-climbs, so maybe I'm a little out of the norm in this regard. But for a huge group of people, there's nothing that virtual reality is going to replace because there is no greater thrill than summiting a mountain—and you may have risked death along the way. This makes us think about the fact that the Forest Service is going to have to be involved as we move into this kind of recreation, in managing risk in a new way. We're going to have to be willing to put up with more risk. And we're going to have figure out how to get it so that we get them to sue the concessionaires instead of the agency. But we're going to have to get good at managing that whole issue and not be chicken about it because that's what's going to draw a lot of the people out there. I look at my own children—they're "dropping" waterfalls and all the things that they do in the national forests, and I believe that that's an important part of what we provide.

Another thing that's going on in the world of technology is transparency. It's getting easier and easier to monitor things. We're living in a world in which a bunch of technologies are suddenly coming together: really cheap sensors are being produced in the same way that we produce microchips for almost anything, wireless communications, data storage that is virtually unlimited, and intelligent data mining so that we can pick out of this mass of data anything that we would want to know. What this means is that surveillance is reaching a level that is just unimaginable. It's a real *1984* thing from one point of view, but on the other hand we will be able to keep track of what's going on in our forests in a cost-effective and incredibly detailed way.

That's going to mean quite a lot changes for what's going on in our forests. We can stop poaching, and we can accurately monitor forest conditions. Perhaps we can hold people accountable for what happens in the forest, as opposed to the process that they engaged in, in order to deal with the forests. We've been talking about that for years—how are we going to be accountable. Now it's going to be possible. On the other hand, privacy and solitude, which may be some of the greatest virtues of the forest, may be hard to come by if we've got little cameras mounted in all the trees watching everybody. It's not going to be just the Forest Service putting those cameras there, but every environmental organization that wants to gather data for its court cases. In fact, people are going to be watched out there. They're going to be watched in their homes; they're going to be watched when they make their purchases. This is going to be a universal fact of life. I believe the national forests need to really work hard on being a place of solitude, so that you can get away from it all there—and really feel like you are away from it all.

There is a danger of technology arrogance as we move into this. I have a fear that we're finally going to figure out how to clone the perfect Douglas-fir and we're going to put that perfect Douglas-fir everywhere. Then there's going to be a blight that destroys all the firs, and we're going to look at a forest that is empty of trees. I hope that we are not going to make that kind of mistake. I worked at the San Bernardino and San Jacinto mountains, just before the fires, on a vision of what they would want. One of the things I learned was that there are about two hundred trees to the acre, but there was only room for about forty, and given the conditions of drought and global warming, perhaps even less than that. We're going to have to face the fact that we're going to have to make changes on all the forests in which we're still dealing with earlier management practices, when we did fire suppression and clearcuts and then let even-aged stands grow up. There's just a great amount of work that has to be done in the forests. This is a small part of the challenge that the Forest Service is facing.

We face an unprecedented need for action on the ground. We've got to do things in the forests in an expeditious manner. We've got to take out a large number of trees if they're not going to burn. We have to do this with urgency and speed, and we have to do it with a willingness to do selective cutting, which is expensive when compared to saving the forests by eliminating (clearcutting) them. And that won't meet the public's needs.

How are we going to do all of this? In the first fifty years of the Forest Service, we had, to a large extent, the public's trust. Admittedly, we were being sued by the timber interests and the grazing interests, but in general we were in a period in which we were one of the most trusted of government agencies. It was a trust that we lost perhaps in the 1980s as a result of overcutting and practices that really offended the public. Congress responded by creating processes that tied our hands behind our backs so that we ultimately had great difficulty doing anything on the land without court appeals and so forth. It became a very difficult time. Professional extremists on both sides became the winners of the process because the only people who could stand the length and duration of the process were those who were getting paid. No volunteer could put up with the length of time it took us to make decisions.

We used to trust our forest rangers. They went around with the *Use Book* and they had the forester's eye, and they were going to do the right thing. People accepted that. Then we had a massive PR campaign for conservation, and people who were merely employees spoke out. Increasingly, we don't trust our employees anymore. We gag them and don't allow them to speak in public for fear that what they say might not look good in court or in Congress. We've developed a legalistic approach. We have a breakdown in trust. The public doesn't trust us, and we don't even trust ourselves anymore.

I don't believe that you can become the active agency you need to become to face the challenges that are happening today—the need to take an incredibly more active role on the ground at high speed—and not operate from a base of trust. We have to regain the public's trust. That's probably our most important thing in order to respond. We have a great opportunity and a great danger right now. We have a rule change [new planning rules issued in December 2004], and you are all probably wondering what's going to happen. The rule change addresses something that was really necessary—maybe we should empower people in the Forest Service to actually do something without five years of study first, at least in some cases. Maybe we should use a little discretion here. We all know that that's needed. You can't solve the problem of getting to work if we spend all of our time in front of our computer screens making reports. On the other hand, this rule change could be used to go back to the 1980s, release the "timber beast" mentality, and offend the public once again. And many in the public expect that that is what we're going to do.

I look at this as one of the great opportunities that the Forest Service has had. You've been given substantially more freedom, or it appears that you have, and the public is going to ask, what did they do with that freedom? You can do intelligent, sensitive fuel reduction; you can partner with the nongovernmental organizations and get them involved about what to do, and then, without immense study, go out and do it; you can get third parties monitoring and work closely with them as allies rather than as people that you're scared of; you can predict results and be accountable for them; you can provide a reliable supply of small-diameter wood and do all the things that the Forest Service ought to do. Then I think we can earn the public's trust. Or we can give into various pressures and do foolish things. It's going to take enormous courage to stand up to the pressures that will be on you as you are given a bit more freedom and do the right thing. I know you are up to it. Thank you.

James Gustave Speth

Dean, Yale School of Forestry and Environmental Science

The Forest Service and the Climate Change Threat

As the USDA Forest Service moves into its second century, its people will do well to recall that the Service was never chartered to be a neutral broker or mere manager. Gifford Pinchot talked frankly about launching a movement. He was not shy about it. He wrote that "outside the tropics, American forests were the richest and most productive on Earth, but nobody had begun to manage any part of them with an eye to the future." On the contrary, he wrote, "the greatest, the swiftest, the most efficient, the most appalling wave of forest destruction in human history had been swelling to its climax in the United States." Pinchot launched the Service to take on that challenge.

Today, America's forests face another great threat—one at least as serious as that seen by Pinchot: the threat of climate change. Let me offer two predictions. If greenhouse gases continue to rise as projected by the business-as-usual scenarios—even some of the more optimistic ones—then our country's forest estate and the values we associate with forests will suffer huge negative consequences. Over significant areas there will be devastation. And second, Service employees will find their work increasingly dominated by the need to cope with climate change, both its impacts and its mitigation.

Let me try to bring home the seriousness of what is going on by referring to articles in reliable news outlets and scientific journals over the last two years.

First, we can no longer doubt that the climate change threat is real, already large, and growing fast:

- *Science:* "Top scientists conclude human activity is affecting global climate"
- *Science:* "Climate change is real…Globally the ten hottest years on record have occurred since 1991, and, in the past century, temperatures have risen by about 0.6°C"
- Environment News Service: "Chinese meteorologists warn of climate catastrophes"
- ENS: "American Geophysical Union issues climate change warning"
- *Business Week:* "Consensus is growing among scientists, governments, and business that they must act fast to combat climate change. This has already

sparked efforts to limit CO2 emissions. Many companies are now preparing for a carbon-constrained world"

When things begin to warm up, one of the first things to check is what is happening to the ice:
- BBC: "Melting glaciers threaten Peru"
- ENS: "Greenland glacier retreating rapidly"
- U.S. Department of State: "Climate warming causes breakup of Arctic's largest ice shelf"
- *New Scientist:* "Ice melt may dry out US West Coast"
- BBC: "Kazakhstan's glaciers melting fast"
- Reuters: "Long summers force polar bears to hunt on thin ice"
- BBC: "Patagonian ice in rapid retreat"
- Reuters: "Alaska natives say warming trend imperils villages"
- *Science:* "The Arctic will be almost free of sea ice during the summers toward the end of this century"
- Reuters: "Denmark to claim North Pole, hopes to strike oil"

And when the ice melts, the oceans rise:
- *Science:* "The ice covering Greenland holds enough water to raise the oceans seven meters—and it's starting to melt"
- *New Scientist:* "The sea level would rise dramatically if Antarctic ice keeps vanishing"
- BBC: "Flooding cost may rise 20-fold" with climate change
- Reuters: "Low-lying Dutch fear rising seas"
- AP: "Rising oceans threaten Pacific island nations"

And climate change can affect more than the ice and the water.
- Reuters: "Swiss study predicts scorching European summers"
- Reuters: "Scientists report global warming kills 160,000 annually"
- *New York Times:* "Drastic shifts in climate are likely, experts warn"
- *Nature:* "Gulf Stream probed for early warnings of system failure"
- Reuters: "Global warming seen as security threat"
- AP: "Global warming threatens Great Barrier Reef"
- *Science:* "Biologists say climate change may already be affecting high-mountain ecosystems around the world"

And here is the most disturbing information of all for your work. The best current estimates suggest that, unless there is a major world correction, climate change projected for late this century will make it impossible for about half the American land to sustain the types of plants and animals now on that land. In one projection, the much-loved maple-beech-birch forests of New England simply disappear off the U.S. map. In another, the Southeast becomes a huge grassland savanna unable to support forests because it is too hot and dry.

We know that today the biggest threat to species and biodiversity is habitat destruction, with invasive species running second. But scientists are now projecting that by 2050, climate change will rival habitat destruction as a source of species loss.

These consequences are huge, especially for any bounded area, but destruction of forests could be far more extensive than even the models suggest. Let us consider what is not included in most of the studies of climate change's impacts on natural areas:

- *Rate of climate change.* Most observers believe that even the gradual changes associated with the conventional models will be too rapid for many species—much faster, for example, than the retreat of the glaciers.
- *Barriers to species migration.* The models tend to assume away highways, agriculture, cities, and suburbs.
- *Ecosystem disruption.* The models tend to assume that one ecosystem type is magically replaced by an intact system of another type, whereas we know that one effect of climate change will be to tear ecosystems apart, with species moving and migrating at different rates and perhaps in different directions.
- *Abrupt climate change.* Models assume gradual transitions, but a recent National Academy of Sciences report said climate change is likely to be more like throwing a switch than turning a dimmer.
- *Fires.* Climate change will make some areas hotter or drier, increasing forest fire risks.
- *Droughts, floods, storms, hurricanes.* Extreme weather events could become more frequent.
- *Insects, infestations, and diseases.* Here we may have already seen what climate change can do to forests in the devastation in the U.S. West, western Canada, and Alaska due to bark beetles and budworms, which are kept in check normally by harsh winters but not by the milder winters since 1995.

I hope the Service and its leaders will remember the mission to save our forests that motivated Pinchot and Theodore Roosevelt and will bring that sense of mission to this climate threat. You must speak truth to power fearlessly, before it is too late. Petitions such as that filed with you in 2004 by the Blue Water Network should be welcomed by you because they speak to your professionalism and your highest values. That petition called upon the Forest Service to integrate the best climate science into planning at all levels.

The U.S. response to climate change today is held back by economic interests so powerful, they have for over thirty years stymied all efforts to forge a sensible national energy policy. It is precisely because these interests are so powerful that your professionalism and your mission are so important. In this context, what Theodore Roosevelt said a century ago remains pertinent today:

Here is your country—do not let anyone take it or its glory away from you. Do not let selfish men or greedy interests skim your country of its beauty, its riches or its romance. The world and the future and your very children shall judge you according as you deal with this sacred trust.

Sally K. Fairfax, *Henry J. Vaux Distinguished Professor of Forest Policy, Department of Environmental Science, Policy and Management, University of California, Berkeley*

My task is to talk about the changing face of government that is going to occur over the next century. I'm going to address the changing institutional world that the Forest Service will exist in by talking about a subject that I've been studying for the last ten or fifteen years—land acquisition and the definition and mapping of specific parcels as a conservation tool. I'm going to focus on the latest bend in that path—land trusts and conservation easements—both because they are a part of the Forest Service's future problems and because they so well illustrate the institutional changes that I want to talk about.

After just having finished a lengthy study of land acquisition, I'm deeply aware of the institutional changes that are accompanying less-than-fee acquisitions. As a tool, less-than-fee acquisitions or conservation easements are not new. In fact, we've been using conservation easements in a number of different contexts since the 1890s. They were very heavily used during the Great Depression to put together the U.S. Fish and Wildlife Service reservations in the Upper Midwest and in the Prairie Potholes area. I'm going to talk about them in two ways: first as a sign of the times that are changing, and second as a problem for the future.

They are most important as a sign of the times. One of the most interesting things that we heard as we were conducting our research was that within the Forest Service, there is a general perception that when a Forest Service manager wants to acquire land, it's inappropriate to speak with the supervisor or the regional forester. Instead, you call the Nature Conservancy.

That is important as a sign of the changing political times for at least two reasons. First, the ideas and understandings that the American people have about government that underwrote the Forest Service's first seventy successful years are changing. The idea of centralized, scientifically based, paramilitary colonial government such as characterized the Forest Service in 1905 and today is less and less important, it is less and less legitimate, and it is less and less relevant to the issues that we face. We are going to have to confront global warming, changing demographics, and changing technology in an environment in which authority is not only being devolved to localities—that is, there is a decentralization of government authority—but also, government authority is being dispersed to nongovernment entities, such as the nonprofit land trusts that I'll emphasize later; corporate entities, which are obviously a key element of globalization; and global institutions, such as the World Trade Organization. The institutional context in which conservation proceeds is very different now than it was one hundred years ago, and it's going to get more different, not less.

The second important sign of the times that I think bears emphasis here— the first is rather obvious—is the major change that is going on in people's understanding of the whole undertaking of conservation. It is true that since the 1930s the public has been pushing conservation organizations like the Forest Service more toward the John Muir end of the spectrum and away from the use end of the spectrum that we have seen emphasized—for obvious reasons—so strongly at this gathering. This push to preservation that gave us the whole wilderness movement and the whole Roadless Area Review and Evaluation exercise was and remains strong. But what is interesting about our times and about less-than-fee acquisitions and about changing government structure is that we are now seeing a new and different trend. We are talking about landscape-level conservation which focuses less on parcels of individual ownership and recognizes the potential of and indeed the mandatory nature of the participation of landowners as stewards of conserved lands. Transcending mere or particular ownerships, the focus increasingly seems to be on working landscapes as a part of our vocabulary of conservation. Easements, or less-than-fee ownership, are a key element in involving owners of land in protected landscapes. That gives them a privileged position in the discussion about conservation, which I think is underacknowledged and particularly important. My first point is that conservation easements or less-than-fee acquisitions are a totally important part not only of our understanding of conservation but of how legitimate government activity is being redefined.

Conservation easements are also potentially a great problem for the future. This is no global warming, but this is certainly going to be a key element in how we respond to global warming. As a preface, let me say that one of the things we learned while studying land acquisition as a tool of conservation is that even an acquisition in full fee is not a reliable or clear win for conservation. Without condemnation, nothing happens without the landowners' consent. Landowners, therefore, decide what will get conserved and under what terms and conditions.

Conservation easements are a clear move evermore in the direction of the landowners' priorities. It's more of the same—lots more of the same. Easements, among other things, lower the owners' costs of maintaining and perpetuating large land holdings. Think "Jane Austen." Think all that stuff that has become familiar to us as they have begun to make such splendid movies of *Pride and Prejudice* and *Sense and Sensibility*. That is not clearly, in my eyes, a public benefit.

Public expenditure pretending to be private is also not clearly a public benefit. And, indeed, it is important to notice that easements are a way of substituting privately negotiated contractual agreements for what has heretofore been a reliance on publicly agreed-to regulation of the land. It gives the landowner almost absolute control over the rights that the public can acquire, and it also defines the ones that are reserved by and to the owner. This is not obviously the best way to protect land, and more profoundly, it is clearly not a good way to define and defend the responsibilities of landownership which underlie any of our abilities to protect or conserve anything. Conservation easements erode the potential for public policy for public and private lands. When you start to admix them, as we are doing with the Forest Service buying and funding easements, it gets even more confusing.

Easements are a problematic as well as an emblematic tool. I'll conclude by wondering whether they will do what we say they will do. Annual monitoring is likely to be perceived as very much more insensitive than mere regulation, and enforcement of private contracts is potentially—and I think unavoidably—no less politically risky and certainly more costly than enforcing government regulations. Furthermore, the landscape that is nominally conserved by this undertaking is not a coherent landscape but in fact a mosaic: a mosaic of different goals, priorities, landowners, and management styles in addition to all the stakeholders that surround the mosaic. It's my humble prediction that these landscapes will be most stable on day one, when the contract is signed, and over time they will become less and less stable.

The experience that we do have with government monitoring and enforcement of easements is not uplifting. The government is generally viewed as a poor monitor and steward for easements, and for good reasons. Another reason why I think these acquisitions are problematic is that they provide relatively little recreation access. Fewer than ten percent of the acres under easement in the San Francisco Bay Area, for example, are accessible to the public for recreation. This is one of the rights that the landowner generally reserves. If it is true, and I certainly believe our current chief that it is true, that managing watersheds is the most important thing that the agency will be doing in an era of global warming, then easements are not clearly advantageous and this fragmented mosaic ownership is problematic. Using public funds to maintain a subsidized class of large owners of land that is not accessible to the public is not clearly good for conservation. It is not clearly a welcoming sign as well to the urban minorities that are so important to the future of the agency. Furthermore, I've been struck by the number of times in the film *The Greatest Good* and in discussions here that we've been able to say that, in terms of the democracy that drives the decision making, in terms of the responsibility we have for the land, ultimately we own this land. We own this—it's ours and the public is the landowner. This is not right and it is not true any longer for those areas that are being acquired and conserved under easements.

There are clear reasons, I want to readily admit, for doing easements now as opposed to the acquisitions that characterized the Weeks Act of 1911, but they also indicate fundamental changes in the nature and understanding of government that we're going to be operating in during the next century. They create clear and fundamental problems for the managers of those mosaics that are emerging. Thank you.

Breakout Sessions

January 5, 2005
11:00 am

january 3-6
2005
washington dc

US Forest Service

Centennial
Congress

A Collective Commitment to Conservation

Liz Agpaoa
Chief of Staff, USDA Forest Service

Charge to Breakout Sessions

Over the last two days, we have had panelists and speakers who have had some very careful and heartfelt reflections on the history of the national forests, and we hope that you have found those to be both engaging and entertaining. You have also heard discussion and exploration of one of our most recent challenges and opportunities facing our national forests and grasslands.

Today, after lunch, the regional forum delegates will present a summary of the research challenges facing the Forest Service and will describe challenges that could be focused on for the future.

I want to give you a little information about this afternoon and the breakout processes. We're going to ask you to go from here and take your lunches in small groups. Your group assignment is designated by a letter on your nametag, and it should be a letter from A through T.

The purpose of your breakout group is to provide you the opportunity to explore ways that we can collectively meet the challenges and opportunities facing our national forests. This is your time to enter into that wider dialogue about how we can carry out that collective commitment to conservation.

We want you to get a little headstart on the breakout groups, so we scheduled your lunch today as your first opportunity to meet your groups. So we will ask you to do that and break out in your small groups, and then you will reconvene in those groups after the forum presentations. After the forum presentations, your breakout group will be a two-hour facilitated time, and we anticipate that you will have full and spirited discussion.

We ask that you also listen to everyone in your group and give the opportunity for everyone to be heard. After your breakout groups conclude, there will be a small team of people who will take your key ideas and help summarize those. Chief Dale Bosworth will present a short summary of those ideas at the lunch tomorrow, and I know Dale is eager to hear your thoughts and the outcomes of this afternoon's efforts.

So in quick summary, from here, you'll go to lunch in your breakout group. Then you will come back after lunch into this meeting room to hear the regional summaries, and then after the regional summaries you'll go back and reconvene at three-fifteen in your groups.

The box lunches for your breakout groups are at two levels, and we ask that you go ahead and pick up those box lunches at the level that your meeting room is in. Meeting rooms A through F are on this main level, and meeting rooms G through T are at the lower-level Independence area. So let's break for lunch, and we'll see you back here at twelve-thirty.

The USDA Forest Service hosted the Centennial Congress on January 3–5, 2005 in Washington, D.C., to launch its one-hundredth anniversary celebration. The theme for the Congress was "A Collective Commitment to Conservation."

On January 5, as part of the Congress, twenty breakout sessions were held with attendees. Participants included Forest Service employees and representatives from partner groups and other organizations. Some were delegates sent from previous regional forums focusing on specific natural resources issues. Attendees represented a variety of interests, some competitive.

The challenge was to bring these varied interests together in breakout sessions to address the following two areas in light of the Congress theme:

- What new approaches will be necessary to ensure that the Forest Service meets the long-term needs of the land and the public?
- How can the Forest Service and its partners more effectively work together to achieve our goal of a collective commitment to conservation?

The Forest Service asked JDG Communications, Inc., to develop a strategy for facilitating, managing, and reporting on the outcomes of the breakout sessions. To foster greater participation and ownership, JDG's central strategy focused on letting the Congress delegates decide for themselves the topics to be discussed under the general theme. The groups then addressed the two questions listed above within those topics, adding a third area of discussion on how each participant might take individual action to carry forward the ideas.

The twenty breakout sessions were limited to approximately fifteen delegates each. Each was guided by one Forest Service facilitator with another Forest Service employee acting as the recorder. JDG created a facilitators' guide, provided facilitator and recorder training, supervised the breakout sessions, and following the breakout sessions, facilitated a session with the facilitators to organize the outcomes. To discuss and organize the resulting eighty-three individual breakout session topics, an electronic software system was used. This system allowed all facilitators to see the results on an overhead screen and further organize them into twenty-three topic areas.

On the day following the breakout sessions, Forest Service Chief Dale Bosworth presented a Centennial Congress Report Out, in which he outlined the key themes of the breakout discussions. In his presentation, Chief Bosworth told the delegates, "You focused on huge issues that will matter for years to come."

The consolidated topics, original topics, and ideas are found in the appendix of the report, along with individual commitments made by delegates and the facilitators' guide.

Key Themes

The objective of these breakout sessions was to explore ways to build better relationships, including better ways to communicate and work together. The desired outcome for these discussions was a collective commitment to conservation with a shared ownership for implementation.

Facilitators reported that the groups held positive discussions with a high energy level. The outcomes featured an underlying theme of "We want to help, we want to give" and contributed hundreds of ideas for carrying forward "A Collective Commitment to Conservation."

From the twenty-three topics selected by the facilitators, comments and ideas are organized into the following eight key themes with the assistance of Cindy Chojnacky, Policy Analysis, USDA Forest Service Washington Office.

New Constituencies

Besides the Forest Service's traditional focus on rural communities close to the forests, many delegates saw the need for urban outreach, where more than eighty percent of the population lives. The agency should engage both urban and rural people and especially focus on youth for education and recruitment.

Environmental Services

Long-term advocacy for amenity values from forests (as well as products such as timber and forage) was recast as "funding for things that forests now provide for free." New "products": carbon sequestered (stored) from trees, clean water, and habitat banking. Innovative funding: "Billing cities, saving ranches" (cities paying for reforestation projects to benefit municipal watersheds, helping ranches market "environmental credits" to maintain livelihood and avoid sale for subdivision) and ways to market renewable energy.

Environmental Literacy

The groups envisioned the Forest Service looking at new ways to partner with schools and also going beyond "environmental education" by engaging in broader conservation outreach and awareness initiatives to reach the public where they are.

Leadership in Natural Resources

The Forest Service should lead across governmental boundary lines, consider global environmental and economic issues, revitalize its mission and vision, and practice more innovative resource management.

Public Trust and Involvement

Focus areas included sharing leadership with communities, making it easier to work with partners and volunteers, engaging the general public and forest visitors, and more use of conflict resolution processes.

Conservation Framework for Balancing Use and Enjoyment

Feedback indicated the need for balance between emphasis on new recreation interests without losing the silviculture function (growing and harvesting trees). Delegates also suggested ways to address changing land use patterns, particularly urbanization and fragmentation.

New Business Model

Delegates were interested in a more flexible organization, integrated resource funding, competing more effectively for federal funding, and entrepreneurship.

Information Delivery and Sharing

Delegates advocated more focus on the use of social science to better understand the public and their values, better sharing and forest use of "cutting-edge science," and better support for research.

Report on the Centennial Regional Forums

January 5, 2005
1:55pm

Northern—*Region 1*
Rocky Mountain—*Region 2*
Southwestern—*Region 3*
Intermountain—*Region 4*
Pacific Southwest—*Region 5*
Pacific Northwest—*Region 6*
Southern—*Region 8*
Eastern—*Region 9*
Alaska—*Region 10*
Puerto Rico
Grey Towers

Statement by USDA Forest Service
Hydrologists, Soil Scientists, and Geologists

US Forest Service

*C*entennia*l*
*C*ong*r*ess

A Collective Commitment to Conservation

Report of the Northern Regional Forum
November 9–10, 2004
Missoula, Montana

—Submitted by Steve Kratville, Partnership and Special Projects Coordinator, Public and Governmental Relations Staff, USDA Forest Service, Missoula, Montana

Conservation Leadership and Wilderness Stewardship: One Hundred Years of Conservation, Forty Years of Wilderness, A New Century of Service

As the U.S. Forest Service prepared to celebrate its one-hundredth birthday in 2005, over three hundred people convened in Missoula, Montana, for the Northern Regional Forum. Forum participants included citizens and conservation leaders from the Forest Service, Wilderness Institute, Rocky Mountain Elk Foundation, Boone and Crockett Club, University of Montana, University of Idaho, and other national and regional conservation organizations. Participants reviewed the history of one hundred years of Forest Service conservation, explored forty years of wilderness stewardship since the passage of the Wilderness Act in 1964, discussed current issues confronting the agency, and looked ahead to the next century of wilderness and conservation challenges.

Key Discussion Points
The following key points are a synthesis of major recurring themes from discussions that occurred during the Northern Regional Forum:

- Prepare for constant change and ecological uncertainty. The rate of social change combined with climatic and ecological uncertainty will result in a future that will be so different from the past that the Forest Service needs to plan and act in the face of uncertainty.
- The future demands collaborative approaches. The magnitude of predicted population, demographic, and technological changes will force the Forest Service and wilderness managers to engage people in new and different ways to get them to participate and care about conservation and stewardship.

- *The agency can't do it alone.* To respond to growing land restoration and facilities maintenance backlogs and increasing public demand for services, the Forest Service needs to work with citizens, nongovernmental organizations, universities, other agencies, and partners to leverage funding and expertise.
- *Recognize and manage volunteerism as a form of recreation.* Forest Service leaders need to recognize the growing interest of citizens who are willing to volunteer for meaningful public service as a form of recreation, particularly if the opportunity involves restoring public lands or the conservation of natural resources. Agency leaders and wilderness managers need to revamp recreation and volunteer recruitment programs to take advantage of this emerging trend.

Northern Region Forum Overview

Missoula Mayor Mike Kadas welcomed the participants, noting that "Missoula is a place framed and changed by landscape." Missoula is the regional headquarters of the Forest Service's Northern Region, comprising Montana, North Dakota, northern Idaho, and portions of South Dakota and Washington. Germaine White, a Salish-Kootenai tribal member from northwest Montana, talked about the importance of wilderness to Native Americans and described her tribe's early establishment of the Mission Mountain Wilderness as a "defining and delicate moment" in the history of federal government and tribal relations. Regional Forester Gail Kimbell discussed how each generation needs to redefine conservation within the context of their times and challenged participants to think about the legacy that will passed on to future generations.

Keynote speakers, including USDA Deputy Under Secretary of Natural Resources Dave Tenny and Forest Service Director of Wilderness Mary Wagner, outlined the stages of Forest Service development from the establishment of the first American forest reserve—the Yellowstone Park Timberland Reserve—in 1891. They described the phases of public consciousness in our forests, from an early interest by stockmen and timber companies in producing commodities to a growing interest in conservation, triggered in part by America's awe of scenic paintings and photographs in the nineteenth and early twentieth centuries. In 1964, Congress passed the landmark National Wilderness Preservation Act, defining wilderness as a land "where man himself is a visitor who does not remain" and setting aside millions of acres for permanent protection. Forest Service Historian Jerry Williams showed a series of political cartoons taken from newspapers over the last century highlighting conflicts and controversies between the budding new agency, commodity users, and the emerging conservation ethic.

A panel of experts spoke about demographic, climatic, ecological and technological trends for natural resource managers to keep in mind in the upcoming years. Emilyn Sheffield of California State University at Chico discussed the projected population growth to 571 million Americans in the next one hundred years, and the impact an aging and more urban population will have on recreation and public land management. The need to provide places for active recreation and meaningful volunteer opportunities was highlighted.

Ron Neilson, bioclimatologist with the Pacific Northwest Research Station, discussed climate variation and current research to model ecological and climatic trends. The need to find a balanced approach between managing fuel buildup and ecosystem carbon storage was explained. Dr. Neilson predicted that the future will look so different from the past that the key to future leadership will be looking forward rather than backward.

Jerry Evans of the University of Montana School of Business Administration described the societal and organizational changes that are occurring as a result of new and emerging technologies. The Forest Service is not alone in struggling to keep up with rapid technological change and adapting to a global and network-centered world that provides unprecedented access to information. The result is a demand for increased openness and accountability on the part of public agencies.

Participants spent parts of both days in smaller discussion groups exploring the challenges of conservation leadership and wilderness stewardship. These groups used a combination of plenary speakers and working sessions to explore key issues and challenges facing the agency in the coming decades.

These breakout sessions produced a number of specific recommendations. For example, national standards for teaching, funding, and training the wilderness workforce were recommended in order to provide much-needed consistency between Forest Service regions and the four federal land management agencies that manage designated wilderness—the U.S. Fish and Wildlife Service, Bureau of Land Management, and National Park Service, along with the Forest Service.

Concern was expressed regarding the lack of public awareness about opportunities for volunteerism, particularly in light of budget realities. In the words of one wildlife biologist, "I think it is important to promote stewardship, because I believe that if people have an ownership of their surroundings, they are more likely to want to preserve it into the future." Participants recommended creating specific projects geared toward volunteers that are significant tasks rather than busywork. These projects then need to be advertised and promoted on a larger scale.

Breakout facilitators challenged participants to respond to the demands for conservation leadership and to prepare the next generation of conservation leaders. One popular recommendation for preparing young professionals to lead was to integrate leadership development with undergraduate natural resource training. A pilot program at the University of Idaho's College of Natural Resources that integrates civics, leadership, and professional development with the natural resource sciences was discussed as a model. This program is designed to give students practical experience by pairing them with agency mentors and providing them with leadership roles in projects and programs vital to the agency's mission.

A Leader-Expert Round Table, "Looking Back and Looking Forward," explored the constraints and challenges faced by the Forest Service as it embarks on its second century. Round Table participants included Gail Kimbell, regional forester for the Northern Region; Doug Scott, executive director for the Campaign for America's Wilderness; Jim Geringer, director of Policy and Public Sector Strategies ESRI and past governor of Wyoming; Jack Ward Thomas, USDA Forest Service Chief Emeritus; Emilyn Sheffield; and Ron Nielson. The panel was expertly moderated by Brian Kahn, National Public Radio commentator, Home Ground Radio.

For many participants the Leader-Expert Round Table discussion was the highlight of the forum as the experts and leaders participated in a lively interchange. Discussion of transcendent values, changing demographics and environmental conditions, citizen involvement, the changing roles of agency professionals, and congressional influence upon the agency's mission resulted in an extremely stimulating exchange. Questions and commentary from the audience added additional perspectives.

In closing, former Wyoming Governor Jim Geringer emphasized the ability of technology to lead us into the twenty-first century and noted that its formidable power can present complex issues in simple terms in order to help decision makers make the best possible decisions. However, he cautioned, "Data is just data until you do something with it; it should lead to action or decision." He also emphasized the need to work together in collaboration and focus on the common good in order to overcome the challenges that will undoubtedly arise in the next one hundred years of conservation and management of the national forests and grasslands. Finally, he urged those present to prepare the next generation to assume the mantle of conservation leadership, working with schools and youth groups such as the Student Conservation Association and 4-H. "Leadership is not a selfish right but an awesome responsibility," he concluded.

The Outstanding Forest Volunteer Centennial Award was presented to Carla Cline Belski, director of the nonprofit Bob Marshall Foundation. Carla has initiated many unique stewardship projects and trained and mobilized crews of volunteers to benefit the Bob Marshall Wilderness Complex. Smoke Elser, a nationally recognized backcountry horse-packing expert, was awarded the Private Sector Centennial Award for fifty years of "Leave No Trace" backcountry leadership. Those who know him describe his contagious enthusiasm as an educator and mentor for horse-packers nationwide. The Outstanding Partner Organization Centennial Award was presented to Steve Dedier, president of the Backcountry Horsemen of America, which has provided over one hundred thousand hours of volunteer service and provided an incomparable amount of support to the Forest Service in the care and maintenance of the agency's backcountry trails system.

Partners and Conveners

The Northern Region Centennial Forum was convened by these conservation partners: USDA Forest Service Northern Region, USDA Forest Service Rocky Mountain Research Station, University of Idaho College of Natural Resources, University of Montana College of Forestry and Conservation, Aldo Leopold Wilderness Research Institute, Wilderness Institute, Arthur Carhart Wilderness Training Center, Montana Discovery Foundation, Boone and Crockett Club, Rocky Mountain Elk Foundation, and the National Forest Foundation.

—Prepared by Ed Marston, Former Publisher, *High Country News*

Saluting the Past, Embracing the Future

To go forward into its second century, we believe that the U.S. Forest Service must first understand what happened during its first one hundred years. Fortunately, the Rocky Mountain delegation responsible for this abstract had the benefit of an outstanding regional forum that portrayed the history and spirit of that first century. Thanks to excellent speakers interacting with an engaged audience, we got to see today's issues, challenges, and the spirit of the emerging Forest Service.

If the Forest Service were the stock market, we would say that the agency's first one hundred years were marked by a long and steady rise to its midcentury point, followed by a boom, culminating in the late 1980s and early 1990s by a bust. The bust took the annual timber cut from ten billion to twelve billion board feet per year down to a few billion board feet.

The timber boom stood in marked contrast to the agency's early decades. For example, an early district ranger is said to have planted one million trees during his career. True or false, this anecdote about a reverse Paul Bunyan sums up what we learned from various speakers: that the early agency was about restoration and protection of land and trees.

Associate Chief Sally Collins said that the Forest Service staff accustomed to a custodian role found the transition to exploitation very hard. From this remove, we can only imagine their pain when the Forest Service responded to a change in national values and shifted to flat-out production of commodities, especially of timber, but also of livestock, stored and conveyed water, and late in the century, recreation.

A word here about recreation. The forum did not have any fights over logging or "overgrazing" or mining. But we did have a firefight over recreation. Recreation is no longer an unquestioned good; it is simply another contentious issue.

The Forest Service does not lack for contentious issues. It has been embroiled in fights over natural resource use for the last several decades, as the nation's values shifted from commodity production back to protection. Just as we must be sympathetic to the earlier agency employees whose custodial values were overwhelmed in the drive for commodities, we are also sympathetic to the communities and companies and agency staff who were caught in the shift away from commodities. Those communities and individuals were standing on the wrong historical corner just as historic forces changed direction…and they were run over.

This change in historic direction decimated communities and even states. It roiled the region's electoral politics. It set one class of people against another and has influenced our national politics.

Now passions and bitterness have subsided. But so has momentum. We are adrift. Again to quote Sally Collins, she said that until recently the Forest Service didn't have a mission statement because it didn't need one. "People knew what we were about." The Forest Service was about multiple use, use, sustained yield, the greatest good for the greatest number.

So one set of problems has been replaced with another. The fight over commodities has largely died down. The old truths are no longer so obvious that they don't have to be written down in a mission statement. The slate hasn't been wiped clean, but it has certainly been smudged. As we enter the next hundred years, there is work to be done plotting our course.

One of the most provocative moments of the meeting came when our regional forester, Rick Cables, held up the 1907 *Forest Service Regulations and Instructions*—the slim, 142-page, vest-pocket-sized bible used by district rangers on horseback to manage their domain.

Written in clear, forceful language by Gifford Pinchot, the agency's founding Chief, this booklet reminded us of two things. First, that the Forest Service was first and foremost not a land management agency but a civilizing force. Its employees carried the values of the larger society to the frontier. Just when the new agency's rangers and supervisors were stopping theft and destruction of natural resources, reformers in cities were stopping child labor and forcing slum owners to introduce running water and ventilation into tenements. The West in the agency's early years was part of a reform movement national in scope.

The skinny, undersized booklet also leads us to ask: How could they have run the forests back then when today we have an eight-foot-long shelf of policy manuals to do the same job? And what is the relation between the handful of men on horseback who administered much the same 191 million acres that are today administered by many more managers, most of whom are bound to their computers?

The short answer is that life is more complicated today, because we have made it more complicated. We put ten demands on the land and its resources where one hundred years ago there was only one or two.

Russell George, director of the Colorado Department of Natural Resources, spoke most directly to the question of managing the land in a complex, contradictory world. His example was water, but it could have been wildlife, grazing, or a dozen other issues. He said one set of laws and rulings says that Colorado's water is owned by the state, and another, equally authoritative set says the water is controlled by the federal government. This is typical: we embrace solitude and mass use of the land for recreation; let burn and demand fire protection; and seek the protection of endangered species and meeting society's material needs. Then we tell our land managers to resolve the conflicts and not bother us too much with the details.

George said that to overcome the built-in contradictions, federal and state agencies must remember that they serve the same people. Equally important, he said, the various agencies must avoid confronting the "big question": never mind which governmental entity owns the water—just go to the ditch or stream or diversion in question and solve the problem on the ground. Manage the land and its resources on the ground. That's the best we can do, he said, and even that is possible only if staffers extend themselves, and if their superiors—he used himself and Rick Cables as examples—give their staffs the room, and the protection, to be flexible and daring.

This is good, it is admirable. But it is also makeshift. Can we go beyond the makeshift?

The first step would be to recognize that the responsibility is shared. From what we saw at the forum, the Forest Service accepts that only partnerships among equals can make progress on the ground.

But there is one element that is the responsibility of the agency: to improve financial management, hiring, firing, and policy making. Unless the internal wheels turn freely, there will not be enough time for the Forest Service to get things done on the ground, with or without partners.

As outsiders, we have no advice to give about internal streamlining. But we are optimistic, as we sense that the Forest Service can sail into its second century with the same spirit and intent to make progress that it had when launched one hundred years ago.

When you look back at what has been done by our predecessors, the path to the future always seemed to have been clearly marked and inevitable. But the early agency, we learned from historian Char Miller's talk, was as mired in controversy and confusion as this era's agency is.

So it makes sense to encourage ourselves by pointing out what has already been done as we get ready for the next one hundred years. The agency has come through the long fight over commodity production and has been transformed. As speaker after speaker said, protection and restoration in the future will always come first, although the production of "goods" will also be important.

In addition, the agency has hammered out one major tool it never had before: partnerships among equals. The agency understands, without resentment, that it is no longer king of the natural resource hill. It can only govern with the help of others.

Finally, we are not trapped in a series of no-win situations. There are solutions. And we believe we know where to find those solutions. We believe the solutions will flow from the ground, via partnerships, hard work, and imagination.

If the money is there. As one speaker said, the Forest Service is being starved.

A more efficient system of internal governance is also needed. Delegate Ellie Towns said each incoming administration tends to set out new priorities that send many staffers running off in unforeseen directions. Somehow, that quadrennial problem—which is avoided this time thanks to a two-term president—must also be avoided in the future.

Finally, it may be that the final answer will be the one we earlier characterized as makeshift: Russell George's prescription for solving problems on the ground, one by one, in their particularity. Given external forces beyond the agency's control, that may be the best we can do. In that case, the Forest Service will need particularly ingenious, risk-taking, commonsense staff. So perhaps the major task for the moment is recruiting those people and setting up a system to give them the training they will need.

—Submitted by Walter Dunn, Collaborative Forest Restoration and
   International Program Coordinator, Southwestern Region
   USDA Forest Service, Albuquerque, NM

Global Connections

*I believe we need a community-based collaborative approach, sometimes
called community-based forestry. The basic idea is this: We sit down with
people from the community and anyone else who might be interested, and
together we formulate some shared long-term goals for the land. Then we
figure out how we can work together to get there.*

—From the opening remarks by Sally Collins,
   Associate Chief, USDA Forest Service

The Southwestern Regional Forum, "Global Connections," was held November
8–10, 2004 in Albuquerque. The forum focused on community-based approaches to sustainable natural resource management and conservation around the
world. It drew 111 participants from the United States and abroad to share
experiences, insights, and ideas for the future. Panel presentations on the social,
ecological, and economic issues associated with collaborative natural resources
management were followed by working groups that discussed more specific
aspects of the panel topics.

The forum emphasized USDA Forest Service international programs and
the role that International Forestry has had on the agency. These experiences
continue to influence agency and their partners around the world. USDA Forest
Service employees who work in international programs are no strangers to
collaborative, community-based approaches to natural resources management. Collaboration is the operating principal behind Forest Service
international programs.

The forum's New Mexico setting drew attention to the Collaborative Forest
Restoration program, which provides grants to support collaborative projects

that utilize small-diameter trees, restore forests and watersheds, and reduce hazardous fuels on federal, tribal, state, county, and municipal land in New Mexico.

This report summarizes the discussions and outcomes of the meeting's panels and working groups. It includes (1) a brief overview of USDA Forest Service involvement in global initiatives and the relevance of those initiatives at the agency's century mark, (2) plenary panels and concurrent working groups, (3) participants, and (4) a summary of the themes and recommendations that emerged from the plenary sessions and fourteen breakout sessions.

Global Connections at USDA Forest Service

The USDA Forest Service currently provides technical assistance and collaborates on natural resource management, policy, and research projects in fifty-nine countries around the world. These projects are accomplished through partnerships with other U.S. and host-country government agencies, land-grant universities, the private sector, and nongovernmental organization. Many of these projects involve hands-on partnerships with host countries and international organizations seeking to improve and advance sustainable forest management.

The Forest Service's global connections are important for a number of reasons. The agency plays a key role in addressing cross-boundary environmental problems, sharing knowledge and information about new technologies and solutions, and operating mutual-aid programs during times of crises.

International cooperation is regarded as essential to sustaining the ecological, commercial, and social viability of global forests, and to conserving biodiversity. Thus, most of the agency's work is done in collaboration with other organizations. International Forestry, which coordinates the agency's global work, partners with government entities such as the U.S. Agency for International Development and Foreign Agriculture Service, nongovernment organizations like Ducks Unlimited and The Nature Conservancy, universities, community groups, and the United Nations Food and Agriculture Organization.

Representatives from those organizations served as panel presenters and participants at the Global Connections forum. Their presentations highlighted ongoing programs, past successes, and importantly, emerging global issues facing the Forest Service and its partners.

Throughout its one-hundred-year history, the Forest Service has played a significant role in developing, initiating, and improving forest conservation and management practices around the world. Still, as participants at the forum pointed out, many challenges lie ahead. Today, the agency and its partners need effective ways to address the fast-growing demand for access and control of forest resources among increasingly factionalized communities of interest. The broad continuum of perspectives on what constitutes appropriate natural resource management poses complex obstacles and opportunities, both abroad and at home, as the agency enters its second century of service.

Plenary Panels and Concurrent Working Groups

Participants at the forum were welcomed by Forest Service Associate Chief Sally Collins and by Southwest Regional Forester Harv Forsgren. Ruben Guevara, regional officer for the International Tropical Timber Organization's Latin American division, and Alex Moad, assistant director for Technical Cooperation, International Programs, delivered keynote addresses.

The meeting was organized around three plenary panel sessions on the ecological, economic, and social issues facing community-based natural resource management and conservation programs in the United States and abroad. Each of the three panels included presentations by representatives of four key sectors: (1) a current or retired Forest Service employee, (2) a partner government agency or tribe, (3) a nongovernmental organization or private sector representative, and (4) an academic with expertise in forestry or natural resource management.

The three plenary panel sessions on ecological, economic, and social issues were followed by four or five concurrent working groups on the same topic. The presenters for the plenary panels and their subsequent working groups follow.

Ecological global connections issues plenary panel: Jeremy Kulisheck, Forest Service archaeologist, Pecos–Las Vegas Ranger District, Santa Fe National Forest, Pecos, New Mexico; Eva Mueller, Forestry Policy and Institutions Service, United Nations Food and Agriculture Organization, Rome; Bill Ulfelder, The Nature Conservancy, Flagstaff, Arizona; and Gary Hartshorn, World Forestry Center, Portland, Oregon.

Concurrent working groups, ecological issues: Protected Area Management, Forest and Watershed Management and Restoration, Inventory and Monitoring, Fire Ecology and Suppression, and Wildlife Habitat Conservation.

Economic global connections issues plenary panel: Jim Sedell, director, Forest Service Pacific Southwest Research Station, Albany, California; Mary Melnyk,

Asia Bureau, U.S. Agency for International Development; and Catharine Mater, Mater Engineering, Oregon.

Concurrent working groups, economic issues: Ecotourism, Marketing, Community and Economic Development, and Timber and Nontimber Forest Product Utilization and Technology.

Social global connections issues plenary panel: Joe Tainter, Rocky Mountain Research Station, Forest Service, Albuquerque; Alvin Warren, Santa Clara Pueblo, New Mexico; Augusta Molnar, Forest Trends, Washington, D.C.; and Jim Burchfield, associate dean, College of Forestry and Conservation, University of Montana.

Concurrent working groups, social issues: Indigenous and Tribal Issues, Communal Land, Land Tenure, Collaborative Community Forest Management, and Multiparty Monitoring.

Each concurrent working group began with a twenty-minute presentation on an applied project or research study, setting the context for a facilitated discussion on accomplishments and challenges in collaborative natural resource management. Discussions focused specifically on opportunities where the Forest Service can play a key role in providing technical assistance, facilitating collaborative programs or initiatives, and effecting internal and external process improvements.

In addition to the fourteen topics discussed in the working groups, an evening poster session highlighted fifteen collaborative natural resource management initiatives around the world.

Participants

The Southwestern Regional Forum drew 111 participants from the United States, Canada, South America, Mexico, and Europe. The participants included 45 Forest Service employees (4 retired); 33 representatives of nongovernmental and private sector organizations; 13 academics and scholars; 9 members of tribes or pueblos; 6 representatives of state, local or county government; and 5 representatives of other (non-USDA) national and international governmental organizations.

Three of the participants, who also served as presenters in concurrent working groups, received Forest Service Centennial Awards for their outstanding work in the area of community-based natural resource management. Awards were presented to Sterling Tipton of Zuni Pueblo Furniture Enterprise, Cornelia Flora of the North Central Regional Center for Rural Development at Iowa

State University, and Juan Manuel Frausto of the Mexican Nature Conservation Fund.

Themes, Opportunities, and Recommendations

Forum participants shared insights and experiences on the social and institutional factors that affect forests and the people who use them. Following on the key themes of the plenary panel presentations, participants in the fourteen facilitated working groups identified a number of ecological, economic, and social accomplishments and challenges. Participants were asked to frame the challenges as opportunities or recommendations for advancing the mission and services of the agency, and for implementing improvements both within the agency and externally to the millions of people worldwide who rely on forests for their livelihoods or quality of life.

A synthesis of the opportunities and recommendations from all fourteen working groups revealed several common themes and areas for future consideration. In general, the discussions and final recommendations indicate a strong desire to expand the Forest Service's connections—both globally and domestically—with communities and other partners, and to improve the agency's systems for meeting the often-conflicting demands of forest ecosystems and forest stakeholders.

The final recommendations are grouped according to four strong themes that emerged from the working groups' reports: (1) collaboration; (2) economic development and poverty alleviation; (3) community-based forestry; and (4) knowledge sharing, training, and education.

1. Collaboration. Working group participants repeatedly cited the need for more cooperative, stakeholder-based decision making regarding natural resource management and forest health, both nationally and internationally. They emphasized the importance of building and strengthening partnerships, improving collaborative problem solving both within the Forest Service and within communities, and collaborative management of traditional and locally owned or managed lands.

Opportunities and recommendations:

- *Strengthen and develop partnerships at all levels.* Partnerships should be strengthened among tribal and indigenous groups; other community and nonprofit groups in the United States and cross-nationally; private landowners; and federal, state, and local agencies.

Among indigenous groups, the agency should partner with tribal colleges (including those in the Pacific Islands and Alaska) to develop appropriate trainings and opportunities, and should support effective cooperative management models with indigenous peoples on national forests and other protected areas.

More collaborative projects should be encouraged and rewarded among nongovernmental organizations focused on social change, community development, and wildlife conservation, and also among local community groups and landowners.

The agency also should encourage and nurture partnerships with other federal agencies with experience, tools, and capacity in stakeholder-driven processes. It should identify opportunities for partnering with state and local governments and develop those where appropriate. Internationally, the agency should continue to support and initiate collaborative programs and partnerships, particularly in the areas of training and cross-national cooperation on conservation, community forestry, and crisis-assistance initiatives.

- *Design collaborative processes to include strategies for building and improving trust in the Forest Service.* To address issues of mistrust and conflicts of interest between the agency and forest stakeholders (which many forum participants described as ever-present and growing), the Forest Service should develop a more transparent, consensus-based approach to project design. For example, agency employees should be straightforward with forest stakeholders about project limitations, goals, available funding, who key decision makers will be, and the potential impacts of specific projects or programs.

Developing stronger partnerships and collaborative initiatives with indigenous groups as well as environmental and wildlife groups—and drawing on their expertise—will help to rebuild those stakeholders' trust in the agency.

- *Adapt the agency's regulatory environment to enable more equal power sharing with local communities and partners.* The Forest Service should find ways to share, or even cede, decision-making control with partners and stakeholder groups. Working groups described power differences as especially skewed in projects affecting local and indigenous communities, and said that this imbalance heightens mistrust and conflicts of interest between those groups and the agency. Regulations should be flexible enough to incorporate local, indigenous knowledge; to respond to dynamic and unique conditions or circumstances; and to include shared or equal decision-making responsibility among partners and stakeholders.

The agency should encourage land-grant and indigenous communities to become involved in collaborative management of traditional or communal lands, empowering them through signed agreements and commitments. It also should consider making grant monies available to small nongovernmental organizations or collaborative community groups that include greater flexibility and responsiveness in developing projects.

- *Improve training and skill-building programs for agency leaders and staff.* To improve the effectiveness of partnerships and community-based collaboratives, the agency should emphasize training and capacity building in the areas of facilitative leadership, collaborative problem solving, and participatory planning and implementation. Training in community development and community organizing for agency officials who work closely with citizens and community groups should also be introduced. Ideally, training would be designed for both agency officials and partnering groups to attend together, rather than offering separate, agency-only training workshops.

- *Reward agency leaders, staff, and partnering organizations for using and experimenting with collaborative approaches to natural resource management.* Collaborative processes often require risk taking and experimentation. Sometimes things can go wrong and bring unwelcome publicity to the agency or to stakeholders. On the other hand, regulatory, litigation-driven or political solutions can do even more to stalemate a project. Agency leaders should weigh these risks in initiating or participating in collaborative processes and should provide incentives and recognition to staff and participants who achieve success in collaborative projects or partnerships.

- *Use postsecondary schools as convening places for collaborative projects.* Student and faculty researchers in fields such as natural resource management, conservation, forestry, or wildlife biology should more often be considered as important technical resources and partners to agency and stakeholder groups involved in collaborative processes. The agency should identify postsecondary institutions that specialize in applied natural resource management programs and have the capacity and willingness to help convene collaborative processes. Student and faculty researchers also can serve as qualified and neutral program evaluators, helping the agency identify what works and what does not in collaborative approaches to natural resource management.

2. Economic development and poverty alleviation. Both domestically and abroad, poverty and the absence of jobs and economic opportunities are seen as key obstacles to conservation of natural resources and sustainable uses of forests. In nearly all of the working groups, participants identified economic challenges and opportunities, from resource development and job creation to marketing, anticorruption initiatives, and cost-sharing measures aimed at creating or improving livelihoods for forest-based communities. Many working groups listed this issue as crucial to future agenda setting and policy development within the Forest Service.

Opportunities and recommendations:

- *Initiate strategic planning and investments in communities to help citizens address their natural resource issues.* Forum participants frequently described a lack of capacity, responsibility, or willingness among communities to address their resource and crisis management issues at community or local levels. The Forest Service should play a key role in designing short- and long-range planning initiatives in communities and should help secure or identify resources to fund partnerships and training programs in those communities.

In addition, the Forest Service also should focus on ways to improve its own as well as local communities' organizational effectiveness, and it should design strategies that help communities mitigate risk and improve the security of their tenure and access to local resources. The agency should look at ways to provide direct investments in forest-based communities in the Unites States, following on similar successful projects overseas.

- *Strengthen marketing research and development around forest products.* The agency should research what works and what does not, both in other countries and domestically, to learn how forest products are successfully improving local economies. Research should identify opportunities for entering the small-business market, success measures for sustaining and growing small businesses, and effective ways to support both large-scale timber production as well as small-scale, nontimber forest product production. The agency should be nurturing and supporting small businesses that harvest, develop, and deliver forest products.
- *Support different scales of marketing projects.* The agency should participate in a number of marketing initiatives of varying scales—from small, local enterprises to large multiforest or multinational projects. Shifting operationally from a resource-based management strategy to a community-based

management strategy could help encourage and enable more unique and innovate small-scale marketing projects. This could also enable more efficient resolution of National Environmental Policy Act issues and other obstacles that currently hinder small-scale, local enterprises. On a larger scale, the Forest Service should partner with other federal or state agencies to use wood products. For example, the Forest Service and the U.S. Department of Transportation could jointly promote thinning along roads and use of forest products for signage. Other agencies could use forest products for shipbuilding, pallets, or other required inventory.

In general, the Forest Service should explore harvesting, processing, marketing, jurisdictional, and permitting issues related to the utilization of nontimber forest products and incorporate their management and harvesting in forest plans.

- *Develop strategies for helping indigenous and legally or economically disadvantaged communities ensure tenure rights and access to forest resources.* The Forest Service should work with indigenous and other legally disadvantaged groups to help them improve the security of their tenure and access to local resources. Training programs in community development and organizing should include education and information about Native or cultural traditional practices, vis-à-vis forest harvesting and gathering.

The agency should encourage and invite land-grant communities to participate in collaborative management of traditional land—and empower them to do so. It should provide grants or other forms of assistance to indigenous groups, land-grants, and other economically disadvantaged communities for developing markets for forest products, acquiring skills and training for forest-based occupations and for designing strategic plans and risk management initiatives on their lands.

To help ensure these initiatives succeed, the Forest Service should hire social scientists and other technical staff who represent indigenous and economically disadvantaged communities, and/or people who have strong cross-cultural communication and facilitation skills.

A number of forum participants believed certification of Forest Service lands would benefit many struggling or disadvantaged communities. The agency should consider a certification process that could lead to improved economic options for traditionally disadvantaged communities.

- *Impart greater decision-making authority to employees to work with community organizers toward improving forest-based economies.* A number of forum participants described community-based processes that were stymied due to field staff's lack of decision-making authority over particular resource or management issues. Forest Service leadership should offer greater flexibility and decision-making authority to field staff working in local communities.

3. Community-based forestry. Panel presenters and working group participants cited the growing importance of community-based approaches to natural resource management and provided numerous examples of community-based models from countries around the world. Yet domestically, such models have been applied primarily in small areas with small-scale impact and have occurred in the context of federal control of resources. Working group participants believe the Forest Service could achieve scale by addressing barriers and providing incentives for experimentation and larger pilots in many of the agency's units.

Opportunities and recommendations:

- *Facilitate efforts to legitimize the role of communities and landowners in community-based resource conservation and management.* The Forest Service should shift toward a community-based management strategy, away from its more traditional resource-based approach. The agency should begin to systematically apply the principles and practices of this approach, whose key tenet is involvement of all concerned stakeholders. "Community based" means that communities managing the resources have the legal rights and the local and economic institutions and support to take substantial responsibility for sustained use of their resources. The Forest Service should work with all forest stakeholders and communities to formalize this approach.

The agency should identify and mentor community leaders and visionaries who champion these approaches and should find ways to build civic and institutional capacity for community-based approaches to forest management.

- *Adopt a more holistic approach to community work by strengthening ties and partnerships with citizens and community leaders, tribes, local and state governments, and federal agencies.* Following the principles of community-based management, the agency should engage in strong partnerships with other governmental agencies, tribes and pueblos, community groups, and non-profits to collaboratively address ongoing and emerging resource management issues. These include long-standing indigenous concerns, particularly with regard to access rights, protection of sacred sites and restoration of tribal lands; resource and jurisdictional conflicts between the agency and land-grant heirs; antagonism and polarization over public lands and grazing concerns; and overlapping jurisdictions and management among a host of federal and state land management agencies.

The Forest Service should look for ways to incorporate traditional and local knowledge about an environment or resource into its overall management plans for an area.

- *Improve community-based monitoring processes.* The Forest Service should implement a number of changes to existing monitoring programs. It should begin to implement community-based monitoring programs over larger landscapes and geographic areas and create incentives (rather than enforcement processes) to encourage multiparty monitoring and collaborative decision making about monitoring issues and programs. It also should facilitate interagency exchanges and knowledge sharing on monitoring processes and successes.

Multiparty monitoring should integrate indigenous knowledge. The Forest Service should be more deliberate in including local people and community input in monitoring efforts. The agency also should encourage cross-boundary initiatives with Canada and Mexico for multiparty monitoring of key projects involving rivers, forests, watersheds, wildlife habitat, and ecosystems.

4. Knowledge sharing, training, and education. Forum participants cited a need for improved education, training, and information sharing and dissemination. Several working groups reported frustrations with community perceptions that forest management and risk mitigation are the sole responsibilities of the Forest Service, rather than concerns to be shared by all forest stakeholders. They believe that better outreach and communication to forest communities and forest users will help increase public awareness of the role citizens must play in forest health and of the complex array of issues facing federal land agencies like the Forest Service. Also, where relationships are strained between Forest Service staff and the communities they serve, all parties could begin to build trust and avoid conflicts by participating in training and capacity building in communications, small-group facilitation, collaborative problem solving, and economic development.

Opportunities and recommendations:

- *Initiate a large-scale education and information campaign ("beyond brochures") to promote the agency's services, challenges, constraints, partnerships, and visions for success.* The roles and responsibilities of the public in natural resource management should be a key part of this campaign, which should target all sectors—from Congress to local schools and households. Materials and information should focus on fire ecology and suppression, the economics of forest management and restoration, the social causes of fire, ways science can enrich local and indigenous knowledge, and ways local knowledge can be incorporated into natural resource management strategies.

- *Work with educators to develop a curriculum for schoolchildren focused on natural resource management issues.* The Forest Service should consider partnerships with national education associations or local school boards to develop an introductory curriculum on the issues facing the agency and forest stakeholders. The curriculum should include general principles and practices in the area of natural resource management, as well as locally relevant information and case studies.

- *Add and improve training and skill-building programs widely across Forest Service units.* The agency should invest time and resources in training programs for employees and leaders in facilitative leadership, collaborative problem solving, participatory planning and implementation, community development, community organizing, cross-cultural communication, and innovations in risk mitigation. Building and improving human and social capital within the agency's existing workforce also should be a priority. Job descriptions should include specific capacities such as "people skills," cross-cultural experience, mediation or facilitation, and the ability to take risks and design innovative programs.

- *Develop knowledge sharing networks among other federal and state land agencies.* The Forest Service should do more to harvest, disseminate, and store key knowledge and lessons learned for agency staff as well as forest stakeholders generally. More robust network building and knowledge sharing will enable a more productive "learning organization"—one characterized by communication and openness, inquiry and feedback, adequate time, and mutual respect and support. The agency should consider ways to help "network" geographic regions facing similar issues and challenges and to join existing networks of larger communities of interest with specific concerns related to natural resource management.

- *Work with postsecondary institutions to develop certificate programs and research studies that support the work of the Forest Service.* To help build and sustain human capital in the natural resources fields, the Forest Service should consider applied partnerships with academic institutions, guiding them in course development and enhancing internships, postdoc, and work-study programs across the agency.

Report of the Intermountain Regional Forum
November 18–19, 2004
Boise State University, Idaho

—Principal author: John C. Freemuth, Ph.D.,Senior Fellow,
The Andrus Center for Public Policy

Fire and Forest Health:
The Forest Service's Continuing Management Challenges
in the New Century

The U.S. Forest Service is about to celebrate its one-hundredth anniversary. It will host a national congress in early January 2005, exactly one hundred years after the first Forest Congress and subsequent to holding a series of regional conferences throughout the country. On November 18–19, 2004, the Andrus Center for Public Policy, *The Idaho Statesman*, and the Forest Service presented one of those conferences in Boise, Idaho. The topics for this conference were wildland fire and forest health.

Summary of Conference Themes
The central need that emerged from the conference is for communication: communication between stakeholders and the agencies; between the Forest Service and the public; between the Forest Service and the media; and among the public, the Forest Service, Congress, and the media. Only when that has occurred can the kind of trust be built that will allow us to deal with the growing physical threats to our forests: wildfire, insect infestations, drought, climate change, demographics, and loss of open space.

Major Issues of the Conference
As the U.S. Forest Service prepares to celebrate this important anniversary, the nation's forests aren't what they used to be, or so it appears. Years of fire suppression, drought, and insect infestations have provoked what some assert is a forest health crisis. Although there appears to be agreement that our forests are not in the best of shape, there are very different views about what the causes of the crisis are, whether those causes have cures, and whether forest health should be the core of today's Forest Service mission. Lying behind that concern is the

question of whether the Forest Service has restored enough trust among its many stakeholders to allow implementation of new policies on fire and forest health.

Setting the Stage

It was widely agreed, going into the conference, that many years of indiscriminate fire suppression have made many forest types prone to catastrophic wildfire. It was also agreed that fire suppression has continued to be the policy even when fire scientists suggested that we rethink that policy. The West is now clearly in the midst of a multiyear drought and of insect infestations. In addition, climate change and demographic changes may be altering western landscapes and rendering fire policy more complex than ever. Even with our best collaborative efforts, it may take years to show results, and those results may be limited by events beyond our control.

The conference participants were aware of the Healthy Forests Restoration Act, recently passed by Congress, as the latest attempt to do something about the conditions of our national forests. The Forest Service views this legislation as perhaps its best (and some inside the bureau ruefully say last) opportunity to show that it has the tools, commitment, and leadership to manage our national forests. Everyone continues to watch to see how the legislation is implemented. For now, there is only cautious agreement on where and how to proceed with that implementation.

The opening speaker, Stephen J. Pyne, Regents' Professor, Biology and Society Programs, School of Life Sciences, Arizona State University, commented that the conference "brought together an extraordinary assemblage of fire lore—literally thousands of years of fire experience in one room."

This report summarizes the themes that emerged from the presentations and panels.

Dale Bosworth, Chief of the U.S. Forest Service: "The way we work with people has changed over time. In particular, we've learned the need for more up-front public dialogue, public involvement, and collaboration in our decision-making."

Issues and Themes

Theme 1. The Forest Service cannot act effectively unless it is trusted. The age of uncritical deference to expertise has ended. By the same token, if the Service performs well, the public should be willing to give the agency some breathing room to move.

To frame his remarks, Dave Tenny, the deputy under secretary for forestry in the U.S. Department of Agriculture, used the theme of trust, the kind that is given as an expression of confidence but that also still requires collaboration and critical questioning. The issue underlies all of our questions about fire and forest health. Do we trust the Forest Service to deal with those questions? How much of a free hand do we give it? What is the role of the media, elected officials, scientists, and others?

David Tenny: "It's an active kind of trust. It requires engagement. It requires collaboration and hard work. It involves asking critical questions at appropriate times about whether we are doing enough or doing the right things at the right pace."

Theme 2. The success of a new fire policy will require a new "fire story," one that clearly expresses the complexity of the issues. The Forest Service should task its public affairs staff to develop a new, clear, and understandable narrative and disseminate it effectively to editors and policy makers around the country.

Pyne, one of the country's most respected experts on the historical and cultural influences on wildland fire, took us through a history of the various fire eras up to present time. Fire was a traumatic influence on the new Forest Service, a "founding menace" that the empowered agency was "eager to fight. But that zealotry was their power, their glory, and their ironic undoing."

Today, we are facing a new "big burn"—large fires, to be sure, but not like those of 1910, which initiated the era of large-scale fire suppression. The fires of today are greatly influenced by mankind's own big burn, "anthropogenic combustion"—industrial use that is causing enough climate change to alter fire regimes everywhere. The question of what to do about those fires leads to intense debate.

Stephen J. Pyne: "The perception among the fire community is that the nation has a deficit of 'good burns,' that the way to solve this shortfall is to reinstate fire across the board, and that the public is unable to absorb anything other than a much simplified message. This time, dissent focuses on whether fire management should be based on the ax or the torch. The great achievement of this era of reformation is surely the indelible bonding of fire to land management. It is testimony to the complexity of that concept that we have no story sufficient to tell what it means."

During a question-and-answer session with the audience, Pyne suggested that one key in telling a new fire story would be linking fire policy to a more explicitly biological framework, moving past a "physical problem that needs physical countermeasures." That framework would need to show that fire was accomplishing an ecological goal that only fire could do.

Theme 3. The media have a responsibility in telling the "new story" of fire as a land management tool.

Panel moderator Marc Johnson, president of the Andrus Center, began the first panel, "The Paradox of Success," by noting that the Forest Service was the "victim of its own success in controlling fire." How to help the agency move into a new era was the question before the panel.

Reporting on large wildfires is one thing, but reporting on the relationship of fire to forest health and the resultant debate over the tools and methods to deal with it is another.

Commenting on the difficulty of telling this story to the public and to Congress, Elizabeth Arnold of National Public Radio suggested that the agency had to work on telling the new fire story in ways that the media could use. Rocky Barker of *The Idaho Statesman* thought that the new message ought to include the fact that fire "is," rather than its being good or bad.

Although the old message on fire was told clearly by Smokey Bear, the new message may be more difficult to convey in clear and concise terms. Retired Forest Supervisor Orville Daniels said that others need to help tell the story and that the issue transcended the Forest Service's ability to solve on its own. It needs political support from the entire society. As he said, "You don't move without others." James Burchfield of the University of Montana thought that a little contrition about past mistakes might help build that support.

Theme 4. Fire use will continue to create issues with smoke and smoke management—issues that will be contentious. As the Andrus Center said in its 2000 report on fire, fire's biological necessity must be reconciled with legitimate concerns over smoke.

Gray Reynolds, a former deputy chief and regional forester, reminded the audience of the difficulty of gaining public support for prescribed fires that lead to smoke, even though that was the historical norm. Tom Thompson, deputy chief of the National Forest System, acknowledged that the governmentwide culture of fire suppression needs to be reexamined. He also cautioned that a "let-burn" fire that grew out of control might make that cultural change difficult to sell to the public.

Penny Morgan, professor of forest resources, University of Idaho: "It's not just threats to people and their property; it's also smoke and the health and visibility hazards associated with smoke."

Theme 5. Forest health is the new Forest Service task. Timber harvest must be part of that task, and the agency should be allowed to produce some timber harvest revenue that is dedicated to forest health work and helps replace general fund monies that will not be available. This must be accomplished in a transparent way.

This was the theme of remarks made by Idaho Senator Larry Craig, chairman of the U.S. Senate Subcommittee on Forestry and Public Lands Management. He expressed hope that the Healthy Forests Restoration Act would work toward restoring trust throughout the forest policy community and "that all interests could see the value of urban watersheds, would put as a third- or fourth-tier value the commercial uses as they relate to our forests, and would do so in an open and public process."

Theme 6. Some of our best efforts on fire and forest health will be inhibited by climate change and demographic factors, about which there is little consensus.

Theme 7. Incentives for suppression, prescribed fire, and treatments often conflict with incentives for new homes and growth in interface areas. Homeowners need to share the responsibility for fire prevention and suppression.

The first afternoon panel, "Things Could Get Worse," was envisioned as a sobering check on any expectations that fire reduction and forest health would be easily accomplished. Prominent climatologist Tim Brown, of the Desert Research Institute, noted that there is scientific consensus that we are in the midst of climate change. For the West in the twenty-first century, this means a warmer winter, less snowpack but more precipitation, and warmer summers. Drought will continue, comparable to the period of the 1930s or 1950s. In Brown's understated summary, he said, "This will be the challenge for management."

Penny Morgan commented that fire was more of a social and political issue than a biological one. Where we "act" on the forest must be within the zone of agreement with the public, and she suggested that the backcountry might be a place where fire could be used as a tool of land management.

Jim Caswell, director of the Idaho Office of Species Conservation and a former Forest Service supervisor, agreed and added that the fire culture still placed undue emphasis on suppression rather than on the use of fire, suppressing fires that could have been allowed to burn.

U.S. Senator Larry Craig: "Let's remember that during the decade of the 1990s, when we brought the level of public timber harvest down nearly eighty percent, we basically turned the Forest Service into a red-ink agency…"

Timothy Brown: "There is scientific consensus that we are in the midst of climate change, both globally and regionally…The next fifteen to thirty years have a higher probability of being dry in the West than the five or seven years we've been through."

Planning for forest treatment was done conservatively because of budget concerns, and many areas were left untreated with the expectation that they would ultimately burn and be paid for with the "blank check" of fire suppression monies.

Walter Hecox, of Colorado College, provided a perspective on western growth and western illusions, noting that many newcomers came west looking for the Marlboro cowboy world. Instead, we see growth in the service economy, second-home ownership that turns over every seven years, and new wildland-urban neighborhoods that do not like smoke and expect fire suppression.

Hank Blackwell, assistant fire chief of Santa Fe County, New Mexico, stressed the importance of partnerships among federal, state, and local entities in attacking the fire and health problem. He did not spare homeowners and suggested that "we shouldn't reward a community for burning itself down."

Jerry Williams, director of Fire and Aviation Management, called for attention to a bigger issue: managing and sustaining fire adaptive ecosystems, which would encourage a focus on building codes and trade-offs among clean air, endangered species, and watersheds.

Theme 8. Collaboration with affected communities is essential for success. People close to the national forests should be part of deciding the desired future of the ecosystem.

Theme 9. Collaborative efforts should have "teeth" that could contribute to building trust at the local level and avoiding the problem of an after-the-fact veto.

The intent of the day's last panel, "Things Could Get Better," was to point in the direction needed for successful policy development and change. Louise Milkman, director of federal programs for the Nature Conservancy, encouraged public participation and pointed to a project on the Bayou Ranger District in the Ozark National Forest where the Forest Service worked hard with the community and gained the support of "pretty much everyone."

Other speakers also stressed the importance of community. Chad Oliver, director of the Yale Global Institute for Sustainable Forestry, emphasized the importance of creating "vibrant" communities, and Wally Covington, professor of forest ecology at Northern Arizona University, thought the number-one task of the Forest Service was to "restore and enhance the economic, ecological, and social integrity" of greater ecosystems. In his view, guiding principles could be articulated at regional levels but discussed and implemented at local levels. The communities and the public must be equal participants.

Gray Reynolds: "If we could get legal determinations from the Supreme Court on some of these issues, it would simplify the work of the Forest Service. Right now…as soon as somebody comes in and raises an appeal, everything stops."

Both Marc Brinkmeyer, president of Riley Creek Lumber, and Jonathon Oppenheimer of the Idaho Conservation League took the discussion back to the need for trust in order to be able to find areas of agreement. Brinkmeyer called for collaborative efforts to include "teeth" that could build trust at the local level, avoiding the "after-the-fact, outsider veto" that often derails collaborative effort.

Theme 10. Outdoor recreation and ecological restoration should be the agency's top priorities within the context of the Chief's list of the four major threats to the forests.

Theme 11. We should act first in areas where agreement exists.

That was the message from Forest Service Chief Dale Bosworth at the opening of the second day of the conference. He noted, however, that the definition of a "restored" forest would depend more on a societal consensus than on a scientific one. More specifically, places where communities, the agencies, and the landowners have "come to some agreement should be the highest-priority areas for forest work."

Chief Bosworth said that debates over timber harvest, grazing, and road-building were distractions that led us away from more important issues, such as the four threats facing the forest system: fuel buildup, invasive species, unmanaged recreation, and loss of open space.

Building consensus on forest restoration clearly implies active conversations with the various publics that are concerned with forest policy. As the Chief said, "There remains public distrust of what is called active forest management." Later in the day, Tom Bonnicksen, professor emeritus of forest science from Texas A&M, remarked that those leading the conversation need to be as "charismatic and persuasive as Theodore Roosevelt and Gifford Pinchot were one hundred years ago."

Theme 12. Forest health is a useful concept, but it requires a publicly accepted definition and a community-centered monitoring process that can help evaluate implementation.

This panel was constructed to provide an entertaining, thoughtful, and useful "debate" about whether the Forest Service ought to make forest health its top priority. Panelists were asked to speak for the affirmative or the negative position on the issue: Resolved: that the Forest Service should make forest health its top priority.

Jerry Williams: "The larger public lands policy issue for at least forty million acres in the West is, How are we going to manage and sustain resilient, fire-adaptive ecosystems? Until we address that larger public lands policy issue, I think we're going to continue to find ourselves at stalemate over science."

Neil Sampson, president of the Sampson Group and former executive vice president of American Forests, took the lead for the affirmative, arguing that forest health needed to be clearly defined in a way that won the day for the active management perspective and that it was the best way to frame the management issue. He agreed with the Chief that the forest health issue transcended national forest lands. He was also concerned that newcomers to the woods often did not understand that forests were not frozen in time and not always green.

Jack Ward Thomas, in some tongue-in-cheek comments, painted a scenario that made clear that a forest health policy can have unforeseen consequences—that is, a lot more homes and people in the woods, raising more urban-wildland interface problems and more expectation of fire suppression. Tom Bonnicksen offered one definition of what he called forest restoration: "restoring ecologically and economically sustainable native forests that are representative of historic landscapes, significant in America's history and culture, also serving society's contemporary need for wood products and other forest services."

Pat Williams, former Montana congressman, objected to a forest health mission for the Forest Service if it meant exemptions from regulations, public review, and an appeals process. Chris Wood, of Trout Unlimited, argued that the forest health question was really about values and urged that people pay close attention to the values contained within roadless areas. He stressed the need for fire as a land management tool in roadless areas rather than thinning and building new roads to allow thinning.

Randal O'Toole of the Thoreau Institute suggested that everyone remember the importance of incentives in affecting agency missions, especially the power of the budget to affect the priorities of the Forest Service. The fire suppression "blank check" was, he thought, an incentive that led the agency not to worry about cost or choice when suppressing fire. He offered three suggestions for how the incentive structure might be changed: allowing the Forest Service to charge for various uses, governing under a fiduciary trust model, and forming a "friends of the forest" advisory board for each forest.

Summing Up: The Next One Hundred Years
Governor Cecil D. Andrus, chairman of the Andrus Center; Chief Bosworth; and Steven Daley Laursen, dean of the College of Natural Resources at the University of Idaho, provided closing comments. Dean Daley Laursen suggested that our culture had changed enough that we should consider new models of decision making. He suggested that the change be in the direction of deliberative democracy, born from the ground up, rather than continuing our current command-and-control regulatory approaches. That may begin to occur as we learn more about ecological processes and about how to put various outcomes together, such as jobs and environmental services, rather than seeing them as mutually exclusive.

Governor Andrus called for people to communicate and work together but also reminded everyone that we still had to make choices and that not every acre of land could be open to every use. Chief Bosworth agreed, stressing the need for communicating, finding common ground, and changing the incentives that people work under. He gave hope that this conference was an example of people beginning to work toward those three goals.

Conclusion
What we are really doing behind our concern for fire and forest health is imagining how we want our forests to look by the end of this still-young century. Stakeholders who care about the national forests and all Americans must come to some agreement and understand what the economic, political, social, and ecological limits might be to reaching that vision.

As we celebrate the centennial of the U.S. Forest Service, the country should remember and appreciate what the Forest Service has done and continues to do well. We need to learn what has not gone so well, why that has happened, and what is being done or can be done to change that.

Gifford Pinchot's stricture to look for the "greatest good for the greatest number for the longest time" can still serve as a signpost to finding that vision.

Agenda
November 18, 2004

Welcome and Introduction
Governor Cecil D. Andrus, Chairman, The Andrus Center for Public Policy
Robert Kustra, Ph.D., President, Boise State University
Leslie Hurst, President and Publisher, *The Idaho Statesman*
David P. Tenny, Deputy Under Secretary for Forestry, U.S. Department of Agriculture

Keynote Address: "Facing the Flames: The Forest Service Takes on Fire"
Stephen Pyne, Ph.D., Professor, Biology and Society Programs, Arizona State University, Tempe

The Paradox of Success: Can We Stand Much More?
Moderated by Marc C. Johnson, President, the Andrus Center
Panelists:
Elizabeth Arnold, Western Correspondent, National Public Radio
Rocky Barker, Environment Reporter, *The Idaho Statesman*
James A. Burchfield, Ph.D., Associate Dean, College of Forestry and Conservation, University of Montana
Orville Daniels, U.S. Forest Service (Ret.), Former Supervisor, Lolo National Forest
Jim Fisher, Ph.D., Editorial Page Editor, *The Lewiston Tribune*
Tom Kenworthy, Journalist, *USA Today* and the *Washington Post*
Gray Reynolds, Deputy Chief, U.S. Forest Service (Ret.), and President, National Museum of Forest Service History
Tom Thompson, Deputy Chief, National Forest System

Perspective from Congress
U.S. Senator Larry Craig (R-Idaho), Chairman of the U.S. Senate Subcommittee on Forestry and Public Lands Management (via satellite)

Discussion: Things Could Get Worse: The Management Challenges Ahead
Moderated by John C. Freemuth, Ph.D., Professor of Political science, Boise State University, and Senior Fellow, the Andrus Center
Panelists:
Hank Blackwell, Assistant Fire Chief, Santa Fe County, New Mexico
Timothy J. Brown, Ph.D., Associate Research Professor, Atmospheric Sciences Division, Desert Research Institute
James L. Caswell, Administrator, Idaho Office of Species Conservation, and Chairman, Strategic Issues Panel on Fire Suppression Costs of the Wildland Fire Leadership Council
Walter E. Hecox, Ph.D., Professor of Economics, Colorado College, Colorado Springs
Penelope Morgan, Ph.D., Professor of Forest Resources, University of Idaho
Jerry Williams, Director of Fire and Aviation Management, U.S. Forest Service, Washington, D.C.

Things Could Get Better: Imagining the National Forests in the New Century
Moderated by Dr. John Freemuth
Panelists:
Marc Brinkmeyer, Owner and President, Riley Creek Lumber
W. Wallace Covington, Ph.D., Professor of Forest Ecology and Director of Ecological Restoration Institute, Northern Arizona University, Flagstaff
Louise Milkman, Director of Federal Programs, The Nature Conservancy, Arlington, Virginia
Chad Oliver, Ph.D., Pinchot Professor of Forestry and Environmental Studies and Director, Yale Global Institute for Sustainable Forestry, Yale University
Jonathan Oppenheimer, Fire Policy and Public Lands Management Analyst, Idaho Conservation League

Closing remarks by Governor Andrus and adjournment

November 19, 2004
Welcome and Introduction by Governor Andrus

Remarks
Jack G. Troyer, Regional Forester, Intermountain Region, U.S. Forest Service

Perspective from the Chief
Dale Bosworth, Chief, U.S. Forest Service.

Mission Impossible? A Debate About the Future Priorities for the Forest Service Resolved: that the Forest Service should make forest health its top priority
Moderated by Marc Johnson
Affirmative:
Thomas Bonnicksen, Ph.D., Professor Emeritus, Forest Science, Texas A&M
R. Neil Sampson, President, the Sampson Group, Inc., and Vision Forestry LLC
Jack Ward Thomas, Ph.D., Professor of Wildlife Conservation, University of Montana
Negative:
The Honorable Pat Williams, Senior Fellow, O'Connor Center for the Rocky Mountain West, the University of Montana
Chris Wood, Vice President for Conservation Programs, Trout Unlimited, Arlington, Virginia
Randal O'Toole, Economist, The Thoreau Institute

Summing Up: The Next 100 Years
Moderated by Marc Johnson
Steven B. Daley Laursen, Ph.D., Dean, College of Natural Resources, University of Idaho
Dale Bosworth, Chief, U. S. Forest Service
Cecil Andrus, Chairman, Andrus Center for Public Policy, Boise, Idaho

Conference adjourned by Governor Andrus

Sponsors
Jack G. Troyer, Intermountain Regional Forester, U.S. Forest Service
Leslie Hurst, President and Publisher, *The Idaho Statesman*
Cecil D. Andrus, Chairman
Marc C. Johnson, President
John C. Freemuth, Ph.D., Senior Fellow
Andrus Center for Public Policy
American Forest and Paper Association
American Forest Resources Council

Bennett Lumber Company
Boise Cascade Corporation
Gannett Foundation
Holland & Hart LLP
Idaho Conservation League
Idaho Department of Fish and Game
Idaho Department of Lands
Idaho Department of Parks and Recreation
Intermountain Forest Association
The Nature Conservancy
Perkins Coie LLP
Potlatch Corporation
Rocky Mountain Elk Foundation
Skinner Fawcett
Stimson Lumber Company
Trout Unlimited
Wilderness Society

—Submitted by Michael T. Chapel, Regional Forester's Representative, USDA
Forest Service, Sacramento; and Kristi Bray, Outdoor Recreation Planner,
Recreation Solutions

Commemorating the Past, Facing the Future

The Regional Forum on California, Hawaii, and the Pacific Islands was held
November 5–6, 2004, in Sacramento, California. The purposes for the forum
were to review the first one hundred years of the Forest Service and to develop recommendations about the agency's future. The information generated
from the forum will be presented at the Forest Service Centennial Congress
in Washington, D.C., January 3–6, 2005.

The morning session of the first day reviewed the history, milestones, and
accomplishments of the agency during the last one hundred years. The afternoon session included a look forward to the region's natural resource
management issues as well as the role of public participation and collaboration. The program was presented in a large group setting for all forum
participants. An evening program was also provided during the first day. The
program included a social time, history displays, and awards. The day's activities were concluded with the highly regarded *On Fire!* a play exploring
firefighting in America's wildlands. The second day of the forum covered the
challenges and opportunities that occur throughout the region. This was accomplished through smaller group sessions that included speakers, panelists, and
time for discussion. The purpose for each session was to seek advice from panelists and the audience about important future issues and opportunities for
the Forest Service.

Day One of the Forum

Forum Co-Coordinator Mike Chapel, the regional forester's representative,
opened the forum by welcoming the group and described the purpose and
background for the Centennial Congress in Washington, D.C., and the Regional

Forum on California, Hawaii, and the Pacific Islands. Chapel covered the agenda for both days, hotel logistics, and explained the materials that were included in the registration packet.

Jody Noiron, Angeles National Forest supervisor, chaired the morning session. Jack Blackwell, regional forester, Pacific Southwest Region, and Jim Sedell, director, Pacific Southwest Research Station, welcomed the group and expressed their commitment to increasing the cooperation between research and the region.

Sally Collins, associate chief, USDA Forest Service, offered a brief look back at the accomplishments and history of the Forest Service. Collins commented on key issues such as ecological restoration and noted that what we leave on the ground is more important than what we take away. She discussed future threats and challenges for the national forests, including fire and fuels, invasive species, off-road vehicle management, and loss of open space. She touched on the opportunity found in collaborative partnerships and stressed that issues and challenges of today's land management would not get solved without community-based forestry.

Ann Bartuska, deputy chief, USDA Forest Service, Research and Development, described the current situation for research as a dynamic environment with important opportunities on the horizon to address: capturing ecosystem values, valuing land biodiversity, urban natural resource stewardship, and large-scale changes such as climate, wildfires, and global warming. Communication of scientific information to land managers is also an area of opportunity.

A Look Back at the Forest Service in the Pacific Southwest Region

The presentation by Tony Godfrey, U.S. West Research, Inc., "The Pacific Southwest Region, 1905 though WW2," was based on a manuscript he is writing to celebrate the centennial of the Forest Service. He began with the period of the "Lost Eden," which he described as the pre-European California setting, which was slowly inhabited by humans starting fifteen thousand years ago. Over this time period, the Spanish and Anglos arrived and brought unregulated resource use to the region. Eventually a conservation mindset evolved, as the national Division of Forestry was created in 1881. In 1905, the Forest Transfer Act moved all forest reserves to the Department of Agriculture's Bureau of Forestry. The Bureau of Forestry was later changed to the Forest Service and led by first forester Gifford Pinchot. During this "Conservation and Paradise Recovered" period, Roosevelt was attempting to manage forests through conservation and closer cooperation with forest users and communities. The

Inspection Division was created as result. The division would later be renamed California District 5 and led by its first district ranger, Frederick Olmsted. Later, California District 5 was led by those such as Coert Du Bois and Stuart Bevier Show. Du Bois contributed simplified timber sales, experimental reforestation, insect control work, and programs to meet the lumber needs of WWI. Bevier Show encouraged fire protection and forestry research during the New Deal era. It is important to note that the mission of the agency was strongly oriented toward the sustainable production of wood products and other commodities during this period.

Dennis Teeguarden, University of California, Berkeley, addressed "The Pacific Southwest Region, 1950 through 2004." Teeguarden began by reviewing the 1950s, when Harry Truman was president, family incomes were rising, the public was spending money, and forest management was still largely directed by the Organic Act. From the 1950s through the 1970s there was a major transition in the Forest Service from the traditional emphasis on timber to more focus on protection of the environment. Rachel Carson's *Silent Spring* was thought to have initiated the environmental movement with her warning about the potential effects of pesticides on ecosystems. From 1960 to 1976, seven laws were enacted by Congress that dramatically changed land management by the Forest Service. These were the Multiple Use–Sustained Yield Act of 1960, the Wilderness Act of 1964, the Wild and Scenic Rivers Act of 1968, the National Environmental Policy Act (NEPA) of 1969, the Endangered Species Act of 1973, the Resources Planning Act of 1974, and the National Forest Management Act (NFMA) of 1976. These new laws reflected the public's concern for the environment and together influenced a major refocusing of the Forest Service that is still in progress today.

Larry Ruth, University of California–Berkeley, discussed "The Pacific Southwest Region, 1950 through 2004." Ruth described how the seven new environmental protection and public disclosure laws unfolded and changed the Forest Service and Region 5. He described three ways that agency management has been shaped by this legislation: (1) major change occurred in the relative emphasis on commodity resources, (2) there was a rapid increase in the sophistication of planning and analysis tools, and (3) with NEPA, the public was given an important new role in the planning process for the agency. He described how litigation has been used to effect significant changes to policy and land management. He concluded by stressing the significance of both the NFMA and NEPA in making major changes in Forest Service methods for land and resource management planning.

*Observations from Former Leaders of the Pacific Southwest Region
and Research Station*

Ron Stewart, Department of Environmental Science and Policy, George Mason University, and former USDA Forest Service Pacific Southwest Station director and regional forester, covered historical trends in the region, including increasing populations, changing demographics, and increasing urbanization as well as changing management paradigms within the Forest Service. He also stressed the need for the agency to gain back public trust. A "wicked problem," a term often referenced throughout the forum, was described by Stewart as a problem with a high degree of uncertainty and risk; no single correct solution; the definition and solution are in the eye of the beholder; solutions are seen as good or bad, not true or false; there are multiple acceptable solutions; and a decision must still be made. Stewart's key message was that the Forest Service must deal with wicked problems with a new approach. That approach must be transparent. And it must position the Forest Service to help facilitate the development of more collaborative solutions that are carried forward under an adaptive management structure that involves all interested parties.

Lynn Sprague, former USDA Forest Service Pacific Southwest regional forester, focused on how public involvement is directly linked to adaptive management. He explained that the current public involvement strategies used for planning are not satisfying a strong public expectation for more meaningful participation. Sprague recommended that future public involvement and adaptive management programs need systematic structural change. He offered that a new process must start by meaningfully involving the public early and consistently. He recommended that the Forest Service should act as facilitator, not leader, of the discussions. Adaptive management can then create a learning environment by which all interested parties can follow along and help the agency guide its programs.

*A Look Forward at Natural Resource Management in California
and the Pacific Islands*

Jim Fenwood, Mendocino National Forest Supervisor, moderated the afternoon session.

Michael Buck, former administrator of the Hawaii Division of Forestry and Wildlife, asked, Where are you going? Whom do you serve? These two questions formed the basis for his talk. He suggested that the agency needs to connect with the public and discuss the environment as an issue from the heart, something that people care about in their day-to-day lives. He believes that stewardship and caring for future generations resonates with the public. Buck also stressed that the Forest Service should help the public realize that the world provides a finite set of resources.

Bill Stewart, assistant deputy director, California Department of Forestry and Fire Protection, spoke about the multiple facets of managing public forests. He suggested that the Forest Service needs to take into account different perspectives about the land. For example, regarding watershed and fire issues in the state, not all agencies agree on how to manage watersheds or "firesheds," especially when they include shared acreage. Stewart noted that the Forest Service is one of many owners of a "flammable" California, and there is now a need to look beyond boundaries, managing and treating lands in a coordinated strategy.

Public Participation and Collaboration

Jonathan Kusel, Forest Community Research, asked, "What has been learned about public participation and collaboration in natural resource management?" Kusel explained that traditional public involvement by the Forest Service and others flows in one direction, with stakeholders commenting on proposals that are largely developed internally by the responsible agency. This is increasingly unacceptable to the public. Collaboration with stakeholders and others in government is the key to solving this issue. Kusel referred to several examples of public participation in need of improvement. He cited the Northwest Forest Plan, where he noted that planning was largely done privately by a small group of agency scientists. He also referred to projects like the Sierra Nevada Ecosystem Project, where a public involvement team launched an intensive involvement process of "civic science"—the process of blending science with public participation to help guide decisions. Kusel closed with an example of a local Forest Service program in southern Oregon where some pioneering work is being done to improve public participation with agency planning.

Chris Nota, the regional forester's representative, considered "How will the Forest Service address public participation and collaboration in the future?" Nota observed that the Forest Service has been directed, expected, and rewarded for acting unilaterally for decades. The Forest Service has recently made great strides to improve public access and employee attitude but can accomplish more by continuing to strengthen public trust, build common understanding with stakeholders, work transparently, provide open monitoring, and carefully lay out goals. In order to do this, the Forest Service is developing new tools, such as fireshed analysis to help facilitate community-based fire protection planning.

Lynn Jungwirth, Watershed Research and Training Center, focused on the future of the four branches of the Forest Service and how they will contribute to community-based forestry. She forecast that the State and Private Forestry program would become the leader within the agency by providing expertise in partnerships. Research will work to better deliver and communicate information. International Forestry will bring its many lessons learned to the mainland. The National Forest System will discontinue working unilaterally and discontinue zoning of natural resources during forest planning.

Maka'ala Kaaumoana, Hanalei Watershed Hui, used the Hanalei Watershed Hui as an example of a project that has become a positive community effort in Hanalei, Hawaii. When the Hanalei River was designated as an American Heritage River, local citizens saw it as both good and bad: bad because the Hanalei community did not seek the designation, and good because it provided potential for creating an environmentally sound river for the community. The Hanalei Watershed Hui action plan allows for flexibility and provides a framework for the community to pursue questions about their watershed.

Amy Horne, Sierra Business Council, suggested that there are two types of issues for the Forest Service: technical and adaptive. She described technical issues as having defined problems and solutions. Adaptive issues include problems and solutions that are not clear. Many of the agency's issues are adaptive issues that include value conflicts and require a different type of leadership. In order to move beyond these issues, the Forest Service will need to give the work back to the people, orchestrate attention to the problem, protect voices of the weaker interests, honor agreements made, and build relationships with stakeholders.

Closing Remarks for Day One, Invitation to the Evening Program

Jim Sedell expressed his support for adaptive management in dealing with wicked problems. He noted that agency problems and solutions will remain unclear but planning assumptions will need to be tested. He believes that efforts to create partnerships and collaboration will be adversely affected by the trend in short tenure for agency decision makers.

Jack Blackwell challenged the group to think about the next hundred years while always keeping the health of the land as key in their minds. He commented on the importance of listening to one another and considering the role that Native peoples can play. He touched on the importance of all four branches of the Forest Service and asked the group to think about the messages that the six delegates should take to Washington from this forum.

Carol DeMuth, forum co-coordinator, Pacific Southwest Research Station, invited the group to the evening program, which included a no-host bar and social, awards, and the play *On Fire!* Kent Connaughton, deputy regional forester, Pacific Southwest Region, encouraged attendees to participate in the seven breakout discussions during the morning of Day Two.

Day Two of the Forum

Seven breakout sessions were conducted during the morning of Day Two. The results of these discussions were summarized and reported by the facilitators during the afternoon session, as described below.

Mark Nechodom, Research Social Scientist, USDA Forest Service Sierra Nevada Research Center, chaired the afternoon session. Following an introduction of the forum delegates to the Centennial Congress, Derrick Crandall, American Recreation Coalition explained that delegates will be participating through a "TV special report"–style program during the Congress. Two of the six delegates will be interviewed for the report. The others will participate in discussions about the regional forums.

Reports from Breakout Discussions

A brief summary was provided to the entire group of attendees and was presented by the facilitator for each breakout session.

Water and watershed management. Watershed management strategies recently implemented in the region reflect an evolution in thinking from the site to landscape scales. These strategies were considered fundamentally sound, but participants felt their implementation needed improvement. In particular, more attention must be paid to identifying issues affecting and affected by management within and outside the boundaries of national forests; analysis of each issue at the appropriate temporal and spatial scale, which often requires crossing multiple administrative and ownership boundaries; and development and implementation of actions to address each issue.

Speakers and participants agreed that collaboration is critical to watershed management, now and in the future. Collaboration is particularly important because most contemporary watershed issues involve numerous parties. Watershed councils are common in the United States and are emerging as a local governance system for watersheds. The Forest Service should actively participate in these councils, as well as much-larger-scale watershed efforts. These collaborative efforts provide a forum for communication and enable the use of joint fact-finding approaches, which facilitate a mutual understanding of watershed issues and solutions. These efforts also enable parties to build the capacity needed to enhance existing watershed programs. Finally, they should improve recognition within the agency that the public, rather than the Forest Service, owns the land that it administers.

Increased watershed investments are necessary to address the key issues of the future, including population growth, climate change, and land use change. This will require connecting people to their water supply through education, outreach, and advocacy. The Forest Service should play a significant role in these efforts. Novel approaches, such as the use of water supply surcharges to fund watershed programs, should also be examined. Such approaches will take strong leadership from the Forest Service and other federal and state agencies.

—Presented by Kim Rodrigues
University of California Cooperative Extension

Recreation. Understanding and correctly responding to the needs of an aging and diverse population is crucial in the future of recreation management. The focus needs to continue to be managing recreation use in concert with what the resources can sustain. With national forests closer to urban populations, people are able to access the forest and connect with nature and each other in a shorter time frame. With this connection comes conflict.

Collaboration is critical in helping to solve user conflict issues and will maximize Forest Service partnerships. Maximizing these partnerships will allow us to achieve what we can't do alone. Another partnership that should continue to be fostered is the one with Forest Service volunteers. Volunteerism not only increases public stewardship but also increases public monitoring of the land.

The Forest Service needs to be more proactive when it comes to educating the public, by utilizing tools like conservation education, which focuses on the health of the land and the public. Use research as a tool while ensuring that we bridge the gap between theory and practice so that managers can use the information immediately. Finally, look to the future and develop professional recreation managers who have the needed core recreation competencies.

—Presented by Beth Rose Middleton
University of California Cooperative Extension
The importance of prefire planning for reducing the impacts of large wildfires. Focus needs to start with defining the problem of fire. A collaborative effort needs to be made in systematically assessing firesheds and the concern over

accumulation of biomass and fuels. This collaboration needs to include all agencies, at all levels, and a network of other partners (realtors, fire safety councils, insurance agencies, etc.). From this collaboration, fuel treatment approaches can be developed utilizing such tools as geographic information systems and landscape scale modeling.

One of the main issues throughout the discussion was how to involve the public. There is now an underlying culture in our communities that the public does not believe they have a responsibility or role in fire prevention. We need to engage the public and maintain their attention through education, community plans and incentives. By working together and realizing this is not a "one-shot deal," we can initiate a plan and follow it through together.

—Presented by Charles Go, 4-H Youth Development Advisor
University of California Cooperative Extension

Invasive species. Invasive species are one of the Chief's four major threats to federally managed lands. The session outlined the current invasive species approach in Region 5 and touched on the new management strategy being developed to stress partnerships and coordination between weed management groups in order to prevent the spread and establishment of invasive species across all landscapes.

Several examples illustrated the magnitude of problems ranging from loss of biodiversity and water quality to effectively managing species that are non-terrestrial. Often compounding the problem and the ability to respond quickly for land managers is the NEPA process. Critical to invasive species management and many of the solutions discussed are the need for prevention information, early detection, and rapid response.

—Presented by Boone Kauffmann, Program Manager
Institute of Pacific Islands Forestry

Future roles for commodity production in managing sustainable forests and rangelands. One primary challenge discussed in this commodity session was the idea of finding balance and constructive ways to manage resources. Commodity production and sustainability issues are political in nature. The Forest Service needs to acknowledge this and address it. One way to do this is through collaboration. By collaborating with partners, the Forest Service can begin to change the mindset, both internally and externally, regarding such commodities as timber, mining, grazing, and water. Begin the process by taking an economic approach as an alternative to commodity.

Timber was a main topic throughout the discussion. Some thought that harvesting more timber through ecological and sustainable practices and including our partners in the process were key. Others suggested that the Forest Service should not be ashamed of the partnership created with timber production. Still others cautioned that the public is very concerned about the effects of timber harvest on the environment, so future commodity production should be planned in ways that conserve public-trust resources.

—Presented by Charles Go, 4-H Youth Development Advisor
University of California Cooperative Extension

Meeting the needs of a culturally diverse society. With California's diverse society, it is important that the programs the Forest Service provides meet the needs of the communities it serves. With a diverse society come diverse forest values and desires. There is now a need for the Forest Service to address these issues by seeking new partnerships with all cultural groups that use national forests. Although collaboration is necessary, the Forest Service should also work hard to help the composition of its workforce reflect the diversity of the surrounding community.

Other valuable relationships to consider are those with tribal governments and opportunities to train youth. The tribe and Forest Service unique government-to-government relationship is one that needs to be fostered, working collaboratively to solve issues and then maintained for the future. Training our youth is an opportunity that the Forest Service could improve. By training youth, the Forest Service could be providing jobs for kids while meeting the needs of the community and natural resources.

—Presented by Beth Rose Middleton
University of California Cooperative Extension

Where world views collide: Forest management in an arena of risk and uncertainty. Risk and uncertainty are issues that affect many management decisions of the Forest Service. Deciding how to quantify and capture the different values that are associated with risk is difficult when multiple interests are each worried about something different. A key planning consideration is how to identify and balance acceptable levels of risk for competing social values? The best way to address these wicked problems is through collaboration and adaptive management. Moreover, the Forest Service can help by understanding and disclosing the uncertainty and risks associated with alternative management decisions.

—Presented by Danny Lee, Project Leader
Redwood Sciences Lab, Pacific Southwest Research Station,
USDA Forest Service

Future Challenges for Science to Shape Forests

Jim Sedell described several issues that will be challenges to managers in the future. Examples were risk assessment, mortality and disease, social and technical issues associated with fire protection, water management in the West, wood products technology, hydrologic forecasting, biological diversity assessments, and land use dynamics. With limited resources the Forest Service must work on these issues through expanding partnerships. Adaptive management is one approach that can be used to look at ongoing management for answers. Plans such as the Northwest Forest Plan and the Sierra Nevada Framework need to be revisited so we can learn from them. Finally, we have a lot to learn from the Pacific Islands and their concept of "ridges to reef."

The concept of integrating science and management was explained by Steve Eubanks, forest supervisor, Tahoe National Forest, as an active partnering to achieve common goals. Important to integration science and management are rapid testing and implementation for the purpose of information sharing and improved management on the ground.

The key message from Bill Stewart was that forest managers need new technologies more than they need new science to address the most pressing challenges today. While he acknowledged the need to advance science, Stewart argued that managers today need new technologies that will provide the decision support capability to support community-based planning. For example, Internet-based technologies could allow different perspectives to be shared and evaluated by interested parties on-line. Similar technologies could be used for fireshed planning. Emerging technologies could allow us to look at optimal patterns in treatment as they related to costs, fire, behavior, and environmental impacts.

Traditional ecological knowledge was the basis of a presentation by Frank Lake, biological scientist, Pacific Southwest Research Station, USDA Forest Service. TEK is a cumulative body of tribal knowledge, practice, and belief handed down through generations. TEK mimics natural physical and biological processes and fosters biodiversity. Utilizing this indigenous and cultural knowledge could enhance and improve effectiveness of current land management and could be integrated into current management practices, such as prescribed burning. There is now interest in evaluating the relationships and the efficiencies of TEK and western science.

Session Wrap-up Panel and Open Discussion

"What have we heard and what do we do about it?" Jim Pena, forest supervisor, Plumas National Forest, expressed his excitement and optimism about "taking on the world" with all the information generated from the forum. The forum reinforced working with stakeholders on his forest and finding leaders who can build relationships internally and externally.

Gloria Brown, forest supervisor, Los Padres National Forest, talked about the issues that surfaced during the forum and the real opportunities for finding solutions to them through partnerships. Listening was key and allows us to hear expectations and facilitate these complex issues.

Peg Boland, forest supervisor, Klamath National Forest, noted that the Klamath deals with many rural community issues. Fortunately, interacting with local communities is much easier on the Klamath than on our urban forests. Working on issues will take mutual learning and understanding—moving people from stakeholders to partners. Rebuilding trust needs to be a two-way street.

Pacific Islands are a hotspot for many of the issues covered at the forum, according to Boone Kauffmann. Management needs to be more proactive in handling issues, many of which are social, not technical or biological in nature. The Forest Service needs to start managing for future generations with such concepts as "conservative forestry."

Jim Sedell reflected on ways to better include youth and even nature writers in our ecological research. Science must be more transparent and accurate and include more opportunities for civic science participation.

Celebrating the agency's one-hundredth anniversary is good, observed Jack Blackwell, but we need to stay focused on the land. Partnerships will be important for recognizing and finding solutions for such wicked problems as overdensity, invasive species, and megafires. Reaching out to a diverse society, our workforce needs to reflect the public we serve and become more culturally diverse. Together we are up to the task.

Ann Bartuska noted that throughout the forum, collaboration was mentioned in almost every discussion. We need to manage our expectations about what collaboration means and practice cautious optimism. Respect will be very important in our willingness to hear different points of view and provide for better understanding.

Closing Remarks
Jack Blackwell and Jim Sedell both thanked the group for their participation and expressed their appreciation for the excellent topics, discussions, and presenters arranged for the forum.

Summary
Throughout the forum the key message that surfaced was the need for the Forest Service to work toward increased use of collaboration and partnerships. Many participants stated that the agency must work harder to engage the public and others in government as partners in the management of the national forests and Forest Service research. Many speakers stated that partnerships are now critical to the agency as it carries out its mission of caring for the land and serving people. More attention is now needed to develop agency staff skills that help build new relationships and find new ways of planning and completing projects in open, transparent, and participatory processes. Building tenure for decision makers was seen as a growing need. And ensuring agency accountability and public ownership in Forest Service programs will be critical for building lasting partnerships. Finally, there was strong support for recommendations from participants from the Pacific Islands, which stressed that conservation must now focus beyond the roles and responsibilities of individual agencies.

Delegates
The following delegates will be representing the Pacific Southwest Region and Research Station at the Centennial Congress in Washington, D.C.:

- Linda Arcularius, District 1 Supervisor, Inyo County Board of Supervisors, Bishop, California
- Maka'ala Kaaumoana, Executive Director, Hanalei Watershed Hui, Hanalei, Hawaiian Islands
- Brenda G. Kendrix, Public Affairs and Communication Staff, USDA Forest Service, Vallejo, California

- Martha Marciel, Public Affairs and Communication Staff, USDA Forest Service, Sierra National Forest, Clovis, California
- Bruce Turbeville, Chairman, California Fire Safe Council, Sacramento
- Bao Vue, Student Intern, Sierra National Forest, Clovis, California

—Prepared by Brian Garber-Yonts, Research Economist, USDA Forest Service, Pacific Northwest Research Station

Commemorating the Past, Facing the Future:
A Forum on Recreation, Access and Healthy Forests and Watersheds

On November 19–20, 2004, some one hundred fifty people met at Skamania Lodge overlooking the Columbia River gorge to discuss the legacy created by the Forest Service in its first century and to confront the challenges of the century that begins in January 2005 with the Forest Service Centennial Congress. Our theme was "Recreation, Access, and Healthy Forests and Watersheds," and the forum was hosted by USDA Forest Service, Pacific Northwest and Alaska Regions, and Pacific Northwest Research Station.

Our task was to draw together a diverse range of people and perspectives to reflect on the past century of service, envision the future of public use and enjoyment of the nation's forests and grasslands, and wrestle with the serious problems that confront us as we adapt the Forest Service to a profoundly different world than that of 1905. Invited participants represented a range of views: agencies at all levels of government, recreation special permit holders and user group representatives, volunteer organizations, advocacy groups, industry and trade organizations, university and government scientists and scholars. All came together to listen and to voice their concerns and aspirations for the future of the national forests and grasslands and the agency that manages them.

We began with a look to the past. The conference began with a slide show of historical photographs of Forest Service personnel and the public on the national forests set to music of the changing times. Seeing the faces of our land stewards, from those who labored to build a nation with resources claimed from the land, of our forebears at work protecting the land, and of those at play on the land, set a tone of reverence for the very human legacy we carry forward together. After being welcomed by Deputy Chief Tom Thompson, we were regaled by President Theodore Roosevelt (portrayed by actor Keith

McGough). He incited us to face the new century with the same boldness as those who, in 1905, began the enterprise of "caring for the land and serving people."

Historian Hal Rothman took up the challenge, bluntly beginning his comments with the statement, "Forests are now more valuable as scenery than as lumber." Rothman presented a rather unsentimental view of the agency's history. Scanning through the march of industrial development and the taming of the American landscape, world wars, the birth of the boom generation and the boom of leisure in the middle class, the birth of the environmental movement and the uprising of the Sagebrush Rebellion, shifting constituencies and ebbing support for traditional forest management, he recounted failures as well as successes. Rothman characterized the present as a time of postindustrial economies and urbanizing, ethnically diverse populations, a time of new demands and new constituencies. Both urbanization and growing ethnic diversity trend toward populations who may regard wildlands as foreign and public agencies as threatening, widening the gap between the U.S. population and public lands. At the same time, in postindustrial America, he argued, the object of aspiration is less consumption now than it is the experience of unique, original adventure, and it is no great leap to envision the intersection of this trend with public land recreation. The key to public support for national forests in the next century, explained Rothman, lies in providing memorable experiences and reaching out to new communities.

With this provocative introduction, forum facilitators asked audience members to partner for one-on-one conversations about the achievements of the Forest Service in our first century. Organizers posted message boards along the walls and asked participants to post responses to the question: What are the Forest Service's greatest conservation accomplishments of the last century? Responses ranged from the contribution to rural economic development of public forestlands to preservation of fish and wildlife habitat. The most common refrains cited the creation of a comprehensive system of public lands and protected wilderness areas, managed in the service of the public and giving Americans unparalleled access to resources, recreation, and renewal. Establishment of the National Forest System and the development of a professional organization to manage and conserve timber as well as watersheds and habitat and other resources were commonly cited. Many participants recognized the capacity of the Forest Service over the last one hundred years to adapt to changing perceptions of the role of public land and the agency's mission, including the evolution from sustained-yield forestry to a broadened conception of multiple use with a growing recognition of recreation and ecosystem management as policy and management priorities. Similarly, the shift away from aggressive fire suppression in recognition of the ecological role of fire and other disturbance was recognized in several comments as an important change. The legacy of the Civilian Conservation Corps projects and development of the National Trails System, and the role of the national forests and grasslands in economic development and in public education were highlighted. Many cited an unrivaled infrastructure for research in natural and social sciences that spans universities and the Forest Service research stations as among the most important achievements of the agency. Decentralized decision making through the relative autonomy of ranger districts, local public involvement, and partnerships was suggested in several comments as being essential to the success of federal forest management in the last century.

With that, it was time to take stock of where we now stand as an agency and as users of public land. The Forest Service's Dave Holland assessed the current status of the Forest Service recreation program. Noting that both the Forest Service and the Bureau of Land Management now collect greater receipts from users of recreation resources than from extractive users, Holland called for the agency to follow through, at long last, on creating a cohesive strategy for managing and funding recreation access and use of the nation's public wildlands. Holland suggested a realignment of agency constraints emphasizing cost recovery, partnership and volunteer development, interagency cooperation, and collaboration with regional tourism interests. "We're moving to a future of shared governance and full participation," he said. "We'll do what we do best and we'll partner the rest." Reflecting on the 1962 report of the Outdoor Recreation Resources Review Committee, Holland suggested that it is time to draw together a commission to revisit the goal of outdoor recreation policy: "to preserve, develop, and make accessible to all American people, such quality and quantity of outdoor recreation as will be necessary and desirable for individual enjoyment and to assure the physical, cultural and spiritual benefits of outdoor recreation."

Former Oregon Governor John Kitzhaber spoke to the forum about ecosystem health and a new vision for resource management. Governor Kitzhaber criticized our current structures for resource policy making as a prescription for conflict and polarization, which fail to address common interests and the interdependence of economic, ecological, and community values. "I have become increasingly convinced that our current natural resource policy-making and problem-solving structure is failing us," he stated, describing those structures as designed for an earlier time of perceived resource abundance. He identified three fundamental problems with current resource management and policy structures: no common objectives among stakeholders, no objective standards for using scientific evidence, and a governance structure defined by bureaucratic boundaries and at odds with ecosystem structure. He described a vision for Oregon forests that focuses on watershed health as the common denominator among stakeholders, adopts a new process for evaluation of science from the field of health care, and redefines governance in context with ecological boundaries. "My challenge to you and to all of the stakeholders in the debate," Governor Kitzhaber stated, "is to find common cause in exploring and finding alternatives to our current broken systems, embracing the possible rather than just clinging to the familiar. If we choose to do nothing, then by default we are letting our future become a matter of chance rather than a matter of choice."

Forum participants were asked to convene in small work groups organized into topic areas matching the recreation, access, and healthy forests themes of the forum. Trained facilitators guided the work groups through the tasks laid out for them: identify the most vital issues confronting the agency in the new century and suggest actions to address these issues. Emerging from each of the discussions was recognition that agency resources are limited and that the 1905 model for funding agency programs is no longer adequate to the more complex organizational challenges facing us and the changing demands brought by a diverse public. The work groups echoed the issues of organizational structure outlined by the morning's speakers. Other issues raised were the need for greater presence of Forest Service personnel on the ground and in communities, and the need for a systematic review of the legal and institutional frameworks that govern public land. Failures to follow through with partnerships and provide the necessary support for volunteers were cited as chronic problems that hamper transition to a more collaborative system.

Work group participants who chose to focus on access to national forests identified gaining a clear agreement on the appropriate amount and type of access as a top priority along with adequate funding to support and maintain access conditions and infrastructure, both on federal land as well as on roads owned by state and county governments, and including both roads and trails. The role of information access was highlighted as well, particularly with regard to providing information and education to users. Two groups meeting to address healthy forest and watershed issues both identified legal and institutional problems as critically in need of resolution. New frameworks were called for to replace paralysis of management in process and litigation with flexibility to manage dynamic ecosystems and reward collaboration instead of conflict. Five work groups convened to discuss recreation topics. All cited inadequate funding or need to elevate recreation to a status within the agency that reflects its importance to the public, local economies, and the rapidly growing outdoor recreation industry. Criticism of the organizational structure of the Forest Service and the 1905 "business model" of funding resource programs suggested that it was particularly inadequate to address recreation priorities. Participants identified the need for an achievable recreation vision and agreement on what constitutes the proper niche for national forests and grasslands within local and regional outdoor recreation resources, and called on the agency to actively support collaborative partnerships with private and public cooperators.

Our keynote speaker, economist, historian and futurist Neil Howe, offered some of the historical flavor of the morning's discussion before shifting the focus of the forum toward envisioning the future. He described the long cycle of generational change over the nation's history and presented the idea of a cyclical pattern in which four generational archetypes have repeated themselves sequentially through American history since the colonial era. With a show of hands, he revealed that some three-fourths of the audience was of the baby-boom generation. Boomers, he asserted, like similar generations of the past, have profoundly changed American culture at every stage of life but have nonetheless failed to move resource management beyond a crisis of institutional gridlock. Howe suggested that many characteristics of the generation just now coming into adulthood, what he called the "millennials," are most similar to those of the generation that came of age during World War II. Like that generation, millennials are much more likely to confront social crisis with collective action, building institutions and engaging in long-term planning. Though speculative, it was a hopeful message for the forum, and a provocative talk that turned our focus toward the longer-term future of the agency.

We began the afternoon with an expert panel on recreation trends moderated by Perry Brown, dean of the College of Forestry at University of Montana. Derrick Crandall of the American Recreation Coalition described the importance of recreation and leisure as an economic sector, both nationally and in communities. Despite the trends of population growth, he noted that outdoor recreation per capita is on the decline and suggested several means to reverse the trend, including better capacity to embrace volunteers, improvement of recreation infrastructure through new funding channels, and greater embrace of information technology to reduce barriers to the outdoors. Emilyn Sheffield of California State University–Chico reviewed the trends in population growth, urbanization, ethnic diversity, growing numbers of retirees and their greater health and activity, and increasingly sedentary youth. Sheffield congratulated those in attendance for helping create a *land-based* system for conservation, but identified the creation of a *citizen-based* conservation system as the principal challenge ahead of us, with outdoor recreation as our most powerful lever to get Americans involved. She described volunteering on public lands as an increasingly popular form of recreation in itself and echoed comments by others calling for better institutional support within the agency for volunteers and partnerships.

Todd Davidson with the Oregon Tourism Commission encouraged participants to adopt the perspective of the visitor when trying to reduce barriers to participation in outdoor recreation. Some of his suggestions included improving access to information, streamlining fee and permit systems, and opportunities for "done in a day" excursions. Frank Hugelmeyer of the Outdoor Industry Association cited the importance of the nation's public lands, both as the basis for a large and growing industry and as a key to a growing public health crisis. He called on the Forest Service to prioritize the protection and enhancement of recreation assets, to update its business model, and to balance the long-term needs of both the recreation and the extractive resource economies. Noting that outdoor recreation is a habit formed when young, he called on fostering mentor programs that get young people into the outdoors. Finally, David Buchner of the Centers for Disease Control and Prevention discussed in greater detail the link between public health and outdoor recreation and the broad health benefits of physical activity. Although national forests clearly provide a forum for increased physical activity, Dr. Buchner noted the greater importance of promoting more physical activity on a daily basis and commended the capacity of public land agencies to promote a consistent health related message.

Between work group discussions and sessions of expert analysis, the forum was rich with information, both given and received. But it wasn't without its lighter moments. The Fiddling Foresters provided a virtuoso performance of old-time music that recalled the days of the original forest rangers, providing a stirring capstone at the end of a heady and demanding day. Alaska Regional Forester Denny Bschor (an original Fiddling Forester) joined the band onstage for a moving performance that drew together many of the themes of the day and recalled a history that includes tragedies among monumental accomplishments. Over breakfast the next morning, Chief Bosworth recognized partner organizations that have provided their own virtuoso performances over many years to support the Forest Service recreation mission. Celina Montorfano of the American Hiking Society and Lori Davis of TreadLightly! accepted awards on behalf of their organizations, and Joan Hobson, Florida's "Hiking Grandmother," accepted a personal award for her many decades of dedicated service in promoting the development and use of the Florida National Scenic Trail.

Chief Bosworth spoke on his view of the Forest Service's history and the challenges ahead. "Today, I believe we are in a new period—a period of ecological restoration and outdoor recreation. Maybe more than ever before, we focus on delivering values and services like clean air and water, scenic beauty, habitat for wildlife, and opportunities for outdoor recreation. These are the main things people today want from their public lands." Adding to the Four Threats of fire and fuels, invasives, loss of open space, and unmanaged recreation, Chief Bosworth also cited deferred maintenance, oversubscribed water resources and deteriorating watersheds, and the effect of air pollution on ecosystem health as long-term problems. He expressed hope that these problems will be addressed through collaboration with partners. He looked to the Centennial Congress as a forum to confront these issues, stating, "We expect the Congress to take the long and the broad view—the view across decades and centuries. The question of collaboration takes the long and the broad view. It transcends the specific challenges we face. It rises to the strategic level we envision for these events. With your help, we can improve the way we work together to meet the challenges of the future."

A final work group session was then convened in which small, facilitated groups were asked to consider the question, "How can the Forest Service better serve the public while caring for the land in the twenty-first century?" Ideas ranged widely and repeated some of those raised in earlier work group sessions. The most common themes focused on continuing and improved communication, both in terms of agency outreach to the public as well as a desire for greater clarity of priorities as communicated to the agency by Congress and the public it represents. Outreach to new forest users was the most commonly cited priority, particularly through engagement with schools to promote environmental education and introduce young people to outdoor recreation and further awareness of the nation's public lands. Developing new constituencies through Forest Service involvement in educational programs in schools and outreach to urban dwellers and underserved ethnic and cultural groups that have not traditionally been public land users was seen as necessary to maintain and build support for public forest lands. New users and constituents along with a new generation of Forest Service employees were seen as objectives of creating a more visible public presence for the agency.

To accomplish outreach and numerous other goals, partnership and volunteer development were seen as crucial. Institutional constraints to working with external groups and individuals were identified by nearly all of the work groups, with administrative complexity, insufficient staffing and organizational capacity, and nine-to-five agency work schedules that conflict with weekend volunteering all acting as barriers. Partnerships were identified as keys to getting work done on the national forests, but collaborative relationships with other agencies—urban parks departments, county transportation planning, local and state tourism agencies, and concessionaires—were identified as essential to providing improved physical and information access for forest users. New administrative and legislative policies were called for to promote and streamline partnership development.

Work group discussions also called for new efforts to define the Forest Service mission for the new century. A high-level, congressionally supported commission was called for to reexamine agency priorities, develop a new business model that aligns funding needs with public demands, and broadly reviews federal lands policy. A common refrain was that the Forest Service is trying to do too much, both in terms of the breadth of resource programs it manages, and in terms of the broad range of recreational demands it is attempting to meet. In referencing the Four Threats that Chief Bosworth has identified and spoke about in his remarks to the forum, some cited the lack of major initiatives other than the Healthy Forests Restoration Act to address three of the four (although discussion of fire and fuels was otherwise notably absent from work group comments). Again reiterating comments from earlier sessions, several of the work groups highlighted increasing centralization as a crisis within the agency and called for redistribution of personnel and decision-making authority to the district level, with less administration and planning and more ground-level accomplishments needed to present a visible result to the public.

Participants called on the agency to place recreation on a funding level commensurate with its perceived importance to the public. Addressing the challenge of existing and new recreation trends was also seen as essential. Need for investment in infrastructure was reiterated and improved accommodation of recreational users was called for, including expanded hours of operation, streamlined permitting and information access, and new developed use areas to provide capacity for growing western populations. Several participants emphasized the role of the Forest Service as an ecotourism provider and cautioned against straying from a focus on ecosystem health in the accommodation of recreation users. Calls for continuing research and monitoring to understand and anticipate users' demands and new recreation uses and trends were again reiterated.

In drawing the forum to a close, Regional Foresters Bschor and Linda Goodman and Pacific Northwest Research Station Director Tom Quigley shared their thoughts on key messages from the forum. Bschor pointed out the importance of research in guiding the response of the National Forest System to broad-scale changes emanating from demographic shifts and climate change. He stressed the need to draw communities and citizens into conservation efforts. Tom Quigley likened the role of research to that of a well-intentioned motorist flashing a "FLAT TIRE" sign to another driver seen speeding along unknowingly on three good wheels. Quigley suggested that managers and policymakers might do well to glance aside from the road ahead rushing at them in order to notice the warnings offered by scientists and avoid a potential crash. Linda Goodman surveyed the horizon of increasing retirements and cited the need to appeal to a new generation to devote careers to service to the national forests and their users, and the need to connect the agency to both communities and the forests by getting our people into the field.

Our forum was imbued with a tone of respect, even reverence, for the accomplishments of the past hundred years, and no less respect for the challenges that lie before us. Those in attendance displayed respect for one another, although a broad range of interests were represented, and a sense of purpose and collaboration in an important endeavor was evident. Participants and speakers exhibited an unflinching resolve to take an honest look at our past and confront the need for change within the Forest Service, as change happens all around us, on the land, in our nation, and in the world. Teddy Roosevelt convened the forum with the charge he gave the first forest rangers and the new agency a century ago: be bold, have no fear of failure or criticism, but seize the moment. It is in this spirit that the forum concluded, with all in attendance embracing the challenges ahead.

—Submitted by Bill Alexander, Landscape and Forest Historian, Biltmore Estate; assisted by Harry Hafer, Executive Director, Cradle of Forestry Interpretive Association

Celebrating One Hundred Years of Conservation

Located in the heart of western North Carolina's Blue Ridge Mountains, Asheville was selected as the site of the Southern Region's centennial forum. Adjacent to the "Cradle of Forestry in America," the venue seemed to be the perfect gathering place for participants *to commemorate one hundred years of conservation, assess current challenges and opportunities, and shape a dialogue for the twenty-first century to address the needs of present and future generations. The theme of the conference focused on forest management and research.*

Bob Jacobs, regional forester, Southern Region, USDA Forest Service made opening remarks and welcomed nearly a hundred participants who represented diverse organizations and associations, including the U. S. Forest Service, other federal and state natural resource agencies, university and research groups, cooperative extension, forest industry organizations, land trusts, conservation and environmental organizations, wilderness, trail and interpretive associations, congressional and senatorial representatives, the tribal nation, historians, student interns, and retired professionals. Carl Mumpower, vice mayor, City of Asheville, gave a warm welcome to the forum attendees.

Bob Jacobs's remarks, which highlighted some of the past successes of the agency, set the stage for the forum. The initial sessions paid tribute to the first hundred years of conservation in the Forest Service and began with an entertaining and enlightening song and slide presentation by the Fiddling Foresters. This enthusiastic and musically talented group of Forest Service employees highlighted important events in the history of the conservation movement in America and how the Forest Service has dealt with the responsibility and challenges involved with the management of our national forest lands. Presentations by Ed Brannon, former director, Grey Towers National Historic Landmark, and Norm Christiansen, professor of ecology and founding dean of the Nicholas School of Environment and Earth Sciences, Duke University, focused on the theme "History of Forests and Forestry in America." Brannon's presentation emphasized the life and work of Gifford Pinchot, first chief of the Forest Service, and his impact on conservation and forestry. Pinchot's forestry concepts had first been applied between 1892 and 1895 at George W. Vanderbilt's Biltmore Estate, where he was employed as forester. Pinchot believed in the new idea of conservation: "a forest could be cut without destroying it," Brannon informed the audience, and "he spent his career successfully marketing the concept to the American public."

Christiansen explored a century of change that has molded the Forest Service into the diverse agency that it is today. "Over its history the Forest Service has not just endured change, it has in many areas been a genuine change agent," he stated. He further stressed that "as the Forest Service enters a new century, the exact trajectory of future change is uncertain. But we can be sure that the tempo and complexity of change will only increase."

Forum participants experienced firsthand some of the pioneering efforts in forestry when they visited the Cradle of Forestry in America, a sixty-five-hundred-acre historic site within Pisgah National Forest established in 1968 by a congressional act. In 1898, on what was formerly a part of George Vanderbilt's vast forestry holdings, Carl A. Schenk, Pinchot's successor as Biltmore's forester, had established the Biltmore Forest School, the first school of forestry in the United States. Today, Schenck's legacy of forestry education is continued through programs at the Cradle of Forestry, the Pisgah Forest Institute, and other venues with the support of the Cradle of Forestry in America Interpretive Association, a cooperative partner with the Forest Service. The evening highlights included remarks by Congressman Charles Taylor relating to the Pisgah Institute, which was established to instruct teachers about environmental issues. Taylor stressed, "Environmentalism is too important to leave people not skilled." Tucker Veach, chairman of the board of directors of the Cradle of Forestry in America Interpretive Association, reported on the shared vision and recently completed strategic plan for the Cradle of Forestry, which was cooperatively developed by the Forest Service and CFAIA.

Pete Roussopoulos, station director, Southern Research Station, USDA Forest Service, opened the second day of the forum, which included a mix of the past century's accomplishments and the challenges currently facing the Forest Service. Leading off in her keynote address, Ann Bartuska, deputy chief for Research and Development, USDA Forest Service, stressed that "scientific research is the crucial solution to the many growing concerns the Forest Service faces," and "healthier forests, as well as an improvement in urban and suburban areas can be achieved." Presentations by three panelists addressed "The Agency's Greatest Accomplishments Behind and Challenges Ahead." Jim Hull, director of the Texas Forest Service; Lark Hayes, senior attorney with the Southern Environmental Law Center; and Craig Hedman, manager of forest economics and water resources, International Paper, each presented their perspectives of the issues. Collectively, the panelists recognized "the importance of working with private and state forests, especially in the Southern Region where most of the land is not federally managed." The "need for southern forests, both private and public, to be a focus on the national level" was also stressed as an important issue. Jim Hull emphasized that the focus in the future should be on three primary areas that he referred to as the "triple bottom line" or a "three-legged stool": the environment, economy, and society.

Forum participants were divided into seven random groups for work sessions to address several questions. Collective summaries of the group responses (not in any particular order) follow.

Question 1: What are the Forest Service's greatest conservation accomplishments of the last century?

- The acquisition of forest lands in the East through the Weeks Act to create national forests.
- The Forest Service's rich heritage as a world leader in forest management, research and development, and education (e.g., Smokey Bear); pioneering in the forest reserve system, globally, which led to pioneering in fire management and protection, insect and disease management, biological conservation, and platform for multiple use management.
- The successes of forest restoration and recovery of forest health on both public and private lands (including urban forest recovery and promotion), wildlife and endangered species habitat protection and restoration, development of long-term management plans for multiple use of the national forests including a variety of quality recreational opportunities, recognition of importance of private and nonindustrial lands, pioneering in the development of state programs, and role as federal funding conduit.
- Long-term research, ecological studies, experimental forests (fifty-plus years of records), and the sustained use of science as a basis for natural resource decisions; systems approach to forest management (Forest

Inventory and Analysis, the Southern Forest Resource Assessment, the Southern Appalachian Man and Biosphere program, the Resources Planning Act, the South's Fourth Forest); management of water (Organic Act and the quantity and quality of watersheds); fire management (awareness and use of fire, Smokey Bear, prescribed fire); "all risk" management leadership.

- Effectiveness of Forest Service in working with partners in developing key legislation and securing appropriated funding for forest related activities (the Healthy Forests Restoration Act, National Fire Plan, the Forest Legacy Program, Forest Inventory and Analysis, the Weeks Act and land acquisition); partnerships with states.
- Establishing the forest profession, first within the agency and then inspiring external careers and related technologies and professions; development of human capital; district- and project-level can-do attitude, stellar amongst federal agencies.

Question 2: What are the most vital issues (social, environmental and economic) that confront the Forest Service today?

Collective summaries of the responses are grouped under the three categories of issues.

Social Issues
- The need to continue to be a conservation organization that practices active management versus an "environmentalist" organization that practices no management.
- The need to work to educate the general public about the relevancy of the Forest Service mission and responsibilities of citizens to environmental issues through an effective conservation education program; keeping agency mission and National Forest System lands relevant to a changing demographic (diversity, rural versus urban); better education about forest management (gaining social acceptance and public understanding of art and science of forestry).
- Keeping the land from being "loved to death"; dealing with and incorporating public values; growing population and fixed land base are creating land use conflicts: fragmentation, more landowners of different types, declining operability, and competing priorities.

- Internal workforce: centralization of administrative support while maintaining skill sets needed for mission—critical work but also diversity for mission is critical.
- Defining the Forest Service role for the future, especially related to the public land expectations and assessing global natural resources and developing U.S. positions; demand for leadership in Forest Service to have global perspective as well as others in the U.S. forestry community.

Environmental Issues
- Restoring forest health and dealing with its issues: insects and diseases, invasive exotics, wildfire, forest fragmentation and effects on ecosystem health; the need to document environmental conditions, quantify values and contributions from forested lands, especially non-Forest Service lands, and provide knowledge and resources to help landowners capture values.
- Need to expand and maintain Forest Inventory and Analysis, especially quantifiable ecosystem attributes, timber, etc., with long-term research and monitoring.

Economic Issues
- Limited availability of funds and increasing competition for existing funds (maintenance of experimental forests and workforce, high costs of fire, conservation education, importance of partnerships).
- Threats to the forest products industry and lack of markets for landowners; globalization and its impacts on markets, invasive species and pathogens and effects on the roles of the National Forest System.
- Quantification of environmental values, creation of new cash flows.

Leah MacSwords, director with the Kentucky Division of Forestry, in her endnote remarks, provided a capstone on the day's discussions and provided a segue to the next day's discussion on the role the Forest Service must play in the future. Bill Alexander, landscape and forest historian for Biltmore Estate, gave a slide presentation on Biltmore Estate's forestry legacy, highlighting 114 years of forestry at Biltmore, noting its leading role in the formative years of forestry in America. At an evening reception at Biltmore Estate, Mimi Cecil, wife of William A. V. Cecil, Sr., grandson of George Vanderbilt and Biltmore's owner, made welcome remarks. Mimi has been a long-time supporter of forestry, the Forest Service, and environmental issues and serves on numerous boards. USDA Forest Service Chief Dale Bosworth presented Forest Service

Centennial awards for continued support of forest conservation and the Forest Service to the Longleaf Alliance, the Wild Turkey Federation, Bill Hubbard, the Cecil Family and the Biltmore Estate, and the Cradle of Forestry Interpretive Association. Bosworth reminded the forum attendees that the Forest Service depends upon its invaluable partnerships to achieve its many objectives of forestry and conservation.

Tom Thompson, deputy chief, National Forest System, USDA Forest Service, presented opening remarks for the third and final day of the forum, which addressed the theme "Caring for the Land and Serving the People in the Twenty-First Century." The speakers offering their insights on the subject were Gifford Pinchot III, grandson of Gifford Pinchot and chairman of the Bainbridge Graduate Institute, and Robert Bendick, conservation director of the southern U.S. region of The Nature Conservancy. "The future of forestry is going to be more difficult than it ever has been," declared Pinchot. He further stressed that "conversations have to happen between Forest Service employees and the general public. We need to look at our employees to see who has the courage to do these jobs well, and we have to be those people, too." Bendick charged the agency: "In its next one hundred years the Forest Service should use its expertise and competent organization to reach out beyond the borders of national forests to facilitate the conservation of forested areas, including those in the South and East and forests that are largely privately owned."

During group discussions, participants tackled the third major question to be answered at the forum: *How can the Forest Service best care for the land and serve people in the twenty-first century?* Collective summaries of the responses are categorized under two themes.

How can the Forest Service best care for the land and serve people in the twenty-first century? through technology?

- Retain science base and develop and apply new technology; use talent to solve land management concerns beyond national forest boundaries and participate in international forest issues.
- Visionary leadership relating to resource use, management, and issues and have a plan to address this in the short-term to long-term: pollution, insects and disease, increased recreation use, and energy and biomass; provide leadership to challenges associated with globalization.
- Actively restore and maintain forest ecosystems; increase resources that protect national forests; acquire more public lands.

- Certify the work. Forest Inventory and Analysis is the ticket to quantify and review the work.
- Move toward being the best, credible source of information that can be used for synthesis and technology transfer; maximize the efficiency of information gathering and assessment relative to all forest values from local to global scale.
- Development of new markets and new products including ecosystem services valuation: Forest Service to take the lead.
- Water resources: the output and the indicators, quantity and quality, will be how public judges, and all practices must maintain it.

How can the Forest Service best care for the land and serve people in the twenty-first century? through a redefined "social contract" (or trust) with the public?

- Identify the mission and market it (Smokey Bear model).
- Determine clear roles for the Forest Service and work with people to determine local needs and priorities; involve the people and communities in every aspect of our work; embrace partnerships, existing and new, that will help us figure out how to get more done with less (critical to success on public and private lands; be an effective partner and leader with states, universities, nongovernmental organizations from the local to global scales, including volunteers and formation of a "Forest Service Club"; secure funding and develop innovative ways to leverage public investment in Forest Service so that programs are commensurate with mission (e.g., land care groups and partnerships are key).
- Remove the roadblocks that keep the Forest Service from being a can-do agency; build trust internally and externally based on communication and participation through community involvement and outreach; conservation education and communication with targeted messages to the diverse cultural groups of the United States, with coherent messages and public relations. It is worth the time and money to tell the world about our good works.
- Adaptive management: listen to our partners (state foresters, tribal groups, communities). We have a lot to learn. Listen to the land, monitor the effects of our management actions, early and often—in effect, change the way we work.
- Market conservation: (1) develop new conservation ethic, with use and active management seen in positive light; (2) reoccupy the middle, increase

role as facilitator for public participation, emphasize relationship between Forest Service, state and private forestry, and private industry; (3) public relations and conservation education; (4) more creative use of volunteers.

- Improve public education programs on core issues related to forest values and management, which will effectively develop a common message relevant to all ages and interest groups to develop the middle ground, demonstration forests, and conservation education; note linkages to concerns about planning process.
- Provide incentives and assistance to nonfederal forest landowners to encourage good management.
- Growing new conservation leaders: actively recruit; must diversify the workforce at all levels and must fully integrate workforce with agency mission; workforce diversity and capacity need to be commensurate with public demand for services.

In his very fitting endnote address, "The Forest Service: A Story of Change," Chief Dale Bosworth did an outstanding job of capsulizing the key evolutionary periods of the Forest Service over the past century and presenting his vision of the future challenges. Some highlights of his remarks are as follows:

"It's a pleasure to be here tonight with so many of our partners and collaborators. I can't think of a better locale for celebrating a hundred years of conservation. As you know, the Biltmore Forest is the cradle of forestry in America, and it's always a personal honor for me to visit this special place. The work that Gifford Pinchot and Dr. Carl Schenck began here more than a century ago gave birth to the teaching and application of science-based forest management that we are carrying on today…

"I do want to give you my own view of where I think we've been and where I think we might be headed, and I'd like to just start with our mission. Here's our mission statement: 'To sustain the health, diversity, and productivity of the nation's forests and grasslands to meet the needs of present and future generations'…There's always been some ambiguity built into our mission, but does that ambiguity doom our enterprise? I don't think so. In fact, I would argue just the opposite—that the ambiguity inherent in our mission has given us the flexibility we need to adjust to changing times…"

Bosworth described the agency's activities of the last century as four periods of change:

Conservation. "We all know the story of how conservation originated a hundred years ago at a time of natural resource waste…Conservation came out of that crisis because people wanted to stop the waste, and the forests here in the South are one of the greatest conservation success stories. Today, southern forests cover an area larger than many countries, something like 212 million acres, almost all on an area that was once cutover and farmed over. It happened through partnerships between the Forest Service, state forestry and wildlife agencies, universities, nongovernmental organizations, and hundreds of thousands of private landowners.

Social responsibility. "A lot of the national forests in the South came about during and after the Great Depression. We'd always envisioned a social role for the national forests—to help homesteaders and small landowners get access to the natural resources they needed…we delivered social programs and jobs, especially through the Civilian Conservation Corps. Every national forest had at least one CCC camp, and we gave jobs to thousands of unemployed Americans in all those CCC camps…World War II ended the CCC, but I guess you could say our social responsibility continued through the war effort, which we strongly supported. A lot of our employees enlisted, and we ramped up timber supplies needed by our troops.

Timber focus. "The war effort had depleted state and private timber stocks, and the national forests were needed to fill the gap. From the 1960s through the 1980s, every administration, with strong congressional support, called for more timber from the national forests. In those thirty years, we went from producing very little timber to meeting twenty to twenty-five percent of our nation's sawtimber needs. We helped millions of Americans fulfill the American dream of homeownership.…

"The 1940s and 1950s were a difficult period of transition. Some of the folks who'd grown up under the old custodial model of the Forest Service found it hard to adjust to the new timber model. Some actively opposed it.…

"Popular demand for more of a balance between timber and the other uses led to the Multiple Use–Sustained Yield Act of 1960. We also had the Wilderness Act of 1964.… The first Earth Day in 1970 sent another major signal, as did the environmental legislation of the 1970s. We learned that the public wanted more of a say in our management, and they wanted us to focus more on delivering values and services like wildlife, water, wilderness, and recreation.

Restoration and recreation. "In response, we started moving toward a new ecosystem-based model of land management. The 1990s were a transitional period…again the transition was difficult. Some of the folks who grew up under the old timber model weren't too thrilled.

"But in my view, it was the right and the necessary thing to do. It was necessary because both our landscapes and our social needs are constantly changing. If we don't adjust to those changes, then we can't fulfill our mission of caring for the land and serving people.

"Today, I believe we are in a new period—a period of ecological restoration and outdoor recreation. Maybe more than ever before, we focus on delivering values and services like clean air and water, scenic beauty, habitat for wildlife, and opportunities for outdoor recreation…And, yes, we also deliver opportunities to harvest timber, graze livestock, and extract minerals. With goods like these come important values, like jobs and community stability. We know that Americans want those values, too…we believe that what we leave on the land is more important than what we take away."

The Chief stated what he thought were the agency's primary future challenges:

"The period we are in will someday end, just as every period did before it. What will the future bring?…The major concerns are, in particular, the Four Threats we've been talking about:

- fire and fuels, including fuels buildups;
- invasive species—kudzu is a classic example;
- the loss of natural areas to development—forest loss and ownership fragmentation are especially troubling in the Southern Region; and
- recreational use that is outstripping our management capacity and damaging resources…"

He listed some other concerns besides the Four Threats:

- "a huge backlog of work to complete—thousands of deteriorating culverts to replace, roads to restore, abandoned mines to reclaim, watersheds to repair, vegetation to treat, and all kinds of deferred maintenance and ecological restoration to catch up on;
- oversubscribed water resources and deteriorating watersheds in many parts of the country, made worse by rapid population growth; and finally,
- rising levels of ozone and other substances in the atmosphere—part of the problem is obvious on most days here in the Appalachians."

Bosworth stated that "…what struck our review teams was the sheer scale of what we face when you take these concerns and combine them with the Four Threats. I believe that the Forest Service is at a crucial moment in history. In the past century, there've been only a few similar moments where we've faced challenges on a similar scale. Meeting these challenges will lay out a career's worth of work for the next generation of Forest Service employees."

In explaining what he thought is to be learned from the past, he enunciated the need for community-based forestry and improving collaboration. He stated, "It's a story of changing values—of changes on the land and changes in the people we serve. It's also a story of how we responded to those changes to protect the land and deliver the goods, services, and values that people want.

"So are we in trouble because our mission focus has changed over time? I don't think so. Change has always been part of our history. The ability to change has always been key to our success.

"What's also changed is the way we deliver what people want. A hundred years ago, Gifford Pinchot recognized the need for working in partnership with local communities if we were to succeed. He planted the seeds of partnership in our first *Use Book* by directing our employees to work closely with local communities to promote conservation.

"Ever since then, we've always been committed to fulfilling our mission through partnerships. Today, the scale of what we face leaves us no other choice: We have got to work together. But the way we work with people has changed over time. In particular, we've learned the need for more upfront public involvement in our decision making.

"Today, I believe that we need a community-based collaborative approach, sometimes called community-based forestry. It involves getting everyone interested to state their ideas upfront and then getting them to talk through their differences and come to some agreement based on shared values...

"In closing, we've come a long way together over the last hundred years. Values have changed and so have the challenges we face...I believe that the only way we can rise to the challenge is through community-based forestry—by working upfront through collaborative partnerships for long-term ecosystem health.

"For that, we're going to need help from our partners...The question of collaboration takes the long and the broad view. It transcends the specific challenges we face. It rises to the strategic level. I look forward to the Centennial Congress as a springboard for improving the way we work together to meet the challenges of the future—and to prepare ourselves for the changes to come."

Deputy Chief Tom Thompson made the closing remarks for a very successful forum.

Organizations Represented at the Southern Regional Forum

Federal agencies: USDA Forest Service (various branches at state, regional, and federal levels), U.S. Fish and Wildlife Service, Bureau of Land Management

State agencies: Cooperative Extension Service-University of Georgia, Kentucky Division of Forestry, North Carolina Division of Forest Resources, North Carolina Wildlife Resources Commission, South Carolina Forestry Commission, South Carolina Department of Natural Resources, Texas Forest Service, Southeast Association of Fish and Wildlife Agencies

Conservation and environmental organizations and land trusts: Appalachian Trail Conference, Cleanwater Management Trust Fund, Environmental Defense, National Council for Air and Stream Improvement, National Wild Turkey Federation, Partners of Joyce Kilmer Slickrock Wilderness, Southern Appalachian Man and Biosphere Cooperative, Southern Appalachian Forest Coalition, Southern Environmental Law Center, The Land Trust for the Little Tennessee, The Longleaf Alliance, The Nature Conservancy

Academia and research: Auburn University, Bainbridge Graduate Institute, Divinity School of Duke University, Duke University Nicholas School of the Environment and Earth Sciences, University of Georgia Warnell School of Forest Resources, Haywood Community College, Institute of Forest Biotechnology, North Carolina State University, Texas A&M University

Forest Industry: American Forest and Paper Association, International Paper, Southern Appalachian Multiple Use Council

Congressional representatives: Senator Elizabeth Dole's office, Senator Lindsey Graham's office, Congressman Charles Taylor

Tribal nations: Eastern Band of the Cherokee Indians, Mississippi Band of Choctaw Indians, Poarch Band of Creek Indians

Regional tourism organizations: Biltmore Estate, Grandfather Mountain, Land of Sky Regional Council

Private forestry: The Forestland Group

Historic sites and support organizations: Biltmore Estate (National Historic Landmark), Cradle of Forestry in America, Cradle of Forestry Interpretive Association, Grey Towers National Historic Site

Retired professionals: Various

Planning and Host Committee

Frank Beum, Legislative Affairs Specialist, USDA Forest Service, Southern Region

Tom Darden, Director, Biological and Physical Resources, USDA Forest Service, Southern Region

Jennifer Hayes, Presidential Management Fellow, USDA Forest Service, Southern Research Station, Asheville

Bruce Jewell, Assistant Director-Pines, USDA Forest Service, Asheville

Pete Roussoupolus, Station Director, USDA Forest Service, Southern Research Station, Asheville

Monica Schwalbach, Deputy Forest Supervisor, National Forests in North Carolina

Nancy Walters, Staff Assistant, USDA Forest Service, Southern Research Station, Asheville

Mike Walker, USDA Forest Service, Southern Research Station, Asheville

Bill Alexander, Landscape and Forest Historian, Biltmore Estate and Secretary, Board of Directors, Cradle of Forestry Interpretive Association

Harry Hafer, Executive Director, Cradle of Forestry Interpretive Association

Tucker Veach, Chairman, Board of Directors, Cradle of Forestry Interpretive Association

Note: Many others were involved in planning and hosting the forum, including facilitators for small-group sessions, administrative staff, and other behind-the-scenes staff from the USDA Forest Service, the Cradle of Forestry, and Cradle of Forestry Interpretive Association.

Sponsors for Refreshment Breaks

The Forestland Group
The Nature Conservancy
National Wild Turkey Federation

Delegates Selected for the Centennial Congress

Robert Bendick, Managing Director, Southern U.S. Conservation Region, The Nature Conservancy

Richard Porterfield, Dean, School of Forest Resources, University of Georgia

Leah MacSwords, Kentucky Division of Forestry

Tony Tooke, USDA Forest Service

David Wear, USDA Forest Service

Report of the Eastern Regional Forum
November 9, 2004
Morton Arboretum, Lisle, Illinois

—Submitted by Sue Barro, USDA Forest Service, North Central
Research Station

Healthy Forests and Healthy Communities in the East: Connecting People and the Land

The Eastern Regional Forum, with the theme of "Healthy Forests and Healthy Communities in the East: Connecting People and the Land," was held at the Morton Arboretum in Lisle, Illinois, near Chicago, on November 9, 2004. The forum was designed to facilitate a regional discussion about key resource issues facing the East and give people a voice in helping the Forest Service to address these issues. Participants in the forum included representatives from conservation groups (24 percent), educators and students (20 percent), representatives from state and local organizations (12 percent), and Forest Service employees (31 percent). A total of 102 people attended. The Eastern Regional Forum focused on the following five topic areas:

- restoring and managing the land;
- retaining open space;
- dealing with invasives;
- connecting urban and rural communities to the land; and
- building a commitment to a land ethic.

Five Forest Service units in the East—Region 9 of the National Forest System, Northeastern Area State and Private Forestry, the North Central Research Station, the Forest Products Lab, and the Northeastern Research Station—worked together to plan and carry out the forum. A seven-person advisory group representing key Forest Service stakeholder groups (i.e., conservation groups, states, Forest Service retirees) helped the Forest Service steering committee to develop the forum agenda, identify potential speakers and participants, and select delegates for the national Centennial Congress to be held in Washington, D.C., in 2005.

Overview of Plenary Session

The morning of the Eastern Regional Forum began with a plenary session. Randy Moore, Regional Forester for Region 9, opened the session and welcomed participants on behalf of the Forest Service. This was followed by a welcome to the Morton Arboretum from the arboretum's president and CEO, Gerry Donnelly. Providing a historical context for the day's events, Forest Service Chief Dale Bosworth spoke on the one-hundred-year history of the Forest Service, highlighting key eras and transition points, including the conservation era in the early years, the social responsibility era during the Depression years, the timber focus following World War II, and the growth of recreation and environmentalism in the 1960s–1980s. He talked about future challenges, such as the threats from fire, insects and disease, increased recreational use, and increasing levels of ozone and other pollutants impacting forests. He acknowledged the huge challenges facing the East associated with urban natural resource stewardship and reconnecting communities to the land. He concluded by talking about the need for a community-based collaborative approach to forest management in the future and the importance of our partners in helping the Forest Service to achieve its goals over the next one hundred years.

Next, Gerry Adelmann, executive director of Openlands, spoke about the relationship that his organization has had with all three branches of the Forest Service over the past twenty-five years. Openlands is an independent, nonprofit organization dedicated to preserving and enhancing public open space in northeastern Illinois. Finally, Susan Flader, historian from the University of Missouri, talked about Aldo Leopold, his association with the Forest Service, and his contributions to conservation.

Overview of Concurrent Sessions

All concurrent session were structured to begin with a speaker or panel of speakers who provided background and laid out the issues related to the session topic for the audience. The audience then broke into smaller groups to discuss the topic as it related to the following three questions:

- What are the Forest Service's greatest conservation accomplishments (related to this topic)?
- What are the most vital issues that confront the agency in the new century (related to this topic)?
- How can the Forest Service do a better job of serving the public while caring for the land in the twenty-first century?

Each breakout group provided their top answers to the three questions above. These were gathered and put onto flip charts. During an afternoon break, flip charts from all sessions were posted so all participants could see what had transpired in the different sessions and add their input and feedback on any of the session topics. At the end of the day, summary comments were made by the Forest Service executives in attendance.

Restoring and Managing the Land: Session Highlights

Randy Moore, regional forester for Region 9, welcomed participants to the session on restoring and managing the land. Two speakers, William Jordan III of the New Academy of Nature and Culture at Loyola University in Chicago, and Kurt Bobsin, Illinois state forester, then set the stage for later discussions with their presentations on restoration and management of eastern forests. Small groups (five or six people) discussed and provided collective group answers to the three questions mentioned earlier.

In response to the question about Forest Service conservation accomplishments, three themes emerged. First, forum participants recognized the Forest Service for its conservation leadership, as illustrated by its expanse of land holdings and its fostering of natural resource professionals and a broad conservation culture. Second, the agency was acknowledged for its leadership in restoration, as demonstrated by restoration of eastern forestlands and promotion and implementation of best forest management practices. Another notable accomplishment was the agency's ability and willingness to make changes and adapt as interests, values, and demands become increasingly complex.

The following themes emerged in discussions about vital issues facing the Forest Service: conflicts and diverse values, such as extraction versus conservation and public desires versus ecosystem health; the importance of restoring forest health by incorporating natural processes (i.e., fire, flood); global impacts on forests, such as invasive species and global climate change; and articulating a land ethic to help connect people to the land.

According to forum participants, the Forest Service could improve in the twenty-first century by doing a better job of communicating what the agency does, why actions are taken, and how decisions are made. Maintaining and improving partnerships and collaborations, such as those with communities and private landowners, were considered important. Support for investments in research and technology to ensure sustainable management was mentioned.

Retaining Open Space: Session Highlights

Linda Donoghue, station director for the North Central Research Station, provided opening remarks and welcomed participants to the session on retaining open space. Charlie Niebling, policy director for the Society for the Protection of New Hampshire Forests, and Carl Becker of The Nature Conservancy made presentations on protecting open space around national forests and near urban areas. These presentations provided background for discussions that followed.

In thinking about the greatest conservation accomplishments of the Forest Service related to retaining open space, participants recognized all three branches of the agency. They mentioned the creation of the National Forest System through the Weeks Law of 1911; the contributions of State and Private Forestry in providing intellectual and financial capital beyond the "green line"; and the importance of Research and Development in providing a science basis for management decisions. The Forest Service role in protecting wilderness and being a lightning rod for debate and discussion about land use were also mentioned.

Forum participants identified a number of vital issues facing the Forest Service related to retaining open space. The increasing stressors and pressures on open space, such as increasing population, development pressure, and ecological challenges at the interface, were mentioned. The importance of communicating about the values of open space to youth was a theme that emerged. Another key issue was the challenge of developing and building coalitions for open space protection that included full engagement of diverse communities. Adequate funding at the national, state, and local levels to support and maintain the land base was considered critical.

According to participants, the Forest Service could do a better job in the future by simplifying its processes and communicating better about what it does. Working more effectively with partners and across multiple ownerships and encouraging volunteerism to reconnect people with the land were two other ways participants thought the agency could improve.

Dealing with Invasives: Session Highlights

Michael Rains, station director for the Northeastern Research Station, welcomed participants to the session and introduced Rob Venette, research entomologist, USDA Forest Service North Central Research Station. Venette's presentation on dealing with invasives set the stage for small group discussions that followed.

The participants highlighted the contributions of research and associated technological achievements as key Forest Service conservation accomplishments related to dealing with invasive species. Other accomplishments noted by the group were the Forest Service management protocols and programs for detection and eradication of invasive species.

Key issues for the Forest Service related to dealing with invasive species centered on gaining a better understanding of the roots of the problem, including globalization and environmental stresses, and developing and supporting effective solutions through cohesive strategies, education, and adequate funding.

In the twenty-first century, the Forest Service could do a better job in this area through better coordination with partners, integrated approaches, and thoughtful application of resources to well-assessed risks.

Connecting Urban and Rural Communities to the Land: Session Highlights

John Nordin, deputy director of Northeastern Area State and Private Forestry, welcomed participants to the session on connecting urban and rural communities to the land. Two speakers, Gary Larsen, Urban National Forest Coalition, and Kevin Brazill, New York City Watershed Agricultural Council, then made presentations to provide background for the discussions that followed.

Three key themes emerged as forum participants discussed the Forest Service's greatest accomplishments in connecting communities to the land. Forest Service outreach and education programs, such as Project Wild and the Smokey Bear campaign, were noted for promoting the overall growth of conservation values and stewardship. New and innovative partnerships (i.e., Chicago Wilderness), programs (State and Private Forestry), and approaches (community-based approaches to land management) were highlighted as great successes in connecting people to the land. The Forest Service was also acknowledged for its multiple use management, which provides opportunities for recreation, education, and interpretation.

The agency is facing a variety of complex issues when it comes to connecting urban and rural communities to the land. Primary among them are public lack of awareness of the values forests provide and a lack of connection between people and forests. A second key issue identified was the increasing diversity of stakeholders who bring different views and expectations about the role and value of forests. A need for the Forest Service to develop messages and establish a vocabulary to reconnect Americans to their forests and natural resources was identified. Concerns about the issues of balancing consumption and protection and restoring forest health were voiced in this session.

In the twenty-first century, the Forest Service can do a better job of connecting rural and urban communities to the land in two key ways. The first is through continuing support for education, communication, and outreach with specific targeting on youth education and better articulation of the Forest Service mission to urban audiences. Second, continued use of collaborations and partnerships will help the Forest Service to operate more effectively in local arenas and better serve urban and rural communities.

Building a Commitment to a Land Ethic: Session Highlights

Chris Risbrudt, director of the Forest Products Laboratory, welcomed participants to the session on building a commitment to a land ethic. Three speakers—Howard Vincent, president of Pheasants Forever; George Rabb, retired director of the Brookfield Zoo; and Michael Nelson, University of Wisconsin–Stevens Point—gave presentations to frame the discussions that followed.

Forum participants considered the demonstrated conservation leadership and history of protecting the land as key Forest Service conservation accomplishments. The Forest Service role in cultivating conservation leaders and thinkers, establishing a wilderness system, and fostering development of an environmental conscience in the United States were mentioned as significant. The willingness of the Forest Service to do some self-reflection and acknowledge the need for change in order to fully apply the land ethic was also considered a key accomplishment.

The vital issues participants identified related to building a commitment to a land ethic were the general lack of public connection to the land and the need for developing vocabulary and messages to better connect a variety of audiences to the land.

According to forum participants, the Forest Service can do a better job of serving the public while caring for the land in the twenty-first century in three ways. First, the agency can work to communicate a land ethic to the public. Better interpretation of what the agency does and why, providing opportunities for hands-on experience and involvement, and communicating the true cost of resource consumption would help accomplish this goal. Second, the Forest Service needs to design better mechanisms for people to share in decision processes and provide feedback. Also important was continuing to develop and promote partnerships, especially with new and nontraditional partners.

Closing Comments

The forum concluded with closing comments made by Michael Rains, director of the Northeastern Research Station. An excerpt of the closing comments is provided below.

"We are a premier agency in conservation. We hold important keys to sustaining our planet (clean air and water, conserving natural resources). Yet according to a broad range of authors, '…our work (protecting the environment) generally does not directly challenge major economic or material concerns.' Accordingly, we lack relevancy to be truly competitive. While I do not agree with this, many do. How could keeping our air clean, for example, *not* be completely relevant, I ask rhetorically. In simple terms, our work holds the key to America's economic and social vibrancy. Yet much of what we do and who we are is not viewed as mainstream.

"The issue, it seems to me, is a profound lack of understanding by the general population about our environment, its condition, and what we do to harm or help its state. The situation is more acute now than at anytime I can recall. Author Jay Gould says, '…you do not fight for what you do not love.' I think it is even more basic. That is, you do not fight for what you do not *know*. We could alter the paradox in our next one hundred years (actually by the next decade) by reaching out more and improving our environmental literacy. In other words, emphasize inclusion and education—the two gems that surfaced repeatedly at our forum.

"Better education about the environment, directly or indirectly through partnerships in public education, improves literacy. According to scholars like Chester Finn and Kevin Hollenbeck, improved literacy translates into better decisions and stronger communities. Better choices breed a stronger support base, which makes inclusion easier and ultimately fosters additional success. Inclusion and education represent a powerful 'right-left' combination for the Forest Service, resulting in a much better balance between social, economic, and environmental outcomes.

"The forum offered a grand venue to review some of our successes. They are impressive and we should be proud. No question, we *do* make a difference. With the emphasis on inclusion and education in the next one hundred years, we just might be the difference in land stewardship and ultimately, helping sustain and improve our livability.

"The Healthy Forests and Healthy Communities Centennial Forum for the Northeast and Midwest was a huge success, in my view. The forum allowed the Forest Service to reflect and project. We are proud of our many accomplishments. We should be. As we look to the next one hundred years, we know the task will be testing. We must stay competitive in the marketplace. Staying relevant will ensure this happens. Expanding our support base and helping make this larger, more diverse constituency more literate about our environment are crucial ingredients to relevancy, and thus the continued success of the Forest Service."

Appendix

Delegates Selected for the National Centennial Congress
Gerry Adelmann, Openlands
Debbie Blomberg, Lake States Women in Timber
John Rogner, Chicago Wilderness
Student, Greenfield Village
Buddy Huffaker, Aldo Leopold Foundation

Award Recipients
Awards were handed out to the following individuals and groups in recognition of their contributions to the Forest Service units in the East:

Outstanding Volunteer:
Gerald W. Adelmann, Open Lands Project

Outstanding Partner Organizations:
Northeast Area Association of State Foresters (NAASF)
The Pinchot Institute of Conservation
Morton Arboretum
Eastern National Forest Interpretive Association (ENFIA)
Society for the Protection of New Hampshire Forests
Chicago Wilderness and the Student Conservation Association

Outstanding Private Sector Partners:
American Forest and Paper Association (AF&PA)
APA, The Engineered Wood Association
CenterPoint

Sponsors of the Eastern Regional Forum
Morton Arboretum

The Nature Conservancy in Illinois
The American Council of Snowmobile Associations
Greenfield Village
Illinois Forestry Development Council

Eastern Regional Forum Advisory Committee
Mike Carroll, Director, Minnesota Department of Natural Resources, Division
    of Forestry
Buddy Huffaker, Aldo Leopold Foundation
Jay Cravens, Retired Regional Forester
Laurel Ross, The Field Museum
John Dwyer, Retired Project Leader, North Central Research Station
Kurt Bobsin, Illinois Department of Natural Resources, Division of Forestry
Andy Falender, Appalachian Mountain Club

Eastern Regional Forum Field Trips
Urban Restoration: Connecting People with the Land in Chicago: Tom Dilley
    (tour organizer) and John Oldenberg (tour speaker)
Retaining Open Space: Midewin National Tallgrass Prairie: Logan Lee (tour
    organizer)

Lunchtime and Closing Entertainment
Susan A. Fowler, Environmental Artist and Educator

Eastern Regional Forum Facilitators
Lisa Burban, Lead Facilitator, Northeastern Area State and Private Forestry
Maureen McDonough, Michigan State University
Dain Maddox, National Forest System, Region 9
Claudia Mielke, National Forest System, Region 9
Elizabeth McCance, Chicago Wilderness
Teri Heyer, Northeastern Area State and Private Forestry

Eastern Regional Forum Steering Committee
Donna Hepp, Forum Leader, National Forest System, Region 9
Terry Hoffman, Northeastern Area State and Private Forestry
Sandra Forney, National Forest System, Region 9
Theresa Heyer, Northeastern Area State and Private Forestry
Kimberly Anderson, National Forest System, Region 9

Tom Dilley, Northeastern Area State and Private Forestry
Susan Maciolek, National Forest System, Region 9
Lisa Burban, Northeastern Area State and Private Forestry
Logan Lee, National Forest System, Region 9
Linda Schmidt, National Forest System, Region 9
Gordon Blum, Forest Products Lab
Connie Stubbs, North Central Research Station
Sue Barro, North Central Research Station
Judy Thiemer, National Forest System, Region 9
Deidra McGee, Northeastern Research Station

Additional Event Support
Jane Cliff, National Forest System, Region 9
Cherie Le Blanc, North Central Research Station
Jessica Lanke, National Forest System, Region 9
Diane Thomas, National Forest System, Region 9
Jodie Vanselow, National Forest System, Region 9
Melissa Ellis, National Forest System, Region 9
Mary Isabell, National Forest System, Region 9

—Submitted by Macky A. McClung, Assistant Director, Community
Relations, USDA Forest Service, Juneau, Alaska

Healthy Forests and Healthy Communities

The Alaska Region's Centennial Forum, "Healthy Forests and Healthy
Communities," was held November 13, 2004, in Anchorage. Seventy-two leaders from industry, academia, nongovernmental organizations, and government
organizations met to discuss the Forest Service's greatest accomplishments
over the last century, the issues that confront the agency in this new century,
and how the Forest Service can better serve the public and care for the land in
the twenty-first century. The comments and recommendations discussed at
the forum will be presented at the Forest Service's Centennial Congress in
January 2005.

Tom Thompson, deputy chief of the National Forest System, opened with
a presentation on the history of the Forest Service with highlights of the history of Alaska. The discussion then shifted to the most pressing problems facing
the Forest Service today, including fire damage and control, invasive plants
and insects, and the collision of wildlife and human habitats. Thompson noted,
"Large-scale fires and the impact of population expansion on the environment are many of the same problems the Forest Service was grappling with
one hundred years ago."

Robert Ott, Forest Health Program coordinator for the Alaska State Division
of Forestry, presented "Current and Emerging Forest Health Issues in Alaska."
Ott said that traditionally, the subject of forest health has placed an emphasis
on insects and disease, but that the field of forest health is actually much broader in scope. He also stressed that when discussing forest health issues, context
is important, because a forest that is deemed healthy by one person may be
considered unhealthy by another.

From there, Ott described current and emerging forest health issues in
different regions of the state. Some forest health issues in the coastal forests
of Alaska include the decline of yellow cedar, and questions about how to

manage young-growth hemlock-dominated stands and old-growth hemlock-dominated forests.

In Alaska's boreal forests, the regeneration of commercial tree species is a problem because of competition from bluejoint grass, other vegetation, and snowshoe hare browsing. In addition, an increasing human population in the fire-dominated boreal forests is resulting in an increasing amount of wildland-urban interface. Other boreal forest issues are the decreasing proportion of early successional habitat for wildlife and browse damage of deciduous trees.

Statewide forest health issues include invasive plants—including concerns about their becoming established in newly burned areas—and invasive insects. Ott also noted that the management of nontimber forest products is a concern of some forest users. An issue that is getting increased attention is climate change in Alaska. Some changes to forest ecosystems that have been documented or are of concern include increased rates of thermokarst, loss of wetland habitats, possible compression of some insect outbreak cycles, possible loss of other insect outbreak cycles, and increased wildfire severity, and shorter fire return intervals.

Jeff Staser, federal cochair of the Denali Commission in Alaska, through an often-humorous account of the Forest Service from the perspective of 2104, then focused the participants in the health of Alaska's communities. Staser stressed the importance of looking to and shaping the future now, particularly with regard to the development of infrastructure and the management of resources and people. He declared, "We must invest in innovation, research and development, education of our young people, and learning how to harvest, mine, and recreate in harmony." In addition, he emphasized the need for economic development in Alaska. Development must come from the private sector," he said, "not from a reliance on the federal government." He placed particular emphasis on finding ways to encourage young people to understand these issues so they can help guide Alaska's future.

Awards were presented to the following people in recognition of their outstanding community leadership and their partnership efforts with the Forest Service toward the health of Alaska's forests and communities:

- Bruce McCurtain, Alaska Recreation Management: For outstanding performance as a Chugach National Forest Business Partner providing exemplary recreation services to the public from 1993 to 2005.
- Jeff Jahnke, Alaska state forester: For sustained performance in partnership with the Forest Service contributing to the health of Alaska's forests and communities.

- Art and Claire King: For outstanding and sustained community leadership in Naukati, Alaska, contributing to the health of Southeast Alaska's communities.
- Roberta Wilfong, manager for Kenai Peninsula Spruce Bark Beetle Mitigation Program: For outstanding support to the interagency "All Lands/All Hands" approach to mitigating the impacts of spruce bark beetle on Alaska's Kenai Peninsula.
- Robert Ott, cochair, Alaska Northern Forest Cooperative: For outstanding leadership as the 2003–2004 cochair of the Alaska Northern Forest Cooperative.
- Tom Paragi, cochair, Alaska Northern Forest Cooperative: For outstanding leadership as the 2003–2004 cochair of the Alaska Northern Forest Cooperative.

The main focus of the afternoon session was to gather input from forum participants via roundtable discussions. Participants were divided into six groups, with a facilitator and recorder at each table. The information captured at these roundtable discussions is listed below.

Question 1: What were the Forest Service's greatest accomplishments to healthy forests and healthy communities in the last century?
The Forest Service was "a credible organization that became the authoritative voice for professional forest management." The Forest Service implemented Gifford Pinchot's premise that national forests should be used by the public and be conserved rather than preserved. The Forest Service put idle land into production, in timber or grassland and grazing.

The Forest Service pioneered the establishment of the wilderness system. The forest reserves that came about through the initial efforts to set aside lands and provide for the long-term sustainability for public use became the body of the National Forest System.

The Forest Service was well respected for using environmental analyses. Allowing public comment on forest planning and project implementation improved the National Environmental Policy Act process, even though the exercise was sometimes a double-edged sword. Open dialogues and good listening led to good decisions. The development of forest plans with public comment was crucial.

The Forest Service produced commodities while managing multiple resources. The agency balanced differing values and provided broad-based management of lands and wilderness. It was flexible in tailoring plans and projects with both rural and urban communities in mind.

As part of its mission, the Forest Service developed infrastructure and upgraded basic road systems, ferry systems, and electric power grids.

The Forest Service pioneered the use of science in forest planning and management, especially in the Alaska Region. After one century, there were 191 million acres of national forest land with balanced plans done democratically through public debate. Even as demands increased, the Forest Service protected key areas of biodiversity while allowing for multiple use of the forest.

Forest science labs supported specialists in many areas and studied timber management, watershed management, ecology, social studies, and wildlife interaction. The Forest Service successfully addressed the question of removing scientists from their customary roles and putting them squarely in political and decision-making roles. Forest Service researchers became leaders in a variety of scientific fields such as entomology, fire, ecology, pathology, and wildlife biology. Their knowledge was used to develop guidelines for forest system management.

After one hundred years of management, the Alaska Region did not have threatened or endangered species. The healthy, vibrant system sustained fish and wildlife. Managers struck a balance between commodity production and sustainability. Large unfragmented, healthy landscapes remained. Researchers looked for ways to maintain the health of the forests while addressing potential problems like the urban–wildland interface.

Alaskans and visitors benefited from the Forest Service's extensive recreational cabin system and water and winter recreational activities.

The Forest Service excelled in developing partnerships for conservation efforts. It became more effective by including partners in decision making.

The Forest Service in Alaska was instrumental in the resolution of the Alaska Native Claims Settlement Act by developing cooperative projects with traditional tribes throughout the state. They increased awareness of Native peoples and helped them preserve their traditional knowledge.

After a history of fire suppression, the Forest Service recognized the role of fire in maintaining healthy forests. The Forest Service provided research and assistance to state and local agencies in management and suppression of wildland fires, and invested in research and development of fire management capabilities and technology.

Programs such as the Civilian Conservation Corp, Youth Conservation Corp, Job Corps, and the Youth Adult Conservation Corp improved the lot of many. The Forest Service was a champion for diversity in hiring.

Forest Service employees were good citizens and neighbors. They played critical roles in community volunteering and became the critical fiber holding communities together.

Goods and services such as timber and grazing built and sustained local communities. In Alaska, the establishment of long-term timber sales aided the development of fully integrated, viable forest products manufacturing. The high-paying year-round jobs that were created at the time would not have happened without those contracts.

The expansion of State and Private Forestry improved the health of communities. S&PF assisted private landowners in reforestation and land management techniques, provided grants, developed partnerships, and aided rural councils.

National forests acted as havens of quiet and serenity.

The Forest Service prospered through decentralization. Decentralization allowed the Forest Service to develop partnerships and close relationships with local communities, since decisions could be made at the forest and district level. The Forest Service reacted to crises with strong leadership, was culturally aware, was responsive to challenges, and exhibited a can-do attitude. Communication was real, and there was an esprit de corps that was tied to its mission of stewardship.

The Forest Service provided college educations for thousands in the past one hundred years, developed cooperative programs with universities, taught natural resources management principles, and sponsored many students in the Student Temporary Employment Program and Student Career Experience Program. The Forest Service established the first school of forestry.

Question 2: What are the three most vital issues that confront the agency in this new century?

Three vital issues or questions that face the Forest Service in the new century were identified:

1. How do we create agency policy and share our intentions to an interested public?

2. What are the scientific and work-related issues that affect our mission?

3. How do we deal with money issues (shrinking budgets, funding changes)? How do we create jobs that are vital to the health of local communities?

There are internal, external, and political forces that impact the creation of agency policy and the way the Forest Service communicates with the public. Can the Forest Service maintain its relevance in view of shifting demographics and values? The Forest Service must adapt to the changing needs, wants, and demands of the public or become irrelevant. (Why do we need the Forest Service if all the land is locked up in a park?) Potentially, we could lose all that we have accomplished in the last one hundred years.

We must package our vision better, make the message more personal, do a better job of telling our story, and address a lack of trust. We must prepare managers for dealing with the media. We must address performance accountability.

The Forest Service must retake the decision-making responsibility from lawyers, courts, and nongovernmental organizations and learn to deal with political pressures in the face of public outcry. We have to balance differing values and address the polarization of public opinion about the environment. We have to deal with conflicting rules, regulations and laws, and gridlocks in the planning process. We will continue to face changing executive orders and philosophies (e.g., the roadless rule).

We must bring young people into the workforce and train them as the next generation of land managers. We must increase our constituency and get young people to say, "I want to work for you."

The Forest Service needs a long-term plan for dealing with the rapidly changing environment. Global climate changes have direct impacts on the health of national forests and communities. We must be flexible, relevant, and adaptable in dealing with these problems. Global climate change also can increase the risk of fire. Changing climates also affect animal and plant species, and could worsen the threat of invasive species. Rapid advancements in travel continue to connect us to all other parts of the world, which also contributes to the threat of invasive species.

The growing population will affect our groundwater. We could be faced with various water issues such as pollution, scarcity of water, or drought. We must be ready to mitigate the effects of water problems on forest health.

Increased population will also create a greater competition for use of the public land base. There will be an increase in the wildland-urban interface. Urban sprawl will affect air quality and fire management. Demographic changes from rural to urban will decrease the connection between the people and the land.

Maintaining the resources we have while providing for future use will become the main focus of determining what is "the greater good." The public often perceives that no individual should profit from resource extraction on the national forest. The Forest Service must stay relevant to an increasingly urban and culturally diverse constituency.

Forest-dependent communities are unable to prosper economically due to lack of private lands and access to public lands. The Forest Service needs to integrate ownership of public lands and nonindustrial private forestlands. We need to restore integrated industries that were lost with the pulp mills, provide job sustainability in communities, and increase the profitability of timber production.

Projects that allow recreation use are not usually litigated. The real issue facing the Forest Service is whether there will be any commercial timber harvesting. The Forest Service should look at the need for a reliable and uninterrupted supply of timber and the reestablishment of an integrated timber industry. Some hard targets in volume and sales should be set.

It is important to define the current terminology of forest health, sustainability, and traditional uses. We need to think about what we want the forest to look like in one hundred or two hundred years. We need to deal with the litigation morass associated with timber sales. Why can't the Forest Service make money? We need to get the decisions out of the courts and into the hands of the land managers.

We must play a key role in developing global and international policy. As the current Third World nations continue to mature and become smarter, they will refuse to let the United States exploit their resources, requiring us to use our natural resources at home. We are one of the few countries that have set public lands for multiple uses. We have to take these concepts to other nations. We should respond to the new global economic reality and help the rest of the world sustain their resources. Lesser-developed countries value land products, but in the United States, the value of open spaces and recreation will continue to grow.

Federal budget reductions are a continuous challenge. In the future, how we will deal with reforestation and many other problems with deficit budgets? Also, there is the need to substantially increase research funds, increase the spending per capita, and maintain infrastructures. We must create the political will to fund and support necessary functions, especially those that aren't easily outsourced, such as law enforcement, research, management, and infrastructure. We must develop the wherewithal to do what we have to do with the resources we have.

The Forest Service must continue to be leaders in natural resource education. We must educate the public so they will give informed input in the public process. We do not want people to lose the knowledge of how the natural systems work. Education affects how the public votes, and even their values. Ethnic demographics are changing so that without receiving natural resource education, people may not value nature, open spaces, and public lands. The Forest Service can help by practicing and promoting the idea of multiple uses of natural resources to Americans and the world.

Education should be geared toward teaching sustainability of our national forests. Students from kindergarten through grade twelve are an importance audience. We should teach social responsibility in terms of natural resource management on a global basis. Education needs to be geared to urban audiences so that they can understand scientific information and management rationale, and what those mean to the public.

We should share the scientific data that drive our decisions. Often public hearing opinions are based what people hear in the media, not on science. We must educate the public so they are knowledgeable of our policies in resource management.

Question 3: How can the Forest Service better serve the public while caring for the land in the twenty-first century?

Education was listed as one of the top priorities for the Forest Service in the next century, for many reasons. The public needs to understand what the Forest Service does. Education will improve our public image and make natural resources more relevant to urban populations. The public should have the chance to learn about natural resources from someone other than the media. Education could reduce conflict and increase public acceptance of our mission.

Education must be based on sound science. Putting an emphasis on grades K–12 will ensure that natural resource basics are taught. Education can shape the values of growing students. The Envirothon program for high school students can be used to bring professional resource managers into the classroom.

Communication will be very important in the future, and the public will look closely at how we shape policy. We must include the public and local communities in our policy-making processes. The public will hold us accountable and expect decisions to be made on sound science. They will want to be informed about the details and dynamics of any change in management decisions and will want to examine the implications those changes may have.

The public wants the Forest Service to search for common ground. Public forums will defuse the stigma of extremists. It will be important for us to build relationships. We must share our message and our principles of forest management practices in a format that is easy to comprehend. We need to understand the concerns and wants of our constituents.

Differences of values and opinions must be confronted in a rational way. We need to maintain an open-door policy and allow decisions to be made at the ranger district level. We must consider traditional Native knowledge and make decisions collectively, not paternally. We should build nonpartisan support, avoid pendulum shifts, and listen to what people want.

The workforce should be reflective of society. We should increase diversity, starting with young people, and work with other agencies to avoid redundancy.

In the next century, the Forest Service must have adaptable management strategies and work toward sustainable management on all levels: social, economic, and environmental. Decisions should become more science based and less political. We must avoid the use of fear to drive forest management policy—it reduces credibility.

The Forest Service will have to operate in spite of regulations and laws from outside agencies that designate operating parameters (through Congress and the executive branch). It will be important in the future to identify appropriate funding to actually implement the long-term plans we develop. Forest plans need to be considered as a contract with the public.

It is in our best interest to manage multiple resources while providing for sustainable consumption. We must continue to identify key areas of biodiversity and ask why programs such as the Healthy Forests Initiative are based solely on fire, and not science. We must help the public understand the difference between prevention and crisis management (e.g., National Fire Plan). We need to refocus the public and the media from problems to positives.

The Forest Service must continue to improve collaborative planning at the local level and be more present on the ground. We should identify strengths and weaknesses and manage accordingly, looking at different management systems from other agencies. We should reinforce forest supervisor and district ranger authority, since that strengthens partnerships with state and local governments. We should encourage public and private ventures to get work done and provide services to the public. The public should be used to monitor and gather needed information for active, wise management (for example, ranchers gathering water and weather data). We can make use of local cultural and traditional knowledge (for example, local place names or alternative forest uses). We should support resource advisory councils.

In the next century, it will be important to maintain public access to public lands. We should continue to inventory resource needs, especially with nontimber forest products. We must allow for traditional uses. We might establish a community forest from state and federal lands.

We must keep pace with technology.

We should have fewer debates and studies and go forward with land management plans. We should streamline our procedures.

The Forest Service needs to include research data in presenting issues and solutions to the public.

We should continue to build on our body of knowledge to become a truly world-class research organization. We can strengthen R&D programs with better funding and expertise.

Our experts should contribute to the establishment of a national energy policy, making the transition from fossil fuels to renewable resources. For example, windmill farms can be set up on national forest lands.

We must use multiple approaches to bring urban dwellers to the forest, so they can understand its value and relevancy to them.

We must be more forward thinking in regard to addressing upcoming problems, such as global climate change and the threat of invasive species.

We have to be innovative in coming up with solutions for budget and fiscal problems. We need to market the economic and social values of the national forests. Our priorities in funding must be linked to what the public wants. We need to learn how to best market commodities, sell them at a profit, and alleviate legal battles. We should keep timber receipts local. We can establish markets for low-grade, low-value timber and look into the ethanol market.

We must continue to work toward healthy communities and forests by helping the public understand their economic ties to the national forests.

We need to improve the social skills of employees who work with a diverse constituency and provide more social science education. We should promote activities that increase local hiring, such as the Youth Conservation Corps. We should involve young people in archaeology or recreation projects to promote understanding and decrease vandalism.

■ ■ ■

After the roundtable discussions were complete, Regional Forester Denny Bschor announced the selection of delegates from the regional forum who would represent Alaska at the Centennial Congress on January 3–6, 2005, in Washington, D.C.:

- Andrew Allgeier, University of Alaska–Fairbanks (student)

- Bruce McCurtain, Alaska Recreation Management
- John Sandor, National Association of Forest Service Retirees
- Roberta Wilfong, Kenai Peninsula Borough
- George Woodbury, Alaska Forest Association
- John Yarie, University of Alaska–Fairbanks

Report of the Puerto Rico Regional Forum
August 25–26, 2004
Caguas, Puerto Rico

—Submitted by Ariel E. Lugo and Mildred Alayón, International Institute
of Tropical Forestry, USDA Forest Service, Río Piedras, Puerto Rico

Tropical Forestry

Tropical forestry deals with the conservation of tropical forests, including forestlands, waters, and all the biodiversity they contain. The objective of tropical forestry is to provide for the needs of people while conserving the tropical ecosystems that provide the products and services that humans require.

Tropical forests represent about half of the world's forests (about 1.8 billion hectares), contain more than half of the world's biodiversity, and support over half of the world's human population. There are more types of tropical forests than temperate and boreal forests combined. The reason is that the tropics contain many climates: from frost-free lowlands to snow-covered mountains and from deserts to rainforests. The absence of frost in the lowlands is one of the main reasons why there are so many species of organisms in the tropics; tropical organisms don't require defenses against cold.

Tropical forestlands experience the highest deforestation rates in the world, mostly because tropical people need land to grow food. Deforested lands are used for agricultural purposes, but large areas are degraded and abandoned. Secondary forests regrow in some of the abandoned degraded lands. Today, the area of secondary forests in the tropics is as high as the area of mature tropical forests. However, the area of degraded deforested land is also increasing. Ensuring sufficient high-quality water for human consumption, repairing degraded lands, sustaining the flow of forest products and services to people, and conserving the biodiversity of the tropical forests are some of the main challenges of tropical forestry.

Tropical foresters focus their activities on the protection of forests, reforesting lands, restoring forests on degraded sites, managing forests for products (fiber, meat, water) and services (clean water, clean air, recreation), conducting research, educating the public, and helping in the development of policies for sustainable land and resource management.

Managing tropical forests is complicated because tropical forests are complex and diverse and little is known about them. In Puerto Rico alone, there are as many tree species as there are in all of North America from Florida to Alaska. The high richness of species applies to all groups of organisms. In Hawaii, of the ten thousand native species, over ninety percent are endemic (found nowhere else in the world). To complicate matters, few scientists live in the tropics and most forestry research takes place in temperate and boreal regions. Therefore, the knowledge base needed to support sustainable forest management in tropical countries is limited.

The Forest Service in the Tropics

The Forest Service and its predecessor, the Bureau of Forestry, have had a presence in the tropics for over one hundred years in Puerto Rico and fifty years in Hawaii. The Caribbean National Forest is the only tropical forest in the National Forest System. The International Institute of Tropical Forestry was established in 1939 to support the management of this national forest and restore forests to deforested lands in Puerto Rico. The Institute of Pacific Island Forestry was established in 1957 to support forest and water conservation efforts in Hawaii and U.S.-affiliated governments of the Pacific. Both research institutes continue with the original mission but also address broad tropical resource management issues, such as dealing with alien species and the global role of tropical forests.

Tropical forestry activities of the Forest Service in the Caribbean and the Pacific are relevant to tropical forests elsewhere in the world, including temperate forests in the United States. The reasons are many but include the small size, long history of human activity, and the diversity of forests in the islands. Small size and diversity of forests allow for greater interaction among forests and between terrestrial and aquatic ecosystems; ecological processes are easier to visualize and study. In addition, processes such as those associated with large human populations are more intense per unit area of land. As an example, human population is from ten to one hundred times higher in the islands than in continents. The long history of human activity under these conditions allows for greater interaction between people and forests, and for observing the long-term outcome of processes such as deforestation, reforestation, alien species invasions, and sustainable forest management. Tropical island forests become laboratories for informing continental debates because islands and their forests are

- harbingers of the future, given the density of human activity and population they support;

- warning signs of change (biodiversity, global change, emerging new resource management issues);
- models for the management of complex natural ecosystems;
- connected to continents by many mechanisms, including migratory species, international commerce (wood, coca, hamburgers, tourism), global phenomena, etc.; and
- the terminus of many environmental gradients—that is, they are useful for comparative research.

In short, tropical islands are mesocosms of compact complexity, and tropical island forestry teaches many lessons applicable to continental areas. The Forest Service has been dealing with these conditions for decades and thus has been a major contributor to the understanding and management of tropical forests.

Tropical Forestry Issues

A partial list of tropical forestry issues that occupy daily debate and concern among tropical foresters would include the following:

- How do we deal with large-scale natural disturbances of tropical forests such as hurricanes, drought, and fires?
- How do we deal with large-scale anthropogenic disturbances of tropical forests, such as urbanization, fires, and unmanaged access to valuable resources?
- How do we approach the dramatic changes in biodiversity product of the large-scale disturbances mentioned above? Examples include the invasions of alien species, the endangerment of endemic and native species, and the high level of rare species.
- How do we satisfy the increasing demand on tropical forests for products and services? For example, people need more food, fiber, high-quality water, open spaces for recreation and nature-based tourism, and ecosystem services, such as serving as a buffer to human activity.
- Which research priorities should we focus on in the coming decades?
- How should we interface with the public and which should be our outreach priorities?
- What level of attention should urban forestry, land management, and forest restoration command in our future programs?

The Tropical Forestry Regional Forum

The Tropical Forestry forum was an activity planned and executed by a small group of International Institute of Tropical Forestry and Caribbean National Forest employees and their collaborators. Institute, national forest, and Pacific Southwest Station employees were asked for nominations of delegates and candidates for formal recognition at the forum. Sally Collins presented centennial plaques to Michael Buck, retired state forester from Hawaii; María Falcón, a television producer in Puerto Rico; and the University of Puerto Rico.

The composition of delegates reflected a wide spectrum of our clientele, collaborators, and professionals. Fifty of the ninety-three delegates were non-Forest Service, and the rest were Forest Service employees. Seventy-six were from Puerto Rico, ten from the United States, three from Hawaii, two from Argentina, and one each from Colombia and Venezuela. Forty-four delegates were federal employees, six were commonwealth employees, and one was employed by another government; twenty were academics, seven were representing environmental organizations, and the remaining fifteen included a high school teacher, biologists, a physician, reporters, an attorney, a commonwealth senator, a producer, an architect, a meteorologist, a city mayor, an engineer, scientists, and environmentalists.

The forum included a half-day plenary where the Forest Service reported its activities in the tropics of Caribbean, Central and South America, and the Micronesia. Talks were supplemented with fifty posters depicting programs in Hawaii, the Caribbean National Forest, and the International Institute of Tropical Forestry. All these materials are available as a CD-ROM through the institute.

Delegates were assigned to interdisciplinary groups (Ausubo, Ceiba, Guayacán, Laurel Sabino, Tabonuco) and were asked to react to the morning talks and the preforum material (what we have done well and where we need to improve), to make recommendations for the future, and resolutions to the whole forum. One group, Guayacán, did not turn in a report. What follows are the observations and recommendations of four groups.

Ausubo

A few delegates stated that the morning presentations were really appropriate in responding to questions about the history of the Forest Service. It was agreed that urban development is a problem in Puerto Rico that can be addressed by the Forest Service. Because of this urbanization approach, Puerto Rico now needs reforestation. Some stated that the Forest Service's original mission had been more science-based but that it was now becoming more recreational.

General consensus was reached on the need for reforestation in the tropics because this is a rapidly depleting resource at a global scale. The agency needs to promote the rescue and conservation of tropical forests and open more marketing opportunities for its products. There is a general trend of involving business as stakeholders in the conservation of tropical forests. However, the Forest Service doesn't know how to synchronize these efforts with companies to achieve a plan that will preserve tropical forests. One delegate mentioned that Senator Hillary Clinton was promoting a project that would use the different woods of the Caribbean National Forest.

Most agreed that the agency needs to improve in providing access to information (maps, geographic information system data, etc.), in developing a website easy for people to retrieve information, in providing educational outreach programs for mentors and communities, in promoting multidisciplinary and applied research, and in increasing liaisons between agencies. The agency also needs to buy additional lands, focus research on identifying and promoting ecological corridors, increase technical assistance to private landowners through nongovernmental organizations and stewardship programs, and request more funds to increase protected areas.

The general consensus appeared to be strong on disallowing military activities in the Caribbean National Forest. There is also a lack of communication because the public does not seem to receive information about ecosystem research. Most research stays with the researchers and the public is not informed on the importance of the ecosystem. Research results should be simplified so the public understands why research is important to them. The ecological impact of insects is not studied sufficiently; therefore, people are not aware of the importance of insects to the environment. The agency needs forest management programs that specify the ultimate cost to the public of ecological disturbances in Puerto Rico. It is not promoting management, and the agency should do so to preserve the national forest in Puerto Rico. Some delegates felt that the Forest Service in Puerto Rico does not teach people to appreciate and conserve their natural resources, but in other small islands, with a smaller budget for this program, they conserve their natural resources better than we do. The Forest Service needs to be more aggressive in terms of fostering education in schools and communities on the importance of preserving natural resources and tropical forests so children will grow up knowing the importance of preserving our natural resources; an educational campaign is expensive but necessary. Delegates also encourage purchasing the land around the Caribbean National Forest.

In general, delegates felt that the agency should continue to preserve tropical forests. However, while some delegates felt that there was not enough educational and community outreach, particularly with those neighbors in the forest, others felt that the agency was working with communities and teaching them the importance of preserving natural resources and tropical forests. More access for the physically challenged was presented as a required improvement as well as clearing access in the national forest for hikers.

There is scientific access, awareness, wide use of the library, availability of maps in both languages, managing of the land notwithstanding environmental obstacles, community participation, job programs, and interpretation programs. Several research programs, such as those being done in tropical forests, are excellent. Also good are the educational programs that will improve the management of schools, creation of future scientists, and the conservation of forest resources. Some delegates wanted to focus exclusively on tropical forests in Puerto Rico, especially as related to the Caribbean National Forest because that is the topic with which they are familiar; however, others wanted to address issues in more general terms.

Recreation, volunteer programs, promoting public participation, international programs, participation in the different processes, assistance to private landowners in managing their properties, protection of all natural resources, collaboration with land buyers for reforestation to recover the forest, and opportunities for communities to manage reserves appropriately and conserve them were seen as areas needing improvement.

Generally speaking, delegates saw as positive action by the agency its efforts at land management, environmental education programs through programs for teachers at El Portal, and the protection and preservation of natural ecosystems, such as watersheds. They also agreed that recreation facilities, infrastructure access, interpretation at the national forest, and the Seniors' Program were areas where the agency was on the right track at the national forest. Delegates felt that no one was better at managing the Caribbean National Forest than the Forest Service.

As for the institute, delegates felt there was good access to research (scientific access through the library and the lab), although some felt that there should be more research conducted in sites other than the national forest, while others felt research should focus more on management practices in the national forest. Some delegates felt that public participation is reached through State and Private Forestry programs such as stewardship, legacy, urban and community forestry, forest health initiatives, conservation education, and cooperative fire programs. Delegates also felt that the institute was doing a good job with the international cooperation program.

Ceiba

Delegates considered many subjects when discussing the Forest Service's performance in Puerto Rico. They began by indicating that the agency should be moving on to the next level in research. Research should integrate land managers and the community. Public demands should not be ignored. More training on cultural diversity and on communication within cultural differences should be enhanced so that the agency can present a more positive image to people of other countries. The agency also needs to be more proactive in many areas. It needs greater interaction with the community and improved communication across language barriers, and it should encourage citizen participation in the processes. People need more education in the field of conservation. In terms of the institute library, access needs to be improved island-wide by opening the library electronically for potential users who would otherwise not have access to its services.

In terms of the State and Private Forestry program, the agency needs to improve the role of private forestry. Continued research is needed on the impact of fire on ecosystems and integration between national (federal), state, and private forestry in dealing with this threat. Cooperative forestry promotes private forestry through landowner grants; however, national forests appear to play a larger role in these grants. More work is needed in the development of forest management plans by seeking greater participation from managers, the public, and academia. In the administration of these forests and its human resources, the agency should keep striving toward a diverse workforce. In the area of recreation, the agency needs to move forward in its quantity and quality.

How much wood is used worldwide? National forests used to provide for this resource, yet now they produce less than five percent. The agency should be looking into providing for more in this area as a means of economic self-sustenance. More research should be geared toward addressing what is needed to provide for wood extraction. Mahogany could be a means to this end, and added funding for research in this area should be actively sought. The agency needs to expand collaboration on tropical forests with other nations at the international scale. It should participate in the development of timber production in forests that have sustainable forest management plans.

In the local arena, the Forest Service should prioritize extending the northeast ecological corridor to the coast, thus opening up greater opportunities to expand knowledge of the services provided by the environment. More efforts need to be expended on the protection of native species, pursuing research that will allow us all to better understand these species. Domestic animals exotic to the national forest (such as cats and dogs) need to be kept away from the forest. The government should provide for shelters to address this issue. In an effort to improve on the management of the national forest, the agency should increase training on forestland management and research, create plantations for rare and exotic plants, provide more interpretive programs for visitors, increase its water management program, and buy more land. In addition, research should address conservation management. Greater efforts toward public outreach should be pursued so that the public can be informed regarding what is being done by the agency. There is great public interest and they want to be informed.

The country needs to work harder at seeing the environment and its products as something of value. An example of demonstrating how the environment provides a valuable product would be ensuring clean water and then bringing it to the community. The agency also needs to formulate methods of producing financing for the protection of the environment. It needs to be more proactive. The Caribbean National Forest should be looked at holistically, from the top of the mountain down to the coast, so that we can see what will affect the forest in the next hundred years. However, the agency should not limit itself to the national forest but also study what is outside the forest. Why not study other forest types? How can damage to these resources be prevented? The agency also needs to recognize that there is a worldwide shift toward recreation as a result of the growth in population; however, managers need to limit uses within these lands to ensure its sustainability. To do this, tough laws are needed, and people to enforce them. It is becoming a social problem. Managers need to be more aware of this shift in focus and provide for protection by controlling access. People need to be taught to take care of the land. How do we manage both population growth and land preservation? Educate the people: "If you want to protect your water, protect your mountains."

It appears that there was disagreement among the delegates concerning what the Forest Service should stop doing. However, they did come to the following items as things that should be discontinued.

The Forest Service should stop projecting itself as the know-it-all agency. There is an image problem at the core of this agency's delivery. Instead of dictating, a better approach would be one of working together. Rather than ignoring situations experienced by other countries, learn from them. Don't be afraid to sever ties. The Forest Service should challenge local government and at some point work toward stopping development on some lands. Stop experimentation that would be detrimental to the national forest or the environment. This type of experimentation, if necessary, should be pursued elsewhere.

As far as things that the agency should continue, scientific research in tropical forestry has been doing a good job in preparing teachers and leaders worldwide. What was once long-term forestry is now long-term research, and this focus has been successful. The level of research has risen, and productivity can be seen in its publications. The information available as a product of this research is very accessible and helpful—for example, through the Internet and through consultation with dependable experts. The library is a valuable resource, and free access to the expertise it provides is available.

The agency is protecting our natural resources, and this can be increased by adding land. Safety at the national forest is excellent, and this could only have been achieved through improved forest management. The Forest Service has also excelled at helping other countries, such as the Dominican Republic, Jamaica, and Costa Rica, not only in emergency responses but also in management strategies for their lands.

The Forest Service provides an independent voice that helps with decisions and is not afraid of saying things publicly. This voice is not just an opinion but also a credible source recognized for its good work. The agency in Puerto Rico has hired many locals, respecting cultural differences and diversity in the workforce. By doing this, it has provided a workforce with staying power that has been exposed to long-term issues with a cultural advantage that aids in communication and makes it unique. In general terms, the Forest Service in Puerto Rico has done well, with room for improvement, in four areas: education, collaboration, research, and management.

Laurel Sabino

Delegates feel that the Forest Service in Puerto Rico is known for the quality of its research and its relevance to tropical forest management. Research has been conducted in a wide range of areas, and the International Institute of Tropical Forestry's products are the technical and scientific publications that reach the general public. Recognition of the agency's research program in Puerto Rico is international in scope, particularly in the tropics. Although there is room for improvement, the institute's library is a resource for local undergraduate and graduate students. The institute is a center for technical training for the islands of the Caribbean and Latin America.

The delegates noted the philosophical differences between the Caribbean National Forest and the International Institute of Tropical Forestry. Again, although there is room for improvement, based on surveys, passive recreation in harmony with natural resources is enjoyed in the national forest. The national forest has a management plan, and as public policy all forest activities are analyzed and put in practice based on this plan. However, there is room for improvement in some areas, as for example, the parrot aviary needs better facilities. In addition, the forest plan is not easy to read, nor clear in its definition of terms. Given land use around the periphery of the national forest, it appears that there is no buffer zone. The agency needs to be more aggressive in preventing development in this zone; they need to write letters, attend public hearings, and look toward seeing that this special zoning law is enforced.

Access to the director and forest supervisor is very good. They are open to the media and are honest in their responses. Nevertheless, some delegates felt that the Forest Supervisor's tenure at the head of his unit has been too long. Although communication with the media by both units is very good, that does not always appear to be the case with communication with each other. The appearance is that there is a war going on between the national forest and the institute.

Interests between federal and state laws clash, and this fosters a feeling of being in a "no-man's island." Forest Service policy at the national level conflicts with policy in Puerto Rico. Many in the group felt it important to note that the agency does not seem to realize that the national forest (El Yunque) belongs to the people of Puerto Rico. The national forest is well managed but could improve: more land should be acquired, proposals need to be developed, and continued interaction with forest communities must be pursued. The Seniors Program, which provides education and training, could be improved in the area of providing tour guides, and in preparing them for this task.

The agency needs to review its internal processes at the national forest. While on the one hand, the permit request process is highly bureaucratic and difficult, on the other hand, some in the group believe that research permits are granted for an excessive period of time. These permits should be evaluated on a yearly basis and all special-uses permits need to go through a consultation procedure.

The national forest either needs to have better-trained management personnel or perhaps hire more people. Law enforcement is so minimal it doesn't appear to exist. The western side of the forest requires attention, and the national forest in general could be improved by an increase in signs and better hiking roads.

Poor communication exists at the intra- and interagency level. As an example, there has been such poor communication between the U.S. Fish and Wildlife Service, which manages the aviary, and the national forest, which manages the forest, that some fear that the parrot will be managed into extinction. The agency needs to improve the parrot recovery program and build the aviary in a more appropriate ecological zone.

There is a patent need for an interpreter to serve as intermediary in the translation of research to the public—some kind of liaison between scientific personnel and their products and the community. In addition, research focus should address other areas such as timber and wood usage, ethnobotany, native species, and nonwood product use. Although research in Puerto Rico is addressing a wide range of technical fields, there are additional areas that should be pursued: more study should be devoted to inventory and its use, more research is needed on secondary forests and on restoration. The agency should ensure that the research done is relevant to management problems not only for the national forest but also for Puerto Rico's state forests and tropical forests in general. In addition, continued support for the institute's work in Brazil was recommended.

While some delegates voiced concern over what they considered poor management and recovery of threatened and endangered species, as well as endemic species, others proposed that the standing policy against exotic fauna be modified to allow planned introduction of terrestrial and arboreal nonvolant land mammals that would replace extinct native species. They felt this could contribute to restoring the national forest's original ecosystem.

In general terms, other areas of improvement voiced by some delegates included public relations, environmental education that was seen as not being provided to low-income communities, poor representation of Puerto Rican and Latin American scientists at the institute, and fewer opportunities for professional development for employees in Puerto Rico as opposed to mainland United States.

Tabonuco

The delegates agreed to refer to those areas where, although the Forest Service in Puerto Rico has been effective, improvement is encouraged. In terms of human resources, the agency has been a trainer of tropical foresters at an international scale. It has provided postdisaster assistance to tropical countries, supported sustainable tourism as an economic resource, been at the forefront in multicultural efforts, and in Puerto Rico, kept the cultural distinction of hospitality and service to visitors.

Highlights in forest management include island reforestation, monitoring and inventory, contributing to the improvement of forest practices, and reducing impact logging. Conservation efforts by the agency have fostered an open door (or portal) to tropical forest conservation. The agency created the conservation icon of the Puerto Rican parrot as an ever-present reminder of how conservation efforts can rescue an endangered species. However, rescuing this species was also a product of research.

The Forest Service conducts a significant amount of research in Puerto Rico. Scientists in Puerto Rico conduct tropical forestry research in several countries around the world. Research on threatened and endangered species and the implementation of this research has an impact, as witnessed by the previously mentioned rescue of the Puerto Rican Parrot. Research conducted by agency scientists on the island is also adapted to meet local natural resources goals. Statistics and data are collected by Forest Service personnel and specialists, and technical publications are made available worldwide, thereby establishing what external users and environmental advocates see as evidence of the agency's credibility.

The agency should, however, improve on sustainable practices to reflect the integration of environmental, social, and economic factors and benefits. It needs to improve or increase the human dimension of its research to incorporate social concerns and issues. More resources need to be devoted to forest inventory and monitoring at an international scale. The agency also needs to increase its efforts and successes in tropical forestry research in an effort to deal with natural forest management and fast-growing plantations in large-scale logging.

Internal communication between the different programs also needs improvement. Research should be used to contribute to the development of an interdisciplinary approach and to integrate all the sciences. The agency needs to improve monitoring and documenting the impacts and benefits received by communities. You need greater self-criticism of your scientific approaches and more emphasis on the study of the links between human health and ecosystem health. The Forest Service needs to understand the connection between human health and biodiversity and not discard traditional ecological knowledge of indigenous peoples. More communication between tropical forestry regions is needed, and an international tropical forestry policy should be developed. The agency needs to understand its markets and audience—a benefit of having Ariel Lugo on the road.

Specific recommendations include committing to long-term assistance to the continuation of the Tapajos project (national forest in Brazil), increasing relevant research on invasive species, committing to long term technical assistance in Central America, and committing to improving inventory and monitoring data from stands to landscapes in the Caribbean region.

Resolutions of the Tropical Forestry Regional Forum

Twelve resolutions were presented by the individual groups and voted by all delegates. Of these, the following five received more than seventy-five percent of the vote. In addition to continuing to pursue its mission in the tropics, the USDA Forest Service should

- incorporate human dimensions and social concern aspects into its research program;
- increase its technical assistance and training in tropical countries;
- improve its visibility with internal and external customers;
- support and enhance efforts directed at the conservation of the karst region of Puerto Rico; and
- increase collaboration between the Institute of Pacific Island Forestry and the International Institute of Tropical Forestry.

A New Name for the National Forest

Delegates also considered changing the name of the Caribbean National Forest. While the majority suggested a name change, there was no consensus on what the new name should be. Some suggestions were El Yunque National Forest, El Yunque Caribbean National Forest, Luquillo National Forest, El Yunque National Forest of Puerto Rico, Bosque Caribeño, Yuquiyú National Forest, Yuke National Forest, and Sierra de Luquillo National Forest.

—Submitted by V. Alaric Sample, President, Pinchot Institute for Conservation

The Greatest Good:
Organizational History and Philosophy of the USDA Forest Service

The concept of "the greatest good of the greatest number in the long run" has, in one form or another, been the guiding philosophy of the Forest Service throughout its first century. As the Forest Service, along with its many partners in other public, private, and nonprofit organizations around the country, look ahead to the agency's next century, this philosophy is taking on new meaning. The planet has become smaller in many ways, and there is a pressing need for leadership in addressing both the challenges and the opportunities in conserving and sustainably managing forests around the world—the kind of leadership the Forest Service can offer. But sweeping global initiatives won't accomplish much if they cannot be made practical and operational at the local community scale. The Forest Service's history suggests that it has some experience and insights to offer from this perspective as well.

As one in a series of regional forums leading up to the Forest Service's national Centennial Congress in 2005, a group of individuals representing a diversity of backgrounds and perspectives gathered at Grey Towers National Historic Landmark in to examine the organizational history and philosophy of the Forest Service. Ross Whaley, chairman of the Adirondack Park Agency and retired president of the College of Environmental Science and Forestry, SUNY-Syracuse; Char Miller, professor and chair of the Department of History at Trinity University; Dennis LeMaster, professor of forestry and natural resources at Purdue University; and Dale Robertson, Chief (retired) of the USDA Forest Service presented their perspectives how "the greatest good" has been articulated in the philosophies and policies that have guided the Forest Service over the past hundred years. Ann Forest Burns, attorney, Burns and Williams, Seattle; Roger Sedjo, director of Forest Economics and Policy at Resources for the Future; and Char Miller each offered a scenario for how the Forest Service as an organization might be expected to continue evolving over its next century of service. This report was compiled by Al Sample as a summary and synthesis of the presentations and discussion that took place at Grey Towers, and as a stimulus for a broader national dialogue on how the Forest Service can build upon its experience in its first century and play an integral role in addressing the conservation challenges of the next.

The "Greatest Good" in the History of Forestry in the United States

Conceptual roots. Gifford Pinchot knew a good idea when he saw one. "The greatest good of the greatest number" is an idea first articulated by British social philosopher Jeremy Bentham (1748–1832) in his now-famous treatises on "utilitarianism."[1] Pinchot was searching for a way to capture the essence of his philosophy on how natural resources should be managed to benefit the public interest in the nation as a whole, rather than to enrich a few wealthy and well-connected individuals in the short term, as was being done throughout America at the time. Bentham's phrase hit the nail squarely on the head for Pinchot, and somehow it soon found its way into a 1905 letter from Agriculture Secretary James Wilson, instructing the brand-new U.S. Forest Service (and its first Chief Forester, Gifford Pinchot) on how the equally new national forests were to be managed: "[W]here conflicting interests must be reconciled, the question will always be decided from the standpoint of the greatest good of the greatest number in the long run."

For Pinchot and his cadre of foresters in the early days of the Forest Service, this became in effect the definition of conservation. Though it lacked the specificity of an operating rule, it became a regular point of reference for the men (and later women) of the Forest Service, a goal to be constantly striven for. Today, we might view "the greatest good" most accurately as a useful slogan, a short phrase representing an important and inspiring thought or characteristic position. And for more than a century, observed Dennis Le Master, this phrase has defined the organizational philosophy of the USDA Forest Service more than any other.

From philosophy to policy. For much of the first century of the Forest Service, "the greatest good" was the philosophy that provided a general foundation for the day-to-day decisions by Forest Service officials managing the public's forests. Over the decades, it also found its way into new laws and policies that authorized and enabled the Forest Service in its work with state and tribal agencies, forest industry, and private forest landowners to improve forest management not just on the national forests but of all the nation's forests. The "greatest good" was achieved by protecting forests from destructive and wasteful wild-fires and pest outbreaks, by planting thousands of trees to restore cutover or burned areas, and by guaranteeing prompt reforestation following timber harvesting. During the post–World War II baby boom, "the greatest good" included supplying ever-increasing supplies of wood for abundant, affordable housing. With the nation's increasing affluence and leisure time, "the greatest good" also accommodated Americans' growing interest in outdoor recreation, wildlife management, and wilderness use.

By the time the Forest Service entered its second half-century, the magnitude and variety of demands on America's forests were making it increasingly difficult for forest managers to reconcile conflicting uses on the basis of such a general statement of philosophy. The multiple use and sustained yield principles, verbal extensions of "the greatest good," were enacted into law in the Multiple Use–Sustained Yield Act of 1960. A more technical approach was needed, one that would be objective enough to help forest managers navigate their way through issues that were fast becoming matters not just of competing uses, but of conflicting social values. "Benefit-cost analysis" was employed to quantify public benefits, even those without direct dollar values, and thus justify public expenditures on resource management activities. Later, sophisticated computerized optimization models were developed, with "objective functions" aimed at maximizing net public benefits, and row upon row of linear equations representing constraints designed to protect environmental values and limit resource utilization to levels that could be sustained. Out of all this analysis, "solutions" were expected to emerge, which would prescribe for forest managers the optimal allocation of land and resources that would achieve "the greatest good of the greatest number in the long run." Economists offered theoretical "production possibility curves" plotted on two, sometimes three, axes to show how the most could be gained from our forests and where there were opportunities to squeeze out more of one resource without sacrificing others. The forest was a factory, and the best way to satisfy increasing demands was through maximum production and peak efficiency.

The environmental movement became of political consequence in the late 1960s, and several environmental laws soon followed, including the National Environmental Policy Act of 1970, the Clean Air Act of 1970, and the Federal Water Pollution Control Act Amendments of 1972. The Endangered Species Act followed in 1973. These laws, noted Dennis Le Master, together with their extensive administrative regulations, which include complex procedural requirements for such things as public involvement and interagency coordination, have made management decisions in the national forests much more expensive, uncertain, unpredictable, and contentious.

The clash of conflicting values regarding forest management got louder, and technical analytical techniques for divining "the greatest good" proved increasingly unsatisfying to a now-fragmented public. Disputes over timber harvesting practices on a few national forests combined like several small forest fires merging to form a conflagration, and the Forest Service found itself consumed in national controversies over forest policy. The National Forest Management Act was passed in 1976, setting standards and guidelines for national forest planning and management. Federal courts became the venue for raising forest management complaints against the Forest Service, and management practices on the National Forests came to be determined more and more by judges.

Through what Chief Dale Robertson terms "the judicializing of forest management," field-based decisions grounded in experience and professional judgment gave way to data-driven analysis, which gave way to a primary focus on process as agency officials sought to improve their record of success in the courts. In Robertson's view, the agency was concentrating so much on procedure that it had lost sight of its mission. The Forest Service struggled to regain its footing, adopting a more simplified, objective-oriented slogan, "caring for the land and serving people." At the close of the twentieth century, however, many observers both inside and outside the Forest Service were concluding that the agency was no longer capable of effectively doing either one of these.

It is easy to view this as the result of a multitude of external political forces closing in on the Forest Service from all sides until it was completely bound up in a sort of process gridlock. With the benefit of hindsight and the perspective that comes with time, however, the Forest Service has acknowledged that it must itself take responsibility for what has taken place in its organizational life—and that this is an essential first step to ensuring that the Forest Service will be an effective and successful organization in the future.

"The Greatest Good" in a New Century of Service

The Forest Service today is a product of this rich and varied history. The pathway that has brought the Forest Service to where it is at this moment has had its share of twists and turns. As an organization, the Forest Service is a product of its history, and it is defined by these experiences. What will define the Forest Service in its next century of service? How will it continue to build upon the foundation that has been laid down, to meet the needs of an uncertain future, and continue to serve as a leader in the conservation and sustainable management of natural resources?

The Forest Service lives in an unpredictable world, which will continue to reshape the needs, challenges, and opportunities it will face as an organization. During the past century, the forces that defined the Forest Service's operating environment in the second fifty years were certainly different from those that defined its first fifty years, and this has severely tested the limits of the agency just to keep pace, if not to lead. At the start of the Forest Service's second century, it seems that the rates of social, economic, political, cultural, technological, and environmental changes affecting the agency have only accelerated. Will the Forest Service be among the organizations racing breathlessly to keep up with the pack, straining to react to each new twist or turn in the road ahead? Or will the Forest Service be boldly out ahead of the pack, anticipating new turns with foresight and confidence, and with innovative strategies that will lead it to succeed as an organization and excel in its mission to serve the public interest?

An evolving economic and societal context. What are some of the forces that will define the Forest Service's broader operating environment over the next few decades? With the continuing process of globalization, national boundaries and the decisions of national governments will become less and less important. Transnational corporations will become increasingly stateless, more independent of and less accountable to the governments of the nations in which they do business. The "united states" of the European Union and the ambitious bloc of "Asian tiger" nations will drive the global economy. Multidirectional immigration over increasingly fluid national borders will drive labor, population, and the diversity of ethnicities found within any given country. National governments, even those of the twentieth century's superpowers, will be turned to less and less for leadership, guidance, or support.

Tomorrow's leaders will be less nationalistic and behave more as "citizens of the world," according to Ann Forest Burns, even though they continue to live their lives largely in one country. This pattern is already well established in the corporate community, where the "nationality" of a given company is increasingly difficult to distinguish and is becoming less and less meaningful. These "rooted cosmopolitans," as Burns calls them,[2] will have a well-developed sense of place but find it quite natural—and perhaps essential in terms of their livelihoods—to be involved globally.

In this world of fluid political boundaries, highly mobile financial capital, and a complex global circulatory system of shifting populations, foresters will become important "stewards of place." People may identify with a particular "home ecosystem," perhaps where they spent the early years of their lives, but many will be personally familiar with—and treasure—other landscapes and ecosystems as well. But this "residential identity" will be determined less by state or national boundaries than by ecological and cultural boundaries of multistate or transnational regions, as anticipated by author Joel Garreau more than two decades ago. [3]

One aspect of this trend that is of particular importance to federal natural resource agencies like the Forest Service is the increasing social, economic, and political independence of the western United States from decisions made in Washington, D.C. Burns suggests that the continuing shift of population and political power to western states will give them a degree of autonomy and self-determination not seen since the closing of the American frontier in the late nineteenth century. For the Forest Service, this could mean that the agency's administrative regions become increasingly autonomous as well, with each regional office implementing the nationwide mission more explicitly in the context of the needs and concerns of communities within its own region. Depending upon what changes are made in the statutory guidance for Forest Service activities—or perhaps in new judicial interpretations of the existing statutes—such a shift could mean relatively less influence in the future by narrow interests representing the political extremes.

Through much of the Forest Service's history, beginning with the days of Gifford Pinchot himself, the agency's local management activities were accomplished routinely, largely shielded from controversies that raged at the national policy level, mostly within sight of the Potomac River. According to Burns, today's demographic, political, and economic trends point toward a return to this sort of regional autonomy. The challenge will be, as it always has been for the Forest Service, to balance the promises made to local communities with its broader mission to protect the interests of the nation as a whole in ensuring the conservation and sustainable management of the country's forests.

Shifting demographics. If the Forest Service of the future will indeed operate in ways that are more attuned to the needs of particular regions and local communities, what are those needs expected to be, and how similar will they be to what these regions' needs have been in the past? In Roger Sedjo's view, the demographic and economic changes that have taken place in recent years, particularly in the western United States, have profoundly shifted societal priorities regarding natural resource management. New and different political constituencies are knocking on the doors of federal natural resource agencies and are increasingly insistent that their needs be acknowledged, understood, and addressed. Constituencies that were dominant in the past have undergone important changes themselves in recent years, and their needs in the future will not be the same as they once were. One of the most important questions facing the Forest Service, according to Sedjo, is whether the agency will fully comprehend this change of events and adapt itself to addressing a new set of needs that are different—but nonetheless critical—from those that inspired the Forest Service mission during its first hundred years.

Over the past century, the population of the United States has shifted from predominantly rural to overwhelmingly urban. Nowhere has this been more true, strangely enough, than in western states—famous for their wide-open spaces and scenic grandeur. The U.S. census in 2000 found that nearly eighty-five percent of Americans reside in metropolitan areas. Of the fifteen percent in rural communities, only two percent derive their livelihoods directly from agriculture. Among the most urbanized states, in terms of the proportion of their populations that reside in metropolitan areas, are Utah and Nevada; among the most rural are Pennsylvania and Vermont. As Char Miller points out, the American landscape has largely recovered from the wave of resource development for timber, agriculture, and minerals that built America as a nation. People are moving back into these restored forested landscapes in the proximity of urban areas, which are themselves new centers of a maturing economy based on technology, trade, and knowledge.

In the West, these trends have brought about a new set of challenges for natural resource managers, some of which are already becoming acute. Foremost among these challenges is providing reliable, adequate supplies of clean water for municipal, industrial, and agricultural purposes. Rapidly expanding urban populations in the intermountain West have led those states to reclaim water supplies once given over to the most populous regions of the country's most populous state, California. Science is not yet clear on just how the West's forests would be managed differently if there was a definitive policy to manage them for maximum water yield, and what the implications would be for other forest resources and values, but such a policy may not be far in the future.

Running headlong into this first challenge to forest resource managers in the West is the second challenge, that of the rapidly expanding scope and scale of wildfires and outbreaks of insect and disease. Two of Denver's major reservoirs and their immediate watersheds have been heavily damaged by wildfires in the past decade, and it will be at least another decade before they fully recover. Other watersheds serving Colorado's Front Range, and watersheds of other communities throughout the West, are at significant risk of severe damage from wildfire. It is widely agreed that actions to minimize this risk are among the highest priorities for forest management in these regions. Nevertheless, a working consensus on the Forest Service undertaking specific management activities aimed at reducing the risk of wildfires has been difficult to achieve. A significant number of people continue to mistrust a Forest Service they once saw as too closely aligned with the forest products industry, and they are doubly cautious about allowing a return to high levels of timber harvesting on federal forests, whatever the reason.

A changing constellation of constituencies. But the Forest Service largely has lost the forest products industry as an important constituent interest and, according to Roger Sedjo, is unlikely to regain this constituency even if the opportunity to significantly increase timber harvest levels on the national forests should arise.

Over the past decade, there was a sharp drop in timber harvesting on federal forests resulting from efforts to protect habitat for threatened and endangered species. In spite of this, says Sedjo, timber supply in the United States has remained steady or slightly increasing; timber prices, after a brief initial spike, are not significantly different in most regions from what they were when timber harvesting on federal lands was near its peak. The initial timber supply response from private forestlands is now being sustained by the results of substantial investments in tree growing made by private landowners, forest products companies, and a new breed of forest owner, the timber investment management organizations. To help ensure the anticipated financial returns from these investments, forest owners have resisted changes in wood supply that could result in lower market prices for their timber, such as increased wood products imports from Canada. An increase in federal timber supply to pre-1990 levels, though it might be welcomed by a few companies in some regions of the country, could work against the financial interests of many others, Sedjo finds.

From this perspective, the national forests have successfully fulfilled one of the key purposes for their establishment, and that part of the job is now done. The three overarching management objectives for the federal forest reserves, according to the Organic Act of 1897, were to (1) conserve the lands within their boundaries, (2) protect the headwaters of major river systems, and (3) sustain a continuous supply of timber for homebuilding and other purposes.[4] A clear and present danger motivating the establishment of forest reserves was that of a timber shortage. In a nation where wood was not only the leading building material but also the primary source of fuel, such a shortage carried serious implications for continued economic growth and prosperity. With "cut and run" still the prevailing timbering practice on privately owned lands, these public reserves were intended to provide an insurance policy, guaranteeing adequate supplies of timber at reasonable prices should wood supplies on private lands become depleted.

Fortunately, at the start of the twenty-first century, most private forestlands in the United States are managed productively and sustainably. It thus can be argued, says Sedjo, that federal forests as a hedge against timber shortages have served their purpose, and forest industry may no longer need—or possibly even want—federal lands adding significantly to U.S. timber supply. Long before the "timber wars" in the United States came to their uneasy truce, forest industry had concluded that "foraging" for wood supplies in natural forests would not meet their needs as efficiently as intensive management of planted forests, where tenfold increases in productivity over natural forests are common.

If the national forests are no longer to be significant sources of timber supply, then perhaps it is time once again to ask the question posed three decades ago by economist Marion Clawson, "for whom and for what"[5] shall the national forests be managed? From a more practical perspective, who are the Forest Service's key constituents now, and are they likely to go to bat in Congress in support of the agency's annual budget requests, the way the forest industry did in years past?

There is broad public support for managing the national forests to conserve wildlife habitat, biodiversity, water, recreation, and other ecological services. Managing for ecological restoration and forest stewardship may be less costly, but the costs will still be substantial. Will new constituencies step forward to advocate for funding adequate to manage the national forests for these purposes? Rather than waiting passively for this to happen, can the Forest Service identify and reach these new constituencies? Given the key importance of forests as watersheds, it has been suggested that the Forest Service follow the water, from the forests to the faucets, and help people, through environmental education and assistance, make that connection themselves. By thinking more creatively, the Forest Service has the potential to create a new array of constituents that is broader, more diverse, and more numerous than ever before.

Learning from the past and building toward the future. The Forest Service has some important challenges ahead. Whether accurate or not, there is a widespread perception, both inside and outside the agency, that the Forest Service is mired in process requirements and unable to accomplish basic elements of its mission effectively or cost-efficiently. Many of the laws enacted to rein in the Forest Service during the forest management controversies of the 1970s and 1980s continue to require costly and time-consuming documentation, planning, and evaluation, even though most of the agency's activities today focus on ecological restoration. The vulnerability of these processes to being halted by a small minority of interests makes it difficult for the Forest Service to keep the broader array of interests actively engaged, leaving the agency without valuable advice and insights from a broad diversity of perspectives. From a local perspective, the Forest Service's vulnerability to process gridlock makes national forests an unwelcome neighbor—better to hand over the forests to some other public or private entity that is not subject to such debilitating constraints.

Many of these constraints may be of the Forest Service's own making, however, and therefore within the agency's own authority to address. It has been pointed out that Senator Hubert Humphrey, in introducing the National Forest Management Act to "get the Forest Service out of the courts and back into the woods," envisioned forest management plans of twenty-five pages. Officials at the Council on Environmental Quality, which oversees federal agencies' compliance with the National Environmental Policy Act, have indicated that the environmental impact statements that the Forest Service prepares to accompany its decision documents could be far shorter, far less complex, and more like the environmental documentation provided by other federal agencies. But the Forest Service has an extraordinarily tortured history with some segments of its public, and it is unclear whether these interests have regained enough confidence in the agency to relax their vigilance.

As with any organization, public or private, there is no guarantee that the Forest Service will continue to exist in its present form. Almost since the day the forest reserves were transferred from the Department of the Interior to the Forest Service in 1905, there have been repeated efforts to consolidate all natural resource management functions into a single department. Besides the sheer raw politics of power and turf control, the chief reason the Forest Service has remained in the Department of Agriculture is the compelling persuasiveness of the argument that silviculture—the cultivation of repeated "crops" of trees on a sustained basis—is more akin to agriculture than it is to simply protecting federal lands in parks and wildlife refuges. This argument has become more tenuous as recreation, wildlife, and wilderness protection have become more prominent activities at the Forest Service, and the Interior Department's Bureau of Land Management has adopted a multiple use management mandate modeled on that of the Forest Service.[6] Since the most recent concerted effort at reorganizing the Forest Service into a single natural resources superagency, during the Carter administration, this key argument has been further weakened by the shift away from timber harvesting on the national forests in favor of habitat protection and ecological restoration.

Nevertheless, as the current problems with wildfires and pest outbreaks have demonstrated, the Forest Service must continue to actively manage the national forests, if only to fulfill their most basic responsibilities for resource protection and land stewardship. Because these problems arise outside the national forests as well, the Forest Service still plays a key role in developing new science and technology and providing assistance and support for sustainable forest management on nonfederal lands.

Federal agency consolidations have usually been sought in the name of greater efficiency and improved internal coordination, but whether any have actually had this result is highly questionable. Unlike private profit-making organizations, public agencies have no clear indication when they have grown to the point where their unwieldiness has cancelled out any efficiency gains associated with consolidation. In the end, the central question remains: Is the organization effective in achieving the results required by its mission and needed by society?

Conclusion

As the Forest Service enters its next century of service, it is discovering that there are other ways—and perhaps far more effective ways—for the agency to continue playing a leading role in the conservation and sustainable management of forests, both in this country and abroad.

If one looks at the composition of today's workforce in the Forest Service, with its diversity of professional disciplines as well as in terms of gender and ethnicity, it is clear that the agency's culture is already shifting toward future needs and constituencies. Perhaps even more importantly, the Forest Service is discovering the power of partnerships—of teaming up with a wide variety of other federal, state, tribal, corporate, and nonprofit organizations to accomplish key objectives that are consistent with the agency's mission and goals. Through such teamwork, the Forest Service is discovering almost limitless opportunities for synergy, in which the overall result is far more than simply a sum of the parts. In many instances, the Forest Service is finding that it can be more effective not by tackling the task alone but by providing others with the tools, technical knowledge, and support to get the job done together. Not only does this accomplish needed resource management activities, it builds social and business capacity and contributes to stable, self-reliant, and confident communities.

Much of what has been accomplished over the past century to improve the management of America's forests would not have been possible without the institutional, legal, and policy framework established early in the twentieth century by the Forest Service and its supporters. The broad and bipartisan consensus for forest conservation that emerged from the 1905 American Forest Congress became the springboard for the establishment of a number of key forestry institutions and policies, the U.S. Forest Service and the national forests being among the first of these. With the impetus of the Forest Congress, the Forest Service moved forward to establish the most capable forestry research organization in the world; cooperative programs with state governments, forest industry, and private landowners to improve forest management and protect against insects, disease, and wildfires; and a 192-million-acre National Forest System that, in spite of its defects, has become a global model for sustainable forest management. Through this institutional, legal, and policy framework, the Forest Service has facilitated improved forest management on both public and private lands throughout the United States.

A century ago, Gifford Pinchot envisioned the future of the Forest Service. By articulating that vision and inspiring others to fulfill their potential for contributing to the public interest—to being part of something bigger than themselves—Pinchot helped make that vision a reality. Pinchot and his contemporaries in the conservation movement of the late nineteenth century inspired a generation of Americans to take decisive action in defense of their natural resource heritage so that we would not share the fate of resource depletion and impoverishment of classical civilizations, described so eloquently by George Perkins Marsh in his book *Man and Nature* in 1864.[7] America faced a clear and present danger at the end of the nineteenth century. Pinchot and his colleagues didn't wait for it to come to them; they went out to meet it head-on.

The Forest Service today, looking ahead to the twenty-first century, is hardly an organization searching for a purpose. At no time in human history has there been a broader, deeper, or more widely shared concern for the future of our forests, at home and worldwide. There is plenty of need for an organization that can help society to understand the challenges to conservation and sustainable forest management, and to craft ecologically sound, economically viable, and socially responsible strategies to successfully address those challenges. The question for the Forest Service is whether it is ready to build upon its experience and strengths and adapt itself to become that organization.

Note: Grey Towers National Historic Landmark, in Milford, Pennsylvania, was once the home of Gifford Pinchot, first Chief Forester of the Forest Service and twice governor of Pennsylvania. Grey Towers was given to the American people by the Pinchot family in 1963, to serve as a place for people to come together to develop the ideas that will continue to advance conservation and sustainable natural resource management. Grey Towers is administered by the USDA Forest Service and is home to the Pinchot Institute for Conservation.

Notes

[1] Bowring, J. 1843. *The works of Jeremy Bentham.* Reprinted 1962. London: London University Press.

[2] Kaplan, R. 1998. *An empire wilderness: Travels into America's future.* New York: Vintage Books.

[3] Garreau, J. 1981. *The nine nations of North America.* New York: Houghton Mifflin.

[4] 16 U.S.C. 475, Organic Administration Act of June 4, 1897.

[5] Clawson, M. 1975. *Forests for whom and for what?* Baltimore: Johns Hopkins University Press for Resources for the Future.

[6] The Federal Land Policy and Management Act of 1976 (43 U.S.C. 1701) was passed into law one day before the National Forest Management Act of 1976 (16 U.S.C. 1601). It includes similar requirements for land and resource management planning, and it established multiple use as the basic management model to be used on federal public lands by the Bureau of Land Management.

[7] Marsh, G. 1965 (1864). *Man and nature: Or, the earth as modified by human action.* Cambridge: Harvard University Press.

—Submitted by Bruce P. McCammon, Regional Hydrologist,
USDA Forest Service, Portland, Oregon

Managing Water and Watershed Resources of National Forest Lands: Preparing the Agency for Future Challenges

A national conference involving USDA Forest Service hydrologists, soil scientists, air resource specialists, and geologists was held in San Diego, California, in October 2004. Representatives from several other federal and state agencies also attended. Similar to the Centennial Congress, this technical conference was organized around themes of honoring pioneering earth science personnel and accomplishments, acknowledging today's state-of-the-arts, and preparing for the future of the physical sciences in the agency. Watershed management and water were key focal areas of the conference that were not fully represented in regional centennial forums that were being planned. Recognizing that water and watersheds are fundamental to the agency, organizers of the Centennial Congress of 2005 encouraged the technical conference organizers to submit a paper for the Centennial Congress proceedings. The opportunity to contribute to the Centennial Congress proceedings was very much appreciated. Bruce McCammon, technical conference chair and regional hydrologist for the Pacific Northwest Region, led a group of regional and national personnel in preparation of the following text to represent the views of conference attendees.

Introduction: Strengths in Land, Skills, and Authorities
The 192 million acres of National Forest System lands and grasslands are uniquely situated to provide sustainable natural resources for the benefit of people at local, national, and global scales. Ranging from the nation's highest elevations to coastal estuaries, public lands administered by the Forest Service span a broad range of ecosystems and provide a unique diversity of natural resources and opportunities for public use. The National Association of State Foresters (Policy Statement: The Connection Between Healthy Forests and

Clean and Abundant Water, 2004) states that "water, in all its uses and permutations, is by far the most valuable commodity that comes from well-managed forest lands." Proper management of national forest watersheds and soils is critical to the well-being of our nation, since national forests represent the single largest source of the nation's water. These areas have the greatest potential for continued yield of high-quality water for all downstream users and aquatic organisms in the future.

Multiple use management of forest resources requires a mix of interdisciplinary skills. The Forest Service's conservation mission relies on approximately six hundred earth scientists (soil scientists, hydrologists, geologists) to provide essential technical skills. Employed in Research, State and Private Forestry, International Forestry, and management of National Forest System lands, these individuals support the agency's mission through application of technical knowledge to today's resource management needs. As a decentralized agency, these individuals are placed at all levels of the organization—ranger districts, supervisor offices, regional offices, Washington Office, research units, and state and private areas. No other federal agency has such a strong assemblage of watershed management skills poised in positions ranging from technical analysis and design to policy formation.

Integration of technical earth science knowledge with other disciplines is essential to solve many of today's resource challenges. Increased integration between all branches of the agency (Research, State and Private, International Forestry, and National Forest System) as well as with other agencies and landowners is needed to solve increasingly large-scale resource challenges.

Today's management of National Forest System lands is built on a history of legislation, congressional direction, legal decisions, scientific understanding, and individual skills. Gifford Pinchot and others succeeded in establishing policy and case law for national forest management based on a strong sense of stewardship and sustainable use. The primary legislation guiding Forest Service management of public lands makes clear that one mandate of the agency is to promote soil and watershed conditions that provide for and protect water resources. The Forest Service's enabling legislation, the Organic Administration Act of 1897, provides three broad objectives for the Forest Service: to improve and protect the forest; to secure favorable conditions of flow; and to furnish a continuous supply of timber. Other legislation enacted during the early to mid-1900s further demonstrated the nation's commitment to improving watershed conditions for all resources. The Weeks Act of 1911 authorized the federal government to purchase lands as national forests for stream flow protection. The Multiple Use–Sustained Yield Act of 1960 clearly established that the national forests are administered for recreation, range, timber, watershed, and wildlife and fish purposes. The Forest and Rangeland Renewable Resources Planning Act (1974) and the National Forest Management Act (1976) further reinforced the mandate that natural resources are protected and conserved through multiple use management.

Protection and conservation of water resources were important concerns to the American public when the forest reserves were created. Emphasis on watershed protection and conservation will only increase as demand for water continues to expand. Agency watershed management programs have not been maintained at an adequate level to meet the growing demands on our water resources and have in fact declined during the past decade. This trend must be reversed if we are to continue providing clean water and meet our public needs and expectations for the Forest Service.

Today's water policies and laws are highly variable and complex. Clearly, however, functioning healthy watersheds are critical to sustaining sources of clean and abundant drinking water. Forested lands also provide for many other products and services besides water. In fact, the public expects that our forests will provide for wildlife habitat, a sustainable wood supply, carbon sequestration, aesthetics, and even spiritual reflection. While contemporary court cases continue to clarify the scope of agency authorities, existing laws and policies provide a strong foundation for protection and conservation of soil and watershed resources on national forest system lands. The current Forest Service slogan—Caring for the Land and Serving People—reinforces that the original land stewardship ethic is foremost in today's agency mission. Laws and policies guide agency management, but a strong land ethic and commitment to land stewardship are core values of Forest Service employees.

Periods of Change: The First and Second Hundred Years

The Forest Service's strength rests with the land it manages, its employees, and the critical partnerships that sustain and promote improved resource management programs. As the Forest Service prepares to enter its second century of public land administration, it should celebrate its strengths and prepare for the dramatic changes that are clearly on the horizon. During the first one hundred years, the agency witnessed an expansion of the land base, increased access to public lands, and greater resource utilization. This was a period in which physical scientists brought the skills and understanding needed to improve management decisions and foster long-term resource stewardship. In spite of contentious and litigious behavior, great advances were made in institution-alizing core stewardship values into management policies and laws. It was a period in which the agency learned that natural systems do not recognize or respect ownership boundaries and that ecosystem management requires humility and an acceptance of the agency's role as one partner among many with a common vested interest in the land.

Dramatic changes are coming. The second hundred years of the agency may well become known as the time of globalization for the Forest Service. World population growth, viewed both as total numbers and shifts in population centers, will force more critical attention to the wise and sustainable use of the unique and highly valued public lands administered by the Forest Service. As populations shift from rural to urban centers, the value placed on water will increase. Climate changes are predicted to dramatically alter plant communities and animal species diversity and viability as well as human needs. The value and critical nature of water resources from National Forest System lands will clearly increase with these dramatic changes. The agency's ability to manage for continued high-quality water resources will be challenged by increasing demand for exports of and simultaneous in-place recreational uses of water. Custodial management of national forest watersheds, where soils and hill slope processes are balanced or maintained in concert with natural and anthropogenic disturbances, will never be more critical.

In the future, there will be a greater demand for high-level earth science expertise at all levels. This need will span from local governments to states and countries around the globe. The fate of our water resources is contingent on our ability to sustain the land and maintain the health of our watersheds. The Forest Service, as an agency charged with stewardship of public watersheds, must strategically and tactically prepare for these changes. The "Guiding Principles for Water Resources on National Forest Lands" and the "National Strategic Plan," which emphasizes watershed improvement, provide a strong foundation for soil and water management on national forest system lands in the future. Three broad areas need agency focus: (1) valuing ecosystem services on National Forest System lands, (2) preparing for globalization of resource programs and economies, and (3) reconnecting agency personnel with the land.

Valuing Ecosystem Services of National Forest System Lands

Rivers, wetlands, and riparian systems on National Forest System lands perform numerous "ecosystem services"—the processes carried out by natural ecosystems that benefit human societies and economies. Wetlands absorb pollutants, moderate surface flows, and influence the quality of surface and groundwater. Riparian areas are critical for water quality maintenance, flood damage reduction, channel and aquatic habitat formation, and providing habitat for highly diverse wildlife populations. Unregulated rivers distribute sediments and create essential habitat for fish and other aquatic organisms. Diverse stream flows trigger biologic activity, such as the upstream migration or spawning of fish. All these ecosystem services, and many more, are provided at no cost to the humans who also rely on these ecosystems.

Globally, and to varying degrees on National Forest System lands, societies have benefited from the development and use of surface and ground water. The expansion of irrigation, hydropower, and human uses of water has been the norm as populations expand. There is increasing awareness that the ability to sustain population growth and water use trends is problematic. Aquatic species are clearly showing the results of decades of depletion and degradation of natural water quantity and quality. At least twenty percent of the world's freshwater fish species have become endangered or threatened with extinction or have gone extinct. Increasing numbers of mollusks, crayfish, and amphibians are becoming threatened or imperiled. Sandra Postel and Brian Richter (*Rivers for Life: Managing Water for People and Nature*, Island Press, 2003) provide a succinct summary of the current situation and future needs:

> *Society is now confronted with a monumental design challenge. A large body of scientific evidence tells us that we have installed billions of dollars of engineering infrastructure that is killing the aquatic world. Freshwater species extinctions are rising. The ecosystem functions that sustain all life, including the provision for services that benefit human economies, are declining. Meanwhile human population and consumption levels continue to climb— driving humanity's demands for water, food, energy, and material items even higher.*

> *Meeting the challenge of satisfying human needs while at the same time protecting the health of the aquatic environment will require a much more fundamental shift in how society uses, manages, and values fresh water—one that recognizes from the outset the importance of healthy ecosystems and humanity's dependence on them. Anything less than a conceptual shift will not suffice.*

Globalization of Resource Programs

The global dynamics and trends associated with climate change, water occurrence (place and time), and population growth and distribution point to the need for broad, bold, and strategic plans to address global sustainability of the natural systems on which humans depend. The challenges of finding the balance between sustainable aquatic systems and societal needs will require unprecedented levels of cooperation and understanding between governments and water users. Each incremental gain made at local levels can be used as an example of increased understanding as well as models for cooperation and negotiation in which common needs include those of the ecosystem.

As managers of headwater watersheds, the Forest Service should continue to support local communities that are organizing to restore watershed conditions for the purposes of establishing long-term, sustainable ecosystems. Currently, there are thousands of local watershed groups working to improve their local watersheds through community volunteers, partnerships and grants. Involvement at the local level and relatively small geographic scale provides the Forest Service with an opportunity to offer skills, information, and better understanding about how natural systems function. Although few people are formally trained as natural resource scientists, the broad population has typically become more concerned about the character and condition of the area in which they live. Local participation by Forest Service personnel helps build relationships and transmit understanding and will lead to a higher probability of successful intervention in declining natural systems. Local communities and economies will benefit from the protection and restoration of sustainable natural systems. Local participation by Forest Service personnel needs to be viewed as a core management responsibility, funded appropriately, and rewarded as much as possible.

The Forest Service has a history of assisting other countries with technical and managerial support. Emergency services are commonly provided when fires or floods occur in countries with which agreements have been developed. These relationships and services are highly valued but are limited in scale and scope. The Forest Service has substantial technical and management understanding that would benefit the global search for balance between ecosystem service stability and societal needs. The international program of the Forest Service should be much more visible and more accessible to a greater number of countries that are leading the way toward implementing changes that support sustainable ecosystems. Not only can the agency help others, it can learn from others who are developing new approaches or policies.

Connecting with the Land
One of the greatest strengths of the Forest Service is the public land it manages and the diversity of values and needs that the land base serves. The agency

is built on a strong history of committed personnel who have worked on and knew the land. The romantic notion of a person who accessed wild places, who encountered many difficulties, and who protected the nation's natural resources is the theme of books, poems, songs, and movies. In large part, the agency's culture was built on a strong sense of "knowing the land" and a very personal interest in caring for the many resources.

Walking the land, wading streams, watching wildlife, and responding to natural disturbances like floods, fires, or insects increase each person's understanding of how watersheds and ecosystems respond or react. First-hand field knowledge is essential to understanding the significance of new or evolving scientific information. The Forest Service's strength is also embodied in the people who walk the land under all conditions and know the agency's mission as well as the value of the land and how it functions during natural or man-made disturbance.

Today's Forest Service takes pride in its history. Books have been written to document the history of the organization and the laws that guide the agency and to recognize the people and the way they have managed the land. There is frequently a sense of awe or appreciation when one looks at historical photos of lookout towers or landscapes of the past. Picking up an old journal or Forest Service map reinforces the hard work employees have done to better understand and manage these lands. Today's Forest Service employees have a great deal of appreciation and admiration for those who worked in past times and set excellent examples of land stewardship.

Forest Service employees today work in a continually shifting technological, political, and social arena. Hand-drawn maps have been replaced by modern geographic information system technology. The Internet provides access to weather and climate information that was historically unavailable as a practical management tool. Programs that were favored or emphasized in the past have been replaced with new concepts and initiatives. Management of data and information about the public's natural resources has always been a part of business for the agency. What used to be held in file drawers is now held in databases. The agency has changed and will continue to evolve. Furthermore, the public has access to the same information and is often well educated about how our lands are being managed. They are concerned and hold the Forest Service accountable for seemingly every action taken on public lands.

Today's laws, policies, and procedures demand a substantial amount of time in the preparation and documentation of a single management decision. Resource specialists who have historically walked the land, waded the streams, or watched a watershed's response to storm flows are frequently bound to office desks, preparing reports or responses to challenges about a decision. Writing reports and responding to public challenges are a necessity, but these highly valued employees now spend less time on the land where their skills are needed to address the increasingly complex issues and greater public demands. The agency's budgets and personnel have been reduced, and the priorities have changed from walking and knowing the land to "office" analysis, responding to challenges or to emphasizing the development of a database. The number of Forest Service personnel with on-the-ground responsibilities at the ranger district level has decreased, while the number of information specialists and technology keepers has increased. The agency is losing critical skills that were common in the past. Logic should dictate that a road cannot be surveyed solely in a computer-aided design system. Specialists are needed on the ground to ensure that the road is appropriate, that stream crossings are designed appropriately, and that all resource concerns are addressed. The same holds true where on-the-ground management to improve a riparian zone can't be properly done in the office by editing on a word processor. Judicious and effective management of these critical resources requires that people put on their boots, walk the land, and apply their knowledge and skills.

As the Forest Service moves forward in the next one hundred years, it will face unpredictable challenges. One thing is certain, however. The land will be there, responding to the forces of nature and the pressures we as a society continually apply to its surface and resources. If the agency is to continue its legacy of caring for the land and maintaining our nation's most valuable resources, it must have a definite commitment to supporting a workforce that has the resources and ability to be on the ground—applying the kinds of skills and knowledge that have served the land so well in the past.

Future Directions for Water Management

In order to achieve our vision of healthy forests and sustainable ecosystems that are reflective of our rich natural heritage, the essential nature of watershed and water resources must be embraced and acted upon. Water, or rather the lack of sufficient quantity or quality, is an imminent threat to forest and grassland ecosystems and to the people who depend upon them for their physical and spiritual sustenance. While no one is implying that resolution of the centuries-long debate over water uses will be easy or that providing multiple goods and services from National Forest System lands is straightforward or bereft of competing views, the necessity of resolution is upon us. We are at the beginning of a new century. The Forest Service, as keepers of America's headwaters, must establish a course now that can achieve long-term goals and preserve our rich heritage. Several avenues could be pursued to achieve this end.

- The uses of the national forests that need a dependable supply of high-quality water must be protected against the inevitable demand for that water. A balance is possible, but limits must be acknowledged, and it is the responsibility of the national forests to establish and maintain water resources within those boundaries or limits.

- Become national leaders by advancing new policies and recognizing water resource values, the economic and social values of aquatic ecosystems, and water resources on national forest lands.

- Implement procedures and policies to quantify flow levels across a full range that will sustain river functions to support human and natural resource uses.

- Do not permit excessive diversions of surface flows that would compromise river, wetland, or riparian functionality.

- Acquire, or assist with acquisition of, lands that contain or are critical to the conservation of flows consistent with river ecosystem needs.

- Embark upon a regimented program that protects existing high-quality waters and restores impaired waters.

- Identify and prioritize river ecosystem needs and protect or maintain any unique or limited water features (springs, seeps, wetlands, riparian systems, etc.) in land management plans.

- Protect aquatic habitat on National Forest System lands to preserve viability and historic diversity. The establishment of exotic species should be rigorously opposed.

- The national forests must undertake a rigorous program to protect, identify, and quantify groundwater (and surface water). Ensure that groundwater and surface water interactions are fully accounted for in any request for diversion of water from national forest lands.

- The Forest Service should become a global partner by providing expertise to other countries in watershed management, water resource conservation, and preservation of their natural resources.

- The Forest Service must actively participate in cooperative inventory, restoration, and monitoring programs at the local level. Local watershed groups should be supported with grants, expertise, and information. The public's dependence on water resources demands their active involvement as well as participation from the Forest Service.

The Forest Service has recently set a course to restore fire-dependent ecosystems. To realize this goal and to restore and protect all ecosystems, we must focus some of our attention upon water and the management of watersheds. The condition of soils, uplands, riparian areas, and channels on National Forest System lands determines the quality and character of water produced. It is clear that society places uniformly high value on clean and usable water. The world is changing in many ways. Climate change and population growth continually exert pressures for increased or shifting demands. These demands have resulted in global recognition of the value of sustainable forests, soils, and water, which is reflected in the Montreal Process. Many nations are aggressively revising their water policies to reinforce and value the role of sustainable natural watershed and stream flow processes to support local and national economies as well as the natural systems on which society depends. As managers of many of the nation's upland watersheds, the Forest Service has the opportunity and responsibility to influence downstream water quality and quantity. Implementation of the programs to secure functioning watersheds requires a dedicated commitment to keeping trained people on the ground and in touch with local and regional communities. The commitment to protect National Forest System lands for future generations can only be kept by recognizing the central, essential role that watershed condition plays in maintaining its productivity and the quality of its rivers, lakes, and groundwater. The fundamental conflict over water use and the threat that this conflict portends to forest ecosystems cannot be overstated. It is time to face this issue squarely, since delay only intensifies the conflict. Sustainable ecosystems that reflect this nation's bounty are an achievable goal, but only if we protect their lifeblood—water.

Lessons for a Future Forest Service:
Assistant and Under Secretaries' Views

January 6, 2005
8:00 am

Jim Moseley *(Moderator)*
M. Rupert Cutler
Jim Lyons
George Dunlop
John R. Crowell, Jr.

january 3-6
2005
washington dc

US Forest Service

$\mathcal{C}$entennial
$\mathcal{C}$ongress

A Collective Commitment to Conservation

M. Rupert Cutler
Former Assistant Secretary of Agriculture for Conservation, Research, and Education, 1977–1980

Reflections from Experiences in the Jimmy Carter Administration

I am "the RARE II assistant secretary."

It was an honor to serve in the administration of President Jimmy Carter. In his new book, *Sharing Good Times*, Mr. Carter reflects, "Experiences are more deep and lasting sources of pleasure when they are shared with others." That somewhat describes my experience as USDA assistant secretary. One dimension of that experience was the good working relationships I had with professionals in the Forest Service, including Chiefs John McGuire and Max Peterson.

Those shared experiences and the can-do behavior of the agency led to the success of several major Carter administration natural resources policy initiatives, including the Alaska National Interest Lands Conservation Act, RARE II, and the first National Forest Management Act Forest Planning regulations.

I object to the characterization of RARE II (the second Roadless Area Review and Evaluation) as "not well done," an expression I heard earlier in this meeting, perhaps in jest. In my view, the entire Forest Service field staff and its recreation staff led by Zane Smith did an excellent job carrying out the difficult RARE II assignment, and I am proud of them for their "beyond the call of duty" efforts to this day.

The RARE II roadless area inventory continues to be the backbone of the important campaign to protect as statutory wilderness all suitable vestiges of wild America left within the National Forest System, a campaign still unfinished. An example of the work at hand is legislation awaiting consideration in the Congress now to add important national forest acreage to the National Wilderness Preservation System in southwestern Virginia (HR 4202 and S 2342, sponsored by Representative Boucher and Senator Warner).

Another, more exotic example is the anticipated passage of legislation to create a ten-thousand-acre wilderness area on the Caribbean National Forest in Puerto Rico, as recommended in RARE II twenty-five years ago! On the other hand, there have been very few wilderness recommendations coming from the Forest Service in recent years, including zero acres in the Tongass

National Forest in Alaska and very little in the Southern Appalachians. Why this across-the-board retreat from any new wilderness designations?

The wilderness experience is priceless. The Forest Service has always been the best federal agency at providing it to the American public, thanks to the long-time support of wilderness in the national forests by agency leaders going back to Aldo Leopold, Bob Marshall, and Chief Greeley. Please give the sub-discipline of wilderness administration and management, and those who choose to follow that career path, respect in your table of organization and in your reward system. It requires "true believers" ever vigilantly working on the ground, monitoring the goings-on, to keep designated wilderness lands free of nonconforming activities, as the Wilderness Act requires. Nothing short of absolute conformity with that act is appropriate, or wilderness will not endure for future generations.

Also, the first generation of forest plans was developed under a regulation adopted, not in 1982 as a Forest Service press release issued last month stated, but in 1978. President Carter's secretary of Agriculture, Bob Bergland, appointed the Committee of Scientists that drafted those regulations. The committee, chaired by Art Cooper, completed its work on my watch. Those initial National Forest Management Act planning regulations were in place before Max Peterson became Chief. They were slightly amended in 1982.

On a personal note: I was the first assistant secretary with a professional forestry education and probably the first one with a lifelong admiration of the Forest Service. That admiration continues to this day. It began when I worked as a lookout–smoke chaser on the Kaniksu National Forest in Idaho fifty-three years ago. It continued in 1955 when, as a wildlife management student and editor of the University of Michigan's natural resources school yearbook, I dedicated that book to the Forest Service on its fiftieth anniversary. In 1980, as assistant secretary, I joined Vice President Walter Mondale at Gifford Pinchot's ancestral home, Grey Towers, to congratulate the agency on its seventy-fifth birthday. And here I am today, pleased to be invited to this party to celebrate the centennial of Mr. Pinchot's creation.

To those of you who, noting how many years I've spent on the staffs of conservation groups such as the National Wildlife Federation, the Wilderness Society, the National Audubon Society, and Defenders of Wildlife, have assumed that I am biased more in the direction of Sierra Club founder John Muir (preservation) than in the direction of Forest Service founder Gifford Pinchot (scientific management), let me tell you that I respect both views and believe both are essential. The National Forest System today provides for the application of both schools of thought, and that is appropriate.

In his address last October to the Fourth Brazilian Congress on Parks and Protected Areas, my author-conservationist friend Michael Frome noted that Gifford Pinchot saw conservation as a social crusade, and that he defined equality of opportunity for every citizen as the real object of laws and institutions. Certainly, Mr. Pinchot is in my pantheon of heroes, together with Mr. Muir.

We've been asked to identify lessons learned for the Forest Service of the next one hundred years. Here are my ideas, from my life experience that includes being a wildlife and wilderness advocate and an elected official of a city located near a national forest.

Lesson one is obvious: Watershed stability is Job One. The Forest Service was created in large part to reduce flooding caused by careless logging. Today, this water management goal includes protecting water quality. We in Virginia's Roanoke Valley appreciate the good job the Jefferson National Forest does in providing clean runoff to our drinking water supply reservoirs. (The silt, undesirable chemicals, and acid rain our treatment plants must cope with come from elsewhere: private farms and forests, construction sites, and coal-fired power plants to the west of us that ought to be cleaned up.)

Lesson two is old but with a new spin: The "sustained yield" goal relates not just to timber but to all the forest's services and values, including wildlife habitat, wilderness recreation, nature education, and clean air. Men and women of the well-paid "creative class" are moving to Roanoke in part because the nearby national forest offers places to fly-fish, backpack, and mountain bike. On their behalf, I urge the Forest Service to continue to tightly control noisy, erosion-causing, wildlife-disturbing off-highway vehicles on national forests. Designated back-road use, OK, but cross-country use, no. A difficult but necessary task in the face of the increasing human population will be to limit access to avoid excessive disturbance of wildlife and watersheds.

Lesson three is relatively new: Ecosystem management (also described as forest health, ecological integrity, and biological diversity) is now the goal, and it is the best target for forest managers and forest plans because it protects our forest capital—our forest wealth—in perpetuity. By now, I hope forest managers have found practical ways to truly implement this goal and are putting them into practice.

Lesson four is related to regional land use planning: National forests contribute importantly to the economy and quality of life of city-centered regions. Planners with the Forest Service and with adjoining counties and cities should informally collaborate. Forest plans and the comprehensive plans of nearby local governments, school districts, and private landowners should be mutually reinforcing.

Environmentalists who fear that local influence on forest plans may skew them toward allowing excessive timber harvest or grazing should appreciate that, in many communities today, local elected officials like me will identify resource-based outdoor recreation opportunities and watershed protection as their top expectations from nearby public forests, while also supporting the sustainable harvest of timber and other commodities to contribute manufacturing jobs to the local economy.

Another benefit of having Forest Service planning staff interact frequently with local government planners, teachers, and the news media is that it gives them a chance to get the message out that national forests are not national parks and were never intended to be managed as parks. My Maryland forester friend Jim Cook observes that, in the public's mind, all the federal lands (forests, parks, refuges) are being merged together into "one big blob to be run like various sizes of Yellowstone." He calls it "the Disneyization of our forest, parks and refuges, an impossible, unrealistic storybook idea and expectation of how they can and should function."

The Forest Service's "lands of many uses" theme can be appealing if the uses, services, and values managed for, and the constituencies served, truly are diverse. Not that foresters need to do what is "wrong" for the resource because of uninformed public clamor. Jim Cook, the forester, says:

> What we need now is tough love by people who know what the hell they're doing, and damn the torpedoes. It's like the extermination of wolves from the Kaibab about seventy years ago and the resulting mass dieoff of deer when they grossly exceeded carrying capacity. No one today can seem to understand that nature is dynamic. People must accept the intrinsic limitations and characteristics of natural resources and their management, plus see the role of conservation in maintaining some semblance of our way of life, or we're going to have some rough times. Those who fail to learn from history are doomed to repeat it. I think we have just killed the wolves (professional managers) and are just waiting for the deer (natural resources) to start dying.

In other words, there's still an important place for professional multiple use foresters who know what they're doing. As retired Regional Forester Zane Grey Smith puts it, "The Forest Service will need to concentrate on winning the confidence of the public that it can include sustainable development with protection on the national forests."

Lesson five is an adaptation to the roadless area controversy of the late Vermont Senator George Aiken's prescription for ending the war in Vietnam: "Declare victory and withdraw." The Forest Service could flatly declare that it has no plans to enter inventoried roadless areas. There is no money to build roads there, and the potential cut from roadless areas is small and not needed to meet allowable sale quantity goals, so the war could be over and that particular longstanding cause of environmentalist irritation with the agency made moot.

State governors, having little authority on federal land, should not have been invited to intervene in the roadless area disposition process and further politicize this issue. Let's just leave the roadless areas roadless and direct intensive forest management attention elsewhere.

Lesson six is that, my opinion, the current administration is wrong to try to bypass the environmental impact statement requirement of the National Environmental Policy Act and the species viability-diversity requirement of the National Forest Management Act in its new national forest plan-preparation rule. I urge Bill Banzhaf and his Sustainable Forestry Board and other third-party auditors, as they interact with the Forest Service on preparation of the envisioned ISO 14001 Plan Environmental Management System and as they audit forest plans, to require the *reinstatement* of these useful procedural steps, to win auditor signoff on the standard and the plans.

I have personally reviewed dozens of national forest plan environmental impact statements and, while I acknowledge that EIS preparation is tedious, I have found them worth their weight in gold as full-disclosure documents. Those who complain about "paralysis by analysis" may also be folks who don't want to be "confused by the facts"—that is, folks who have their minds made up without sufficient information. As Congressman Mark Udall said yesterday, why reverse your field and generate suspicion and skepticism when you know you will need that analysis-of-alternatives planning data anyway, including the identification of who pays and who benefits?

The Sierra Club view of the proposed changes in national forest planning procedures, stated by its Appalachian regional representative, Dave Muhly, in the January 2, 2005, *Roanoke Times*, is that the changes clearly are the idea of the American Forest and Paper Association and constitute the streamlining of federal forest management at the expense of forest protection. Or as my friend Liz Belcher, head of our regional greenway trail program, expresses it, "The

Forest Service still [seems to be] geared to the big boys with the big toys." There's that suspicion and skepticism Congressman Udall was predicting, and you don't need that when you're looking for public support.

I trust that wilderness will continued to be integrated into, and routinely considered in, national forest planning. I raise this issue because Interior Secretary Norton excluded wilderness from the Bureau of Land Management planning process last year. That's a bad pattern the Forest Service should not follow.

Lesson seven, in my view, is that it is important to include generous land-purchase funds in your budget requests and to be aggressive in acquiring land in fee simple ownership. The Forest Service needs to continue to add to its national forest land base, particularly where habitat "gaps" exist. We in western Virginia were terribly disappointed at the inability of the Forest Service recently to take advantage of Westvaco's decision to sell large tracts of important wildlife habitat within and near the George Washington and Jefferson national forests. Tracts sold included Purgatory Mountain, which provides a unique travel corridor for bear and other species between the Blue Ridge and the Allegheny Mountains. That critical travel corridor now is in fragmented private ownership and undergoing clearing and development.

One of the agency's greatest accomplishments was the purchase and reforestation of Appalachian mountain land under the Weeks Act after private interests had devastated those watersheds. Thanks to effective Forest Service stewardship, the Appalachians are now a globally important area for species diversity. You still have the authority to do more of this. Don't stop now!

Finally, lesson eight is to strengthen the Forest Service's important Research and State and Private branches—Research to help forest supervisors figure out in practical terms how to implement ecosystem management and to encourage wood conservation and recycling, and State and Private grants to state foresters to support cities' urban forestry programs and expand the Forest Legacy program.

The Forest Legacy program enables nonindustrial private forestland owners to put their lands under voluntary conservation easements that help keep water clean and slow forest fragmentation while allowing sustained forest harvest. As a trustee of a state agency, the Virginia Outdoors Foundation, that holds perpetual conservation easements on over a quarter million acres of private land, I was brought up short by Sally Fairfax's negative view of them yesterday. I have always regarded conservation easements as complementary to but in no way substitutes for fee simple public ownership of land with very important public values.

Urban forestry is becoming critical as our population becomes more concentrated in cities, yet the Forest Service has often had to depend on "congressional add-ons" to win appropriations for this important cooperative forestry program. Despite the growth of cities like Atlanta, the urban "green infrastructure" (tree canopy) continues to decline. There is a lot of latent popular and political support for the Forest Service associated with a strong technical and financial assistance program directed to help our cities' beleaguered urban foresters restore the trees that enhance urban environments.

Not unlike a soldier's experience in a war, I suppose, the experience of serving in the President's subcabinet is a searing and unforgettable time. Assistant secretaries, after all, have been called the President's second lieutenants. Fortunately, in my case, thanks to the support of President Carter and Secretary Bergland and the responsiveness of the career civil servants who reported to me, it was a positive experience. I encouraged the Forest Service to change with the times, and it has changed dramatically since the 1970s. National forests are now, for the most part, being managed on a holistic basis. Timber is no longer king. Timber sale targets are modest and often are means to other ends.

When my friend Bill Damon, the just-retired supervisor of the George Washington and Jefferson national forests, said to me the other day that "the timber industry has given up on the national forests because they are no longer a dependable supplier," I felt no major sense of regret, and neither did he, as far as I could tell. National forests should always be a source of forest products, but intensively managed private forest plantations on the flatlands probably are where most of our commercial wood should be grown in the future.

I am concerned about the current administration's plans to privatize the management of public lands and to outsource Forest Service jobs to private contractors. Public goals, not private profits, must always take precedence on the agency's agenda, for practical reasons as well as because of your public trust mission. When the Virginia transportation department recently was ordered to downsize staff and outsource maintenance, it was left with no one to remove the snow. Be careful outsourcing, or you'll lose your internal expertise and experienced leadership.

The prospect of future generations of Americans so wrapped up in their television programs, computer games, cell phones, and shopping malls that they never get into the woods and learn where their wood and water come from is an unsettling prospect. Additional efforts should be made to get school classes, volunteers, and local elected officials onto the national forests to assure the forests of a political constituency. Forest Service personnel should not live in federal employee enclaves and stick to themselves, but become part of the life of their communities, to put a human face on what otherwise could be regarded as a soulless bureaucracy.

Work to keep the agency relevant—inertia will be fatal—and the Forest Service will still be around in good shape one hundred years from now.

Good luck!

James R. Lyons
Former Under Secretary of Agriculture for Natural Resources and Environment, May 1993–January 2001

It is a pleasure to join my distinguished colleagues on this panel and to have the opportunity to address you this morning. I will use my eight minutes first to focus on some of the accomplishments during the Clinton era that were not included in *The Greatest Good* but are worthy of mention; and second, to focus on lessons learned during my eight years in office; and finally, to reflect briefly on some of the valuable messages I've heard from previous speakers these past two days.

I am quite proud of our accomplishments during the Clinton administration working with Jack [Ward Thomas], Mike [Dombeck], and many of you who remain agency leaders. Some of these successes include:

- completing the first-ever landscape-level ecosystem management strategy (the President's Northwest forest plan) and then extending that ecosystem management framework to other regions of the country, including the Interior Columbia River Basin, the Sierra Nevada, the Southwest, and the southern Appalachians;

- implementing a rule to protect remaining national forest roadless areas in a scientifically sound, legally sufficient, and publicly supported manner;

- promoting more effective use of science in policy and decision making and enhancing transparency and public participation in decision making (both as part of the forest planning rule that we finalized based on the [1999] recommendations of the Committee of Scientists [appointed in December 1997]);

- bringing into focus the importance of recreation on the national forests;

- promoting watershed restoration as a foundation for land stewardship;

- reaching an increasingly urbanized nation through an improved investment in urban forestry and the Urban Resources Partnership;

- pioneering development and implementation of the Forest Legacy Program;

- adding a million acres to the national forest system through land acquisitions, monument creations, and exchanges;

- ending the stranglehold of two fifty-year timber sale contracts on the management of the Tongass National Forest (one through termination and the other through a negotiation initiated by the remaining contract holder);
- promoting women and minorities to leadership positions in the agency (and in the office of the under secretary); and
- innovative strategies for reinventing government, such as enterprise teams (which Gifford Pinchot III referenced yesterday).

We took on tough issues, a hostile Congress, and at times, a Forest Service culture that is both the agency's greatest strength and its greatest weakness.

On to lessons learned:

1. First, it is true that those who fail to learn from the mistakes of the past are doomed to repeat them. As we celebrate this centennial, we shouldn't be lulled into believing that the world is as it was when Pinchot created the agency or even as it was when many of you in the leadership first joined the agency two or three decades ago. We also shouldn't misrepresent the failed policies of the past as innovative solutions to the agency's present problems. The pace of change is rapid and accelerating. It is important to keep pace with changing attitudes and public values, and to embrace that change as it provides opportunities for the organization to grow and serve the public better.

I fear—and this is best exemplified in more recent policy changes and in the new planning rules unveiled essentially on Christmas Eve [2004]—that we are trying to go back to a bygone era when forests were managed solely by foresters; when his (and it used to always be "his") decision was final; and the public, the "ologists," other agencies, or the courts weren't questioning what we did.

It's not that way anymore. We live in an age when people want access to information, they want to participate in (or at least be informed about) decisions affecting the places they care about, and they demand the right to question. As has been said by other speakers, they also trust government less to simply "do the right thing."

By restricting public access to information by eliminating environmental impact statements, by burying management guidelines and standards in the manual (if they exist at all), and by limiting appeal rights, the Forest Service runs the risk of creating greater distrust of the agency, its planning process, its decisions, and its people. Many others have spoken from this podium of the issue of trust and transparency. Going back to strategies that engender further mistrust of the agency is a bad idea!

2. The second lesson is to ground management decisions in sound science. This is, after all, one of the hallmarks of the Forest Service. Pinchot created the Forestry School at Yale to ensure that his foresters had the best training and expertise. The Forest Service Research Program, unique among land management agencies, was created to ensure that forests were managed with the best available science.

It is disingenuous to create a planning process that requires only "consideration" of best available science, then claim that the process will generate more scientifically sound decisions. Scientific information should drive decision making and provide a light to guide new policies to prevent potential catastrophes (e.g., climate change). Forest Service research and field managers should be partners in developing policies and devising management strategies. That's not to say that the scientists should make the decisions. But their input should be given more weight than simply "consideration."

Whenever the agency lost a court case in the 1970s or 1980s, it was usually because a decision was deemed "arbitrary and capricious." And this was usually because the agency's own scientists had strong evidence to refute the wisdom of that decision. Do we want to go back to that?

3. Lesson three: Think big! Management decisions are best made in the context of watersheds, landscapes, and ecosystems. I've hardly heard reference to ecosystems in the past two days except for Jack's comments. Is ecosystem management simply a passing fad? I hope not.

We have a tremendous responsibility to consider all things in managing our forest legacy. That requires good scientific information, state-of-the-art geographic information system capability, the input and expertise of a whole host of "ologists," and consideration for the impacts of decisions on all the resources and the people who are affected by those resources on a landscape level. Don't allow this desire to return to the days of "local decision making" to distract you from the obligation to see the big picture.

I suspect that defenders of the new forest planning rules will say that environmental reviews will occur at the project level. That's good. But what gets lost is the ability to understand the effects of each individual project across the landscape—the *cumulative effects*. This is something that the timber industry and certain former timber lobbyists and Senate staffers have fought since it was forced upon the agency in an Idaho lawsuit more than a decade ago. But how can you manage watersheds, landscapes, and ecosystems without the ability to understand how each individual decision can affect the whole?

Of course, the rule's authors have a solution. They offer a new process—environmental management systems, or EMS. This is a new, supposedly independent audit system that will ensure that all is well on the landscape. Untried and untested. Who can honestly have faith in a new monitoring system when the agency has never been committed to nor had adequate resources for monitoring? And without baseline information on social, economic, and ecological health, what are we to use to measure progress or success?

4. Number four: Encourage public participation in natural resource management. From their inception, the national forests have been a source of conflict and controversy. Congress, administrations, and the agency like to invent processes to resolve conflict. But as we've seen (and will see with the new planning rules), these processes often generate more controversy.

Process is no substitute for dialogue and collaboration. Changing the process to limit public access to information, to limit appeal rights or access to the courts will improve nothing. Instead, I strongly encourage you to consider the words of Gifford Pinchot, who in developing guidance for management of the national forests in 1905 wrote:

> *National Forests are made for and owned by the people. They should also be managed by the people. They are made not to give the officers in charge of them a chance to work out theories, but to give the people who use them and those who are affected by their use a chance to work out their own best profit. This means that if national forests are going to accomplish anything worthwhile, the people must know all about them [and] must take an active part in their management....*

By making it more difficult for the public to know about their forests and how they will be managed, the administration and the agency are following a path that is in direct conflict with Pinchot's advice and antithetical to the notion of public lands. Furthermore, it leaves many in the public with the impression that the agency does have something to hide.

If we want to better "connect people to the land and nature," as speakers have said this week, then in good faith we need to invite the public to join us in learning about their forests and taking a very active part in their management.

The Forest Service can and should play a new and constructive role in planning—as a source of information, as a place to go for technical advice and scientific expertise, as a facilitator to encourage broad public discussion regarding the use of the national forests. New technologies make that possible. Imagine inviting the public to an information session in which they can play "manager" using virtual reality technology to see how different management decisions affect the landscape over time. My colleague at Yale, Chad Oliver, has developed such a tool. Why aren't we using these kinds of technologies to foster dialogue and discourse rather than fomenting conflict and controversy?

5. Final lesson: Focus on whom we serve and how we can serve them better. I commend Max Peterson and the Forest Service for coming up with the phrase "Caring for the land and serving people" to characterize the agency's mission. I fear, however, that we focus the majority of our effort on the land and too little on the people.

Presentations yesterday emphasized changing demographics, technologies, and management strategies. We're getting more urbanized, more diverse, older, perhaps more sedentary, but we love the outdoors.

Are we preparing to better address the needs of an urbanizing nation? How well funded are our so-called urban national forests? What are we investing in serving urban populations directly through the urban forestry program? If we want to reach these people, we have to invest in the programs and strategies that do so.

Public values are changing, the landscape is changing, and the Forest Service's business model must change as well. Recreation is having a bigger and bigger impact on the national forests. Yet funding is declining, trails are failing, facilities are closing. If the Congress won't fund recreation, then we need new tools, innovative approaches, and partnerships to reinvest in "*re*creation."

The management model used today is still one that is driven, albeit in more subtle ways, by "getting the cut out." The measure has changed to "acres treated," but it fails to give adequate consideration to other multiple uses and resource demands.

The products of multiple use—recreation, potable water, clean air, refugia for native flora and fauna—have greater public value than we recognize or wish to acknowledge. A business model for the Forest Service of the future might include other potential future "products" like carbon sequestration, as both Senator Craig and Dean Speth addressed yesterday. (How's that for both ends of the spectrum?) Could a future national forest "product" be growing and banking carbon in ways that permit us to capitalize existing forest cover and promote "active management" on our most productive forest acres? Yesterday, other speakers noted the increasingly important value of forests simply as a place of refuge or for families to reconnect. That's not to say that commodities shouldn't continue to be produced. But increasingly, other resources have much higher value for the public or can be produced more efficiently on other lands.

I will close with these brief thoughts:

Sally Collins asked the four chiefs to comment on what it takes to be a good leader. All had good responses—entrepreneurship and creativity, hope and humility, faith in people (both inside and outside the agency), and trust. All agreed that reconnecting people to the land and to nature was an essential role for the agency to play.

As the agency looks forward to its second century of service, it faces two immediate challenges: (1) an impending wave of retirements, and (2) an almost certain reduction in agency budgets (excluding, perhaps, for fire). As a result, the Forest Service will look very different (in the very near term) and its ability to sustain itself might be dependent upon new and creative financing mechanisms.

With these changes will come new challenges, new opportunities, and new leaders who will be charged with addressing both.

I would add to the important criteria for leadership, for the benefit of this next generation of Forest Service leadership, the essential ingredient of *courage*.

It takes a great deal of courage to be a leader, to speak out, to challenge what is politically popular or the norm. You can pay a price for doing so. But if leaders like Roosevelt and Pinchot weren't willing to speak out, to stand up for what they believed to be "for the greatest good," then we would not be celebrating this centennial.

It's your turn now. The future of our great forest legacy is in your hands.

Thank you for the honor of working with many of you and the opportunity to address you this morning.

George Dunlop

Former Assistant Secretary of Agriculture for Natural Resources and Environment, Reagan Administration

I want to begin by saying what a significant privilege it was for me to be associated with the Forest Service and the Department of Agriculture in my years in the Reagan administration. We came to the Reagan administration with a great deal of conviction. When I came and found that the Forest Service in particular was possessed of such great enthusiasm for everything that you do and did, it was a great encouragement to me.

In fact, I have to tell you a little story about the infectious enthusiasm of the Forest Service leadership that made an impression on everybody in the Department of Agriculture who had to deal with the issues of public policy. Dick Lyng was a great secretary of Agriculture and a really, truly fine human being. If there was anybody on this planet who was like Ronald Reagan, it was Dick Lyng. They were both Irishmen, they both had that twinkle in the eye, and they loved a good story and a good joke. So, one day Secretary Lyng called me and said, "George, I want you to come down to my office. We're going to play a trick on Chief Dale Robertson. When you come down here, you have a serious and somber look on your face, and just go along with me."

When I got down there, he rings the phone up and calls Dale. He says, "Chief? Listen. I've just had a call from the President. You've got to come up here right away. There's an urgent matter we've got to attend to at this moment." Chief Robertson comes over there all enthusiastic. Secretary Lyng said, "Dale, the President has decided it's an important and vital mission for this country that we go to Mars. And he told me that he knew there was one organization that could get us there, and that was the Forest Service because they can do anything. Are you up for it?" Dale thought about it for a minute and said, "Yes, I've got the people who can do it. We'll line it up and start immediately." Dale, I think that's a true story.

Serving was a pleasure and an honor. Throughout my life's experiences, I've always been a glass-is-half-full kind of guy. The three lessons that I want to share with you all that I've perceived or learned are informed by the fact that I've had a fifteen-year hiatus between the time that I was dealing and struggling with those issues and today. For the past three years, I've come back to those issues, dealing with them again as [Deputy Assistant Secretary of the

Army (Civil Works)] in the George W. Bush administration—dealing with all those environmental issues, particularly under the Clean Water Act instead of the National Forest Management Act, but with many of the same processes and procedures.

Lesson number one is that Gifford Pinchot was right about the science. The whole idea behind the creation of the Forest Service, as I understand it— and you'll forgive me if I abbreviate things so much that they aren't exactly accurate, but we are looking back from a one-hundred-year perspective—is that the resources that we are given responsibility for are the natural resources: the air, the water, the soil, the flora, and the fauna. And the nature of those resources is that they are dynamic, they are resilient, and—particularly from the perspective of the Forest Service—they can be improved by the intervention of mankind's art and his science. That was the idea that captivated the thinking of Gifford Pinchot and his predecessors in the silvicultural science field, and in the mind of Theodore Roosevelt. That concept—that mankind can manage these resources to good effect and for the benefit of those resources and for mankind in a sustainable way—became a decisive idea in the conservation movement and defined what we would call today the environmental movement.

That changed in 1963 with the publication of Rachel Carson's book, *Silent Spring*. The whole idea about the capacity of these resources to be resilient and manageable didn't die, but it got shoveled pretty deep. And it's still struggling to get out of the grave. The idea behind the laws and statutes that we saw enacted as a consequence of this concern—that mankind in fact was not managing these things, and that in fact we had created these ecological catastrophes (because that was the theory behind what Rachel Carson and her handmaidens and subsequent people did with the enactment of all these top-down regulatory statutes)—the idea was that these resources aren't dynamic; they're static. The idea was that these resources are not well managed by people. To them, mankind's very existence is harmful to the air, the water, the soil, the flora, and the fauna. And that by definition, anything that we do to use these resources is a negative thing. That theory, that idea—that insurgency—against the original Gifford Pinchot concept dominated public policy all through the period that I served. And some people would say it dominates it yet today.

However, I think what we have learned (and this is the reason I think the glass is half-full), which pertains to my work today and the Clean Water Act, is that there is a rising and increasing consensus among the people who deal with the science of the ecological matters that these resources are dynamic, they are amazingly resilient, and mankind's management and helpful application of his art and his science will in fact improve them and increase them in quality and quantity. While there are many skirmishes and other episodes to be carried through, I believe over the next eight or ten years in public policy that the Gifford Pinchot idea will have been proven correct. That's rule one, and if the Forest Service never forgets that, then you'll never lose your focus and you'll have a very successful second century.

The second lesson really informs the first. What I've learned over the last fifteen years, especially while I was engaged in the information technology business, is that the advances in information and communication technology are absolutely astounding—they are beyond the comprehension of most people. These information and communication advances, especially in the Internet work capabilities, are something that is going to be able to inform a bottom-up, stewardship-based conservation movement, instead of this top-down, "all the elites know what's best," "we're going to run everything from Washington," "one size fits all" approach that has dominated what I call the Rachel Carson static mindset. This information technology is something that all agencies should be encouraged to fully integrate into their systems.

The third and final lesson is the fact that all of things together then contribute to what I think is an important and significant development that will serve all agencies well to understand. That is, the public is very interested in being involved in processes that will allow good decisions to be made for people in local communities—a site- and situation-specific approach to the way these resources are used and developed. This idea comes under different rubrics and names, such as "civic environmentalism" or perhaps "competitive federalism." If you're from the West, you may have heard former Governor Mike Leavitt of Utah speak of the "Enlibra principles." Another comes from the administration of George W. Bush, which issued an executive order on "collaborative conservation" a couple of months ago. This is going to become the way in which the Bush administration defines this stewardship-based, bottom-up, information- and technology-informed thrust toward the future of natural resources management, based upon these dynamic principles. So if we focus on this collaborative conservation, if we focus on the importance and significance of the information technologies that are available to us and need to be exploited to the maximum extent possible, and if we always remember that Gifford Pinchot was right, the Forest Service will have a successful second century.

John B. Crowell, Jr.

Former Assistant Secretary of Agriculture for Natural Resources and Environment, 1981–1985

Getting Our Money's Worth from the National Forests

It became clear in the last eight years of the twentieth century that those who advocated preservation of the National Forest System without utilization of its existing resources for economic benefits had gotten the upper hand: the modest timber harvest levels achieved in the preceding thirty years were precipitately reduced nationwide, grazing leases were being amended or terminated, the fifty-year timber sale contracts originally entered into for the purpose of fostering economic development and population growth in southeast Alaska were summarily terminated, large acreages in the national forests of Oregon, Washington, and Northern California were devoted to protection of spotted owls and marbled murrelets largely to the exclusion of other uses, and just before the Clinton administration left office, unroaded areas totaling approximately fifty-eight million acres were administratively put off limits for multiple use by administrative fiat by prohibiting future construction of roads on those acres.

Thus, the principal issue concerning the national forests during the first part of the twenty-first century was framed: Is the National Forest System henceforth to be managed largely as wilderness and parks, or is the Theodore Roosevelt–Gifford Pinchot vision of reserves providing multiple uses for the American people to be revived?

■ ■ ■

The U.S. Department of Agriculture Forest Service is charged with administering and managing approximately 191 million acres owned by the federal government and designated as national forests and national grasslands. National forests in the West were withdrawn from the public lands starting in 1891. President Theodore Roosevelt made many of the withdrawals during his tenure of office, from 1901 to 1908. Most of the eastern national forests were acquired by purchase with funds appropriated by Congress under authority of the Weeks Act, which became law in 1911. National grasslands were the result of purchases made in the Dust Bowl of the thirties under authority of the Bankhead-Jones Farm Tenant Act of 1937.

The rationale for setting aside and acquiring forest reserves was the fear prevalent among concerned and forward-thinking citizens of the day that without such setasides, the Nation and its people could, in the not-too-distant future, be left with a shortage of wood, which was then and is now very important for sustaining a steadily improving standard of living for an expanding population.

Administration of the new forest reserves was transferred in 1905 from the secretary of the Interior to the secretary of Agriculture by the Act of February 1, 1905. The Transfer Act also established the Forest Service, so that February 1 became the birthday of this, today, increasingly venerable agency. The Act of June 4, 1897, which is known as the Organic Administration Act for the national forests, had directed that

> No national forest shall be established, except to improve and protect the forest within the boundaries, or for the purpose of securing favorable conditions of water flows, and to furnish a continuous supply of timber for the use and necessities of citizens of the United States." [emphasis added]

On the date of the birth of the Forest Service, Secretary of Agriculture Wilson sent a letter of direction to Gifford Pinchot, who was designated to be the first Chief of the Forest Service. The famous letter is reported to have been drafted by Pinchot himself. The letter set out the purposes and principles to be applied in managing the forest reserves; it made clear at its beginning that the land in the reserves was "to be devoted to its most productive use for the permanent good of the whole people" and that protection and use of the resources was to be conducted under "business-like regulations, enforced with promptness, effectiveness and common sense." The letter closed by admonishing that where local "conflicting interests must be reconciled, the question will always be decided from the standpoint of the greatest good of the greatest number in the long run." Secretary Wilson's letter did not have the force of law; nonetheless, for the next sixty-five years, the precepts set forth in the letter guided successive Chiefs and the agency in carrying out their legally established mandate.

Some of those precepts were enacted into statute by the Multiple Use–Sustained Yield Act of 1960. The act broadened the statutorily stated purposes for which the national forests are established and administered to include outdoor recreation, range, timber, watershed, and wildlife and fish. The act explicitly stated that these enumerated purposes were supplemental to the purposes named in the Organic Act of 1897; it further directed that the surface resources be developed and administered "for multiple use and sustained yield of the several products and services" which could be generated from those resources. The act ended by defining both "multiple use" and "sustained yield."

The Multiple Use–Sustained Yield Act and the Organic Act together provided a rational and stable policy foundation upon which the national forests could be managed. Even the Wilderness Act of 1964, which explicitly was "within and supplemental to the purposes for which national forests…were established and administered" did not substantially alter implementation of the Organic Act and Multiple Use–Sustained Yield Act when it permanently set aside eight million acres of national forestland as wilderness, little of which was commercial forestland.

■ ■ ■

For the first forty years after establishment of the Forest Service, management of the forest reserves primarily involved protecting them and, in fact, all of the nation's forestland, from the ravages of wildfires. Despite occasional catastrophic fires, Forest Service fire suppression and protective measures against wildfire have been hugely successful, not only on the national forests but also, through partnerships with the various states, on other public and on private lands as well. I rank that as the foremost and most significant accomplishment of the Forest Service in its first one hundred years.

The principal purpose of keeping wildfire out of the woods is to avoid loss of value represented by standing trees, man-built structures, and settlements, and to prevent loss of human lives. In short, the basic purpose of wildfire suppression and protection is to prevent waste. The only reason to be concerned about waste is that our society expects, sooner or later, to use the materials saved—at great public expense—from being wasted. The original vision was that the value represented by national forest trees should, sooner or later, be utilized. However, for the first one hundred years of Forest Service existence, that resource has been vastly underutilized.

Even before the Forest Service came into existence, there were efforts supported by the federal government to determine the volumes and types of timber in existence within the United States. Later, the Forest Service periodically issued reports attempting to assess the status of wood volumes growing on the nation's woodlands. It was not until 1974, with publication by the Forest Service of *Forest Resources Report 20*, that improvements in analytical methods and increased accumulation of information provided sufficiently reliable conclusions concerning the timber inventory of the United States that concerns about any imminent shortage of timber finally could be laid to rest. The extent of national forests' underutilization is illustrated by the facts that (1) today the national forests contain approximately eighteen percent of the commercial forestlands within the United States, but (2) approximately fifty percent of the nation's softwood timber of merchantable size is standing on the national forests. In short, the nation has relied on harvests from small private ownerships, industrial ownerships, other public ownerships, and on imports—largely from Canada—to meet its needs for wood.

The fact that the citizens of the United States were never and are not today faced with an imminent shortage of timber for their uses and necessities does not, however, imply that we can afford to waste what we have. Efforts at preventing and suppressing wildfire in the woods must continue unrelentingly, as should research and efforts to control tree mortality caused by diseases and by insects. The only restraint on such efforts should be not to allow the costs of those efforts to outrun the values being protected.

Increasingly, however, the federally owned forests within the United States are suffering from another form of waste—a form imposed by heeding the urgings of a minority of our citizens who are extremely vocal and well organized in opposition to utilization involving harvesting and removal of *any* of our very valuable public timber resource. As a consequence, harvest and removals of timber from the national forests have dropped in the last twelve years to less than one-quarter of even the modest and conservative levels which were achieved in the previous thirty years. The level of sales and removals of timber from the national forests in the last few years has been only about two billion board feet annually, as compared with ten billion to twelve billion board feet annually for the preceding two decades.

Even the previously achieved levels were only half or less of what the national forests are capable of producing in perpetuity *with natural growth rates*. When one takes into account additionally the desirability of removing volumes accumulated over many decades in which harvesting has been insufficient in volume, it would be possible to remove as much as thirty-five billion board feet every year for one rotation of sixty or more years. I should emphasize here that the land base on which such harvesting could occur leaves entirely out of account approximately twelve million acres of national forestlands which are included in the thirty-two million acres which since 1964 have been set aside as wilderness by statute, even though that twelve million acres meets the definition of commercial forestland.

It is to be emphasized at this point that in the discussion which follows, acreages statutorily set aside as wilderness—including the twelve million acres of national forestland capable of growing trees in commercial volumes—is not regarded as "wasted areas" or as "going to waste." A nation as richly endowed with forest areas as is the United States can afford the luxury for the foreseeable future of setting aside from multiple use and sustained yield the acres designated by law as wilderness. The public policy question has been, is, and will continue to be, how much of such setasides is enough?

A case can be made, particularly when one adds up all the acreage in the national parks, the national wildlife refuges, and wilderness setasides in the public domain and in the national forests, that we have already set aside too much land for noncommercial use, with a resulting waste of resources. The merits or demerits of that public policy question are not addressed here. What is addressed in the remainder of the discussion here is the harm to the public welfare which results from de facto exemption from timber harvesting on much of the approximately eighty million acres of national forest commercial timberland which should be managed for multiple use and sustained yield, including, very prominently, timber harvesting.

The waste of timber resources resulting from the follies of undermanagement, which have intensified rather than diminished in the last fifteen years, occurs, essentially, because trees are living organisms which die. They do not live forever, and long before they die of old age they stop growing. Thus, leaving such trees in a stagnated state for decade after decade before they die also wastes the growing capacity of the land on which the stagnated trees stand were they replaced by vigorous young trees. Lost also is the much greater carbon sequestration capability which occurs when young trees are growing.

The nation and its people suffer serious consequences of significant magnitude resulting from the waste of not utilizing trees which no longer are growing vigorously. The sharp decline in volumes sold from the national forests has wreaked havoc among numerous small and not-so-small communities, particularly in the West, in which wood-processing mills were situated. With logs no longer coming from the national forests in sufficient volumes to supply those mills, they closed, throwing thousands of workers in the mills, in the woods, and in the dependent communities who supplied the mill and woodsworkers and their families with the amenities of life. Few of those communities have alternative economic activities available not based on wood supply, with the consequence that the communities have withered and often died.

Along with job losses came reduced federal and state income taxes and loss of local property taxes because of loss in value to small-town properties. Society has borne additional costs as a result of reduced harvest levels from the national forests, the first of which is loss of stumpage payments to the federal government and the next of which is higher end-prices for lumber, plywood, linerboard, and paper, all of which would be lower if more timber were brought to market. Finally, the United States could and should be a net exporter of wood products rather than a net importer, as we are today, with consequent damage to the nation's balance of payments and the continued loss of opportunity to provide often badly needed wood for low-cost housing to people of Third World countries, with a consequent reduction of economic necessity to harvest, more often than not without replanting, their own, often tropical forests.

■■■

The Forest Service is neither entirely nor even mainly to blame for the huge waste in value which is occurring as a consequence of present-day national forest management. The principal blame, I think, is with the board of directors of the Forest Service. It is a big board of directors—the 535 members of the U.S. Congress. It is Congress and congressional enactments of the last thirty-five years or so which have caused the situation in which we find ourselves today.

Since 1969, Congress has enacted various statutes which have vastly complicated the process and have greatly increased the costs of managing the national forests, particularly for commodity production. The National Environmental Policy Act of 1969 requires a statement analyzing the consequences to the natural environment of each management action contemplated by any federal agency; the act applies, of course, to the Forest Service and its management of the national forests. Because of the sweeping scope of NEPA and particularly its requirements to "study, develop, and describe appropriate alternatives to recommended courses of action in any proposal which involves unresolved conflicts concerning alternative uses of available resources," the act has been the basis for numerous challenges in court to Forest Service management of the national forests by any group or person who disagrees with management actions proposed by the Forest Service. The National Environmental Policy Act contains no direction or standards by which its provisions are reconciled to or limited by the Multiple Use–Sustained Yield Act, and because NEPA was enacted later without such standards or provisions, it can be construed as overriding basic directions of the earlier act.

The Forest and Rangeland Renewable Resources Planning Act of 1974 established sensible requirements that inventories of national forest resources be established and kept current. The act also requires periodic assessments of demands to be expected for use of national forest resources. From these inventories and assessments, plans to produce the needed resources to the extent they can be provided by and from the national forests are to be developed and implemented for each national forest.

The ink was barely dry on the Resources Planning Act when it was substantially amended by the National Forest Management Act of 1976. The new act diffused the original purposes of the Resources Planning Act by introducing numerous factors which had to be taken into account in developing the forest management plans; most of these factors can be viewed as limiting factors. Although NFMA limited volumes of timber which could be harvested "to a quantity equal to or less than a quantity which can be removed from such forest annually in perpetuity on a sustained-yield basis," with a couple of highly pertinent exceptions applicable to overstocked stands, the act prescribes no minimum amount which should, can, or must be harvested annually from the national forests.

The Endangered Species Act of 1973 and its various minor amendments since then, as it has turned out, has provided a superseding overlay to the various congressional enactments governing management of the national forests. Any portion of a national forest utilized by an animal, bird, fish, reptile, insect, or plant classified under the act as endangered or threatened must be managed so as to conserve that species regardless of what consequences such management may have for other uses and benefits derivable from the forest. The economic costs and loss of other benefits of that mandate are implicitly irrelevant under the act; preservation of individuals of species designated under provisions of the act takes precedence over any and all other considerations, regardless of whether the species has any economic value, regardless of how much harm may be done to individuals of the human species, and regardless of the biological fact that living species have appeared and disappeared over time without the slightest evidence that human beings have had anything at all to do with such appearances or, except in a tiny number of cases, with such disappearances.

There are other congressional enactments which also impose restrictions on national forest management which can be mentioned: the Clean Water Act, the Clean Air Act, and acts regulating use and applications of various pesticides and herbicides.

∎∎∎

So, what should be done or what can be done about (1) freeing the Forest Service from the straitjacket of "management paralysis by analysis" and (2) reconciling or balancing various conflicting public policy objectives affecting national forest management? Note, first, that these are two different questions;

what *should* be done probably is not what *can* be done politically—at least right away. Congress is, after all, a popularly elected board of directors and, obviously, will be subject to the articulated aims of the national forests' stockholders—that is, the citizens of the United States.

An initial suggestion of what should be done is statutorily to disallow any administrative or court appeals whatsoever of plans developed for salvaging dead, dying, or damaged timber after fire or insect kills. Along with such prohibition, the legislation should direct that salvage plans be developed immediately with the objective of allowing as little as possible of economically valuable dead and damaged timber to be further wasted. Such plans should be required to include specific provisions and a schedule for reforesting or revegetating the acreages, and should make available net receipts from the salvage to effect reforestation without having to go through an appropriations process.

A second suggestion about what should be done now is to enact legislation which could greatly reduce the costs and delays which at present inhere to the forest planning process. Costs and delays could be reduced by legislatively exempting the Forest Service from having to comply with the National Environmental Policy Act in connection with forest plans or amendments thereto; justification for such an exemption is the existing detail provided by the National Forest Management Act's amendments to the Resources Planning Act, which prescribe a great many environmental objectives.

A third suggestion is to amend the Endangered Species Act to require a realistic determination of the economic consequences of designating a species as endangered or threatened and of establishing critical habitat for that species. If the economic costs exceed measurable economic benefits on federally owned lands by a statutorily prescribed amount, the designations should have no effect on those lands. A designation of a species as endangered or threatened should have no effect at all on uses of privately owned lands unless the landowner is promptly compensated for the resulting restrictions on use of the land. Such amendments, obviously, would also require limitation of the consequences legally imposed for a "take" of endangered or threatened species.

A fourth suggestion would be for Congress to prescribe minimum annual volumes of softwood and hardwood timber to be sold from the national forests in each Forest Service region. Such minimums would be based on timber inventories existing on the national forests (exclusive of already-designated wilderness areas) and on reasonable, even conservative, rotation ages. In doing this, the congressional committees implementing the concept should not legislatively delegate the task to the Forest Service, but should equip themselves with staff expertise for developing the rotation ages applicable to existing timber inventories in each region. In this process, other multiple use objectives should, at least initially, be ignored, as they most certainly will automatically be dominant on each patch of land between timber harvests. Some adjustment to the ultimately determined possible harvest levels will doubtless be required to take into account likely market demand for the volumes of wood available under such a mandate, particularly on eastern national forests dominated by hardwood species, which are at present in considerable oversupply relative to the commercial demand for hardwood.

A fifth suggestion would be legislatively to establish goals for each national forest region to generate a minimum decadal profit after covering all annual costs of operating the region's forests (except for fire suppression costs incurred in emergencies) and including annual payments to counties. A related suggestion would be to change the current payments-to-counties provisions to allow counties to impose a property tax equivalency charge on national forestlands within the county. This would assure the counties of a more dependable annual income from national forestlands.

■ ■ ■

In making these suggestions, I am fully aware that each of them alone will be cause for great opposition. Nonetheless, the political war must be declared and the battles fought in order to implement the original vision of Theodore Roosevelt and Gifford Pinchot in establishing national forests for the good of all United States citizens. Personally, being now of an age considered biblically advanced, I do not anticipate having much of a role in fighting even the early battles which must be fought. I anticipate—again in biblical terms—"sleeping with my fathers" long before sensible management principles finally are in place for National Forest System management, but I hope that sometime early in the second one-hundred years of the Forest Service, this will be accomplished. The sooner the better.

The Power of Participation, The Power of Partnership

January 6, 2005
9:15 am

David Bell *(Moderator)*
M. Hosny El-Lakany
James B. Hull
Rob Keck *(no paper available)*
Ann Linehan
Majora Carter

january 3-6
2005
washington dc

US Forest Service
Centennial
Congress
A Collective Commitment to Conservation

M. Hosny El-Lakany

Assistant Director-General, Food and Agriculture Organization of the United Nations, Forestry Department

Collaborative Partnership on Forests: A Viable International Partnership in Support of Intergovernmental Dialogue on Forests

1. What Constitutes a Partnership?

While the idea of working together in partnerships is not new, it was the World Summit on Sustainable Development, held in Johannesburg, South Africa, in 2002, that advocated partnerships as a viable modality in support of the global agenda on sustainable development. The summit characterized partnerships as voluntary initiatives that should have concrete value added to the implementation, bearing in mind the economic, social, and environmental dimensions of sustainable development.

Based on this, I would describe an effective partnership as willingness and commitment to work together on a common cause; effective leadership; sufficient resources; concrete tasks; and a stable parent body which gives guidance.

2. Intersectoral Relationships

Partnerships in forestry at all levels are vital, mainly because of close linkages between forest and other sectors. By nature, forestry is cross-sectoral, with impacts to the air we breathe, the water we drink, the land we cultivate for food, the ecosystems we utilize and enjoy—in brief, the impacts on human well-being as well as preservation of natural resources around the world. Conversely, policies for other sectors, such as agriculture, trade, and finance, have direct impacts on the forest sector.

In addition, there is a high public interest in forest issues. Not only active nongovernmental organizations but the public at large have become more conscious about the environment.

One of the main challenges facing many countries—both developing and developed—is to have a forest sector that is strong enough to contribute effectively to the coordination and harmonization of policies between various sectors interfacing with forestry. Another key challenge is to move toward integrated natural resource management strategies that cover environmental, economic, and social aspects while responding to the needs of people who benefit from forests.

3. From National to International

Why are forest issues dealt with in international fora? The fact is that forests do cross borders, and many forest issues are of global concern. Forest management is being influenced by free flow of labor, capital, goods, and information between countries as well as other effects of globalization. Forests provide global environmental benefits, especially conservation of biological diversity, soil and watersheds, and mitigation of global warming. Certification is also a good example of international influence; much of the pressure in many countries for certification comes from international nongovernmental organizations.

Some of the key questions currently addressed in the international dialogue are the following:

- the continued alarming rates of deforestation (in the 1990s, 9.4 million hectares of forests—an area almost equivalent to the size of Virginia—was lost annually, mostly in the tropics);
- the vital role of forests in economic development, employment and income generation;
- international cooperation to curb illegal logging and forest fires;
- ways to increase stakeholder participation in decision making; and
- the role of sustainable forest management in poverty reduction and the achievement of the United Nations' Millennium Development Goals, agreed to by the heads of state in 2000.

The Food and Agriculture Organization has offered a venue for international discussion over fifty years, bringing forest issues to the forefront and raising awareness of the significant contributions that forests make to the health of the planet and its inhabitants. More recently, the United Nations Forum on Forests is also dealing with forest issues from the global political perspective, seeking solutions on complex issues, such as how to finance and monitor progress towards sustainable forest management.

Given such topics, it is obvious that the intergovernmental forest dialogue spills over to the country level. The decisions made at the international fora do affect work at the local level, and thus cannot be dismissed. The Forest Service and Department of State colleagues who are involved in the international affairs can attest to that.

4. Why Collaborative Partnership on Forests?

There are about sixty international agreements and intergovernmental organizations that deal with forests. However, it is widely recognized that no single body has the capacity to deal with the full range of issues in a comprehensive manner. That is precisely why there was a need to establish the Collaborative Partnership on Forests. It aims at supporting intergovernmental celebrations and improving cooperation among the key international agencies. CPF consists of fourteen organizations, including FAO, the International Tropical Timber Organization, the World Conservation Union (IUCN), the World Bank, and the secretariats of conventions on biological diversity, climate change and desertification, and United Nations Forum on Forests, just to name a few.

Since the Rio Earth Summit in 1992, governments have negotiated a great number of international proposals for action toward sustainable forest management. CPF works with countries in putting into effect these recommendations. Basically, this means assisting countries, especially developing countries, to achieve sustainable forest management by providing information and technical assistance and mobilizing financial resources.

More concretely, CPF members have embarked on many collaborative joint activities that try to make a difference on the ground. For example, they work to advance, promote, and implement criteria and indicators, landscape restoration, conservation of forest biodiversity and many more issues. For example, CPF members currently work jointly on

- updating and disseminating, through a website and CD-ROM, of information on funding sources for sustainable forest management around the world; and
- streamlining forest-related reporting to various international processes and harmonization of definitions, to reduce the reporting burden on countries and national agencies that are involved in filling out the many questionnaires.

One of the significant achievements of the CPF is the strengthened collaboration among its members. However, this partnership has also enriched the work of each member organization by continuous exchange of information and innovative ideas across the member organizations. The partnership has also helped better coordination of members' programs and projects around the world.

5. What Makes the Partnership So Successful?

Many factors contribute to CPF's success as a partnership. First of all, it has a parent body, the United Nations Forum on Forests, where governments provide guidance to CPF. However, CPF's success is linked to the effectiveness of UNFF. The stronger the parent body is, the stronger is also the partnership. Secondly, it has a clear purpose: work together to help countries, specifically developing countries, to implement international commitments toward sustainable forest management. Thirdly, the partnership operates by consensus, and each member organization works within its own mandate and budget.

Above all, CPF works because it is an informal and voluntary arrangement of partners that share a common goal—sustainable management of forests. While the partnership arrangement is informal, the members are committed at the highest levels to contribute to the joint activities. In other words, the arrangement is kept simple and unbureaucratic, but firm in terms of commitment to cooperate.

Each member is assigned lead responsibility for particular forest issues, based on its relative expertise and comparative advantage. Yet it is obvious that CPF includes very different types of partners with different levels of contribution. Bigger organizations can afford bigger contributions. However, all members are involved—there is no room for free riders.

The partnership is also about pooling resources. While a common fund may work in some partnerships, in CPF's case the most viable funding modality is seeking external funding for joint tasks, coupled with in-kind contributions by all the members.

While CPF is kept deliberately small in order to work efficiently, CPF is reaching out to a wide range of other partners, such as nongovernmental organizations, indigenous peoples' organizations, and private sector entities, through an informal CPF network.

The governing bodies of CPF member organizations are pleased that major international fora have recognized CPF achievements in helping countries translate commitments made at the international level into action on the ground. These include the World Summit on Sustainable Development, the FAO Council, the Convention on Biological Diversity, and other major environmental conventions.

CPF has been recommended as a model for other sectors, such as the Convention on Biological Diversity.

6. Role of the USDA Forest Service

I see a twofold role for the U.S. Forest Service. First, you have a job to do both domestically and also internationally: it is about the future of the forest sector. It is of utmost importance to raise the sector high on the policy makers' agenda and to work across other sectors related to natural resources. Secondly, it is the role of all of us, as foresters, to make it clear to the international negotiators that more efforts are needed on the ground. We can, and should, provide the necessary linkages between the realities on the ground and the politics of the international negotiations.

The USDA Forest Service, as well as the U.S. Department of State, has been a great supporter of the CPF's work—in guiding us in the right direction and providing resources for action. I would like to take this opportunity to thank them warmly for this tremendous support.

James B. Hull

State Forester, Texas Forest Service

It seems a bit odd, strange, weird, unique, ironic, puzzling—albeit essential—that after hundreds of years of settlement and development in America, we are still gathering together and pondering what would seem to be the most logical process on earth: real, genuine, cohesive, synergistic partnerships and relationships in all phases of our society.

When the USDA Forest Service was only fifty-five years old, I started forestry school. On my first day in Forestry 101, I was told that *Forestry is a science, an art, a business, and a public policy capable of, and occupied with, effecting continuous production and management of forests on suitable lands and promotion of their beneficial use by mankind.* I thought, "They're not going to run me off that easy!" So, I decided to stay in forestry anyway, but it has taken me most of my forty-five-year career of hands-on experience to figure out what that definition really means!

From the East Coast to the West, the vast forests of America are what they are today because of the strong, vital, and enduring partnership between the USDA Forest Service and fifty state foresters (plus nine territorial state foresters). This partnership, in fact, this relationship that now spans more than a century has never been stronger, nor has it been more essential at the beginning of the next one hundred years of American forestry.

In his brief overview of the history of State and Private Forestry, James Giltmier described the early days of our nation, where the federal government worked hard to transfer public domain lands into the hands of people. It was felt that nearly all wealth was to be created from privately held lands. Most of the land ended up with farmers. Today, our privately owned forestlands account for forty percent of all the privately owned forestland in the world.

For over one hundred fifty years now, the nation has been trying to figure out the role of the federal government when it comes to issues related to all of these private forests. In a nation of new forest landowners with little or no conservation knowledge, nor understanding of a land ethic, and long before the U.S. Forest Service came along, the U.S. Department of Agriculture felt intense need to step in and influence how land was managed or treated.

Forest industry was doing the "cut out and get out" routine. Farmers also followed the new "American way" of cropping the land until it played out.

They then packed up and moved, generally further west, where there was thought to be an inexhaustible source of land and forests.

When the U.S. Forest Service was formally established, and with the troubling concern about private lands, it was only logical that a Division of State and Private Cooperation be established as soon as 1908. Some states had already started creation of state forestry agencies, and the Forest Service continued support until nearly all states were on board by the late 1920s.

The first Chief of the Forest Service, Gifford Pinchot, went to work with a commitment to stop forest industry's "cut-out" practices but had little success. That led him to strongly pursue some sort of federal regulation of state and private forestlands. Fortunately, those efforts never caught on, either, as the sovereignty of states' rights and private property rights arose to the forefront time and time again, one Forest Service Chief after the next.

The leadership of the U.S. Forest Service has now been struggling with this question of private lands for a century. As recently as September 27, 2004, in Jackson, Mississippi, current Chief Dale Bosworth asked the National Association of State Foresters to help him define and craft the role of the Forest Service in private forestry issues. Continual definition and redefinition will no doubt continue to be a major state and federal tenet as population trends continue to explode, placing more and more pressure on the newly coined phrase, *the triple bottom line: economy, environment, and society.* This might currently be the best phrase spouted forth in the past century.

In recent years the states and the Forest Service have maintained somewhat friendly debates as to whether State and Private Forestry programs were state-funded federal programs or federally funded state programs. While the answer probably does not lie in where the largest proportion of the state's program funding comes from, we do see where federal funds amount to as high as seventy-five percent of some smaller states' total state forestry budget. That ranges downward to less than five percent in some other states.

Regardless, in all states the presence of federal funds coming through the Forest Service is considered vital, which is probably why state foresters agonize relentlessly over the federal program funding allocations (how to most equitably split up the pie while meeting the intent of Congress!). It will probably take the full extent of the next hundred years to reach a good solution to this challenge.

These early concerns about private forests did lead to the first establishment of more appropriate federal-state-private partnerships, as witnessed in passage of the Weeks Laws of 1911 and later the Clarke-McNary Act of 1924. The

Weeks Laws established direction and funding for watershed programs and cooperative fire protection with the states on lands impacting navigable streams. Clarke-McNary expanded fire protection to all forestlands across the nation, plus added funding for states to start reforestation programs and technical forestry assistance to private landowners.

Under both programs we have together built the greatest fire protection programs anywhere. This culminated in the phenomenally successful National Fire Plan, which not only provides substantial funding, but occasionally recognizes that the wildfire protection program in America is nationwide, all lands, cross boundary—not just in the western USA, not just on federal lands.

In 1950, Congress passed the Cooperative Forest Management Act, which outlined and funded a whole plethora of programs between the Forest Service and state foresters. This was further modernized in 1978. These have been great programs that were production oriented, incentive based, easily counted, and they could all be delivered by the traditionally trained, *the pure foresters* of America (like me!).

With these programs we were right on target; in fact, we hit the bull's-eye. These one-on-one, hands-on programs were the epitome of what a federal-state partnership could be. We wrote management plans by the thousands, and delivered FIP, SIP, SOIL BANK, CRP, ACP, FLEP, even fire suppression and numerous other problem-solving efforts. These programs were right for the times. Unfortunately, in the best of years, with these traditional co-op forestry programs, we collectively impacted about one percent of the total forest landowners. Ever notice how the bull's-eye of a target covers about one percent of the total target?

Back in the early 1990s, Lamar Alexander of Tennessee was U.S. secretary of Education and made a very pertinent observation, "Education in American is in a time warp—our schools are not doing much any different from the ones my grandparents attended." I am here to tell you again today, that State and Private forestry programs that were very right for America for much of the first one hundred years of the Forest Service and state forestry, are now reaching a point of time warp.

Nearly all state forestry programs were put into place when most American forest landowners were farmers, as I described earlier, and these programs have not changed much since. During the last half of the past century we neglected to acknowledge a few vital points along the way:

- The American population quadrupled.
- Demand for forest products increased tenfold or more.

- The number of forest landowners probably more than quadrupled, and that translates to massive fragmentation to smaller tract sizes.
- The average ownership of property changed hands every seven years.
- The demographics of America and forest landowners changed dramatically, and that translates to new kinds of dreams, visions, goals, passions, and objectives that us traditional, pure state foresters don't want to hear about and are often ill prepared to deal with.
- And in 1996, we blindly entered into a drought cycle, hardly recognizing that for most of our careers we had been in a thirty-year wet cycle, thinking that was normal.

As we look to the next hundred years of partnership between the Forest Service and state foresters, we must figure out how to hit the whole target—how to hit the other ninety-nine of the target that we have been ignoring. One of the greatest challenges for the Forest Service and state foresters will be to retool, reinvent, remold, and revitalize State and Private Forestry. One-on-one forestry programs can still be relevant; current forestry programs still have a place. However, collectively we must find innovative ways to reach all forest landowners, in their real world, not in our perception of how it was or how it should be according to us traditional foresters.

We must realize that today forestry is more than just industry and trade, more than just pulpwood and two-by-fours. Forestry today and into the future is also very much about ecosystems and forest health, biodiversity and biomass, soil and water and air conservation, carbon sequestration, social benefits and ecotourism. Most of these are not exactly new, but forest landowners have been "expected" to provide these environmental services free to society. The marketing of these environmental services is the most exciting development in many years. It is also the common ground we have been seeking between forest landowners, society, and environmentalists.

One of the most significant programs of the first hundred years of the Forest Service was the Civilian Conservation Corps of 1933. My uncle, Cordell Hull, secretary of State under President Franklin D. Roosevelt, administered this critical program. The CCC put thousands and thousands of unemployed young men to work following the nation's 1929 financial crash. That co-op conservation program built some of the offices I still occupy in Texas, built bridges, recreation sites, and performed enormous conservation of natural resource projects until 1940, when it was discontinued. Other smaller but similar partnership-type programs have been most beneficial to the states through the years.

During the first half of the Forest Service's hundred years, other important laws and acts were enacted, but one key factor was present in all that I must identify. Most of these early efforts were led by the Forest Service through active partnership with the Society of American Foresters, established in 1900. For fully half of your existence SAF was led by the U.S. Forest Service. Unfortunately, throughout most of the last half-century, the Forest Service has dropped out of one of the best ways we have to link professionals and, more importantly, build valuable and lasting relationships.

Within my own organization, the Texas Forest Service, young forester applicants know they need not even apply for a job if they are not already members of SAF. Employees know that SAF membership and active participation are not optional. Also not optional is SAF Certified Forester status. I suspect we are the only forestry employer of any size in the nation that has one hundred percent of its qualified professional foresters *certified*, but as public servants I think that is the minimum we can do to help gain the respect of our constituents, plus it makes us more quality foresters.

Speaking of quality employees, the U.S. Forest Service was built on the shoulders of giants in Forestry—Gifford Pinchot, Henry Graves, William Greeley, Edward Cliff, Max Peterson, Dale Robertson, to just name a few. Joining with these leaders have been great regional foresters and district rangers, all with a common purpose.

The next hundred years, in fact, the next hundred days and beyond are going to be equally dependent on the shoulders of equal giants. What I am extremely concerned and perplexed about is the Forest Service's hiring practices today for top leadership positions. I was recently asked to serve on the search committee for a key Forest Service leadership position, and I submitted a list of questions I wanted to ask the finalist candidates during the interviews. I wanted to ask such things as

- What is your vision for forestry in the South?
- What are the three greatest challenges facing forestry in the South?
- What do you consider the top three priorities for this position?
- We all expect employee excellence; how would you define excellence in this position?

I immediately got a phone call saying, "You can't ask those questions!"
I asked, "Why not? Those are the same type questions I always ask when I am looking for leaders." The answer was, "You cannot ask those kinds of questions

because they discriminate against those who don't know anything about forestry, the South, or the U.S. Forest Service!"

I am here to tell you that you best not discriminate, but you sure best figure out a way to immediately find and begin developing some more giants who not only have vast forestry experience, understanding, and insight, but also have innovation, vision, and above all else a passion for what forestry can and must be in the next hundred years. The continued emphasis on developing every segment of employment diversity will be the key to developing giants capable of meeting the complex issues facing forestry and the Forest Service in the next century.

In 1922, a major revelation occurred when the U.S. Census revealed that the USA was becoming an urban nation! The 1907 *Use of the National Forest Reserves, Regulations and Instructions* guide suddenly started to be as much about the management of people as it had been the scientific growing of trees.

For the first fifty or sixty years of the Forest Service, federal scientists were celebrated for their expert contributions to the nation's booming economy and rising standards of living. My career came on the scene in 1960, and foresters' professional judgment has been under sharp attack and our status hotly debated ever since. We have experienced every conceivable kind and style of protest and litigation.

In the South we have been the target, the victim, and at times the great beneficiary of all this litigation. Throughout my career, the Texas national forests have spent more time locked up from lawsuits than they have in scientific forest management.

- We have seen enormous losses on private forestlands because of uncontrolled national forest southern pine beetle infestations that didn't recognize property boundaries.
- We have witnessed forest industry disappear from lack of federal timber on the market.
- On the other hand, here in the South we laughed all the way to the bank over the spotted owl issue.
- We saw unparalleled demand for timber from our southern forests and saw timber prices skyrocket. (Of course, Texas forest landowners are now ready to hang the Texas state forester because those prices could not be sustained.)

In 1908, the U.S. Forest Service conducted the first statewide forest survey in Texas. Actually, that was the last time a statewide survey was done until 2004! However, one of the greatest accomplishments of the past hundred years has been the Forest Inventory and Analysis program. FIA was initially established by Congress in 1928 and designed to periodically, systematically, and scientifically measure and describe the status of the nation's forests every ten years.

It worked pretty well for about sixty years, but in the late twentieth century, especially in the South, it became very apparent that ten-year survey intervals were simply too far apart with our rapid change in population, land use changes, and fast timber growth rates. The decision was properly made to go to an annualized survey by measuring twenty percent of the fixed plots each year to form a five-year survey interval, updated by twenty percent of the plot date each year. FIA forms the basis for the most accurate, real-time, factual, relevant forest data available and is used for all aspects of forest planning, policy, etc.

As we look toward the next hundred years, I have just defined one of the critical roles that the Forest Service needs to regain—that is, the recognized, trusted, and respective global source of every kind of forest-based information. We have proved in Texas that we can collect FIA data a whole lot more efficiently and expediently than the feds can. But where most states need help is analyzing the data and explaining what it really means in the state, national, and global environment.

Over the past hundred years, there are so many other things the Forest Service–state forester partnership discovered, learned, experienced, and in some cases totally missed:

- We discovered urban forestry where eighty-five percent of Americans live and vote.
- We started recognizing and learning to dance the WUI (wildland-urban interface), and we danced with a whole new set of partners.
- We were shocked that wings fall off old air tankers when policy is flawed.
- We learned that today a forester cannot go to the woods without a cell phone, pager, satellite radio, laptop computer, Palm Pilot, GPS unit, and now a Blackberry.
- We finally admitted that we don't have a clue how to effectively run conservation education programs or economic development programs.
- Smokey Bear taught us that the most effective role of government is preventing problems before they occur, not continually trying to fix them.
- We saw a good Woodsy Owl program end up tasting more like crow.
- We learned that quality and relevant decisions are best made with quality, relevant, factual, and real-time information. One of the best and essential roles of the Forest Service must be to get back to developing and providing such information.

- We have witnessed the greatest path to success being through building of partnerships, genuine relationships, and building the capacity of others to take responsibility for their own future. In my early days, my office walls were covered with training certificates from the Forest Service. I became fascinated with administrative management because of Bruce Cartwright in Region 8. He introduced me to Peter Drucker and other leaders. The Forest Service needs to return to that expertise and training model.
- In recent years we have seen some of the most effective and dramatic forestry accomplishments coming from a new model of community-based organizations, such as the Quincy Library Group in California, the Great Lakes Forest Alliance in Wisconsin, the Applegate Partnership in Oregon, the North Olympic Timber Action Committee in the state of Washington, and even county forest landowner associations in Texas. Each of these has great potential, and we need to support and grow others.
- We learned that Winston Churchill was pretty astute when he said, "You can always count on those Americans to do the right thing, but only after they have tried everything else." For one hundred years we have tried every thing else, some with enormous success, some things not so great. I will conclude by going back forty-five years to my first day in forestry school and Forestry 101.

Forestry is a science, an art, a business, a public policy...

This definition is as relevant today as ever, but beginning on the first day of the next hundred years, the Forest Service challenge is to breathe new life into the totality of this definition.

Thanks, and Happy Birthday!

Ann Linehan

Division Director, Program Support, Head Start Bureau,
Washington D.C.

First, let me thank Mr. [David] Bell for his introduction and Susan Alden for inviting me to participate. And very special thanks to the woman whose enthusiasm and vision made Head Start's partnership with the U.S. Forest Service possible: Iris Velez.

When I look at the names and titles of all the other presenters and organizations represented at this Congress, Head Start may appear to be a fish out of water. Yet as I look at the values, goals, and missions of these two cherished government agencies, caring and serving are our common bonds.

As you mark your centennial year, Head Start will celebrate its fortieth birthday. We began in the summer of 1965, offering an eight-week summer program to four hundred fifty thousand poor children who were entering kindergarten that fall. The goal was simple: to help these children achieve success as they began their public school education by helping to overcome the disadvantages that poverty often brought.

Like the Forest Service, we have evolved and changed over our lifetime to meet the new and emerging needs of our children, families, and the communities in which they live. However, despite the diverse population we serve, our cornerstones of parent involvement, community partnership, comprehensive child development, and health services remain constant.

Today Head Start is one of the largest domestic programs in the country. With an annual budget of nearly $7 billion, we fund over sixteen hundred local agencies.

Through our funding, one hundred and fifty Native American and Alaska Native tribes operate Head Start programs. Agencies serving the children of our migrant and seasonal farm workers provide Head Start services to over thirty-five thousand migrant and seasonal families each year as their parents toil in the fields harvesting the wonderful foods we take for granted. In total, these organizations enroll nearly one million children annually, ages birth to five.

To grasp the size and diversity of Head Start, note there are more Head Start classrooms (forty-seven thousand) throughout this country than there are McDonald's.

We have inner-city programs like New York City and Los Angeles that serve over twenty-thousand children, and rural programs like the Havasupi Tribe at the bottom of the Grand Canyon serving as little as twenty children—where you have to travel by chopper or mule to visit. Some Head Start programs have such diverse populations that they may have twenty-three different Native or home languages spoken in one center.

The challenges are great for local Head Start programs, and we know it requires the meaningful involvement of parents and committed community partnerships to make and sustain the progress that children must achieve in order to be successful in school and in life.

The first leader of the Forest Service, Gifford Pinchot, spoke to the possibilities of our great future becoming realities: "Only if we make ourselves responsible for that future." Head Start shares that philosophy and has embraced a collective responsibility for our children, who are our future.

Chief Seattle once said that "all things are connected." The Forest Service works endlessly to promote national responsibility for caring for our land, and I believe that the partnership between the Forest Service and Head Start reflects Chief Seattle's belief.

Together, fostering a caring and informed generation of children who understand even now the importance of their land and their responsibility to care for it offers hope of a great future.

Through your National Symbols program, the U.S. Forest Service has brought the Woodsy Owl program to Head Start. You know Woodsy's message, "Lend a Hand—Care for the Land." Through this partnership, we have the potential, with the distribution of Woodsy Owl educational materials, to help millions of Head Start children and their families discover the natural world and incorporate into their daily routines positive life-long activities that care for their natural world.

Remember, preschool-age children are like a sponge wanting to soak up all that is around them. Sure, they have policemen and firemen and other more traditional figures visit their classrooms, and in many Head Start classrooms, a year is not complete without a visit to the firehouse. Now imagine how we can broaden our children's experiences by a visit from a Forest Service representative…maybe even Woodsy. Think of the stories and knowledge they could impart…experiences and knowledge that no one else has first-hand.

We know that as a result of one such partnership between a local Head Start program and a Forest Service representative, we now have four- and five-year-old children filled with curiosity as they learn about their environment and ecology and recycling—all magnificent vocabulary words and concepts for such young children to master.

Also remember that the mission and values of the Forest Service can be translated and applied to our children and families regardless of whether they live on the tenth floor of a crowed tenement building in Chicago or in a remote Alaska village.

As you know, over the last four years, the President, Mrs. Bush, and scholars from across the United States have repeatedly stated that Head Start children must enter kindergarten with the language and literacy skills needed to achieve success in schools. Part of fulfilling that mandate has been an increased focus on letter recognition and vocabulary development. And just this past year the Forest Service published Woodsy's *ABCs Book*.

Even if you have never taught young children, you remember that when you where first introduced to the letter A as a child, your teacher said, "A is for apple." Guess how Woody introduces A? "A is for air."

My Woodsy favorites are "W is for wetlands," and "X is for xeric." Honest, Woodsy taught me a new word!

You may ask if this is such a big deal. My answer is yes—because through this partnership we have an opportunity to expose a future generation to their land in a way they would otherwise not know. And Head Start's grasp is not limited to the children. We work with their families and siblings and grandparents and more.

This past June, the Head Start Bureau hosted the Fatherhood Institute, where we brought together over four thousand Head Start dads and local Head Start staff. In one workshop, conducted by another federal partner, the Environmental Protection Agency, we discussed the health risks to children from second-hand smoke.

I'll never forget the responses of two dads in the audience. One very young dad from Cincinnati sat in disbelief with tears welling up and said, "I never would have smoked in front of my baby had I known. Why didn't someone tell me?" Another dad from Puerto Rico asked if he could have five hundred packets containing smoke-free materials; he said he wanted to give this information to every family in his community.

I share these two stories because they speak to the power of these partnerships. There are thousands of children and families in this country who do not have access to information or real-life experiences that would enhance the quality of their life today, tomorrow, or in the future.

But in our case, a little help from Woodsy through the marvelous local Head Start staff across this diverse country can and will foster generations of young children who experience, care for, and enjoy their land!

Majora Carter

Founder and Executive Director, Sustainable South Bronx

I am honored, and I admit that it is a bit of an overwhelming experience to make a presentation like this, because it reminds me of how far my community, the South Bronx, has come in terms of realizing that a sustainable, livable community should be a right, *not* a privilege. This is a love story about how a community learned to love itself enough to recognize its own strength, power, and beauty as it strives to create a more livable, breathable, walkable community. It is also very personal for me to tell you this story because I am a proud daughter of the South Bronx who also happens to be the granddaughter of an American slave who struggled to work a little piece of land down in Georgia in order to support his family when he was freed. So with the following experiences, I learned to appreciate what protecting the land and striving to take care of future generations really means.

This is the South Bronx I grew up with. It's the summer of 1973. I am seven years old. Years of disinvestment by real estate, banking, and manufacturing interests often led landlords to torch their own buildings in order to collect insurance money. People that used to walk to work now had neither work nor a home to walk to. Many of my friends and neighbors are forced to relocate. We lose sixty percent of our population. I watch the two buildings on either end of my block burn down. My brother Lenny is killed, a casualty of the drug wars.

No one expected anything good to come from this community. The common perception was that only pimps, pushers, or prostitutes were from the South Bronx. *I was ashamed to be a part of it.*

You can understand why the community was feeling a bit disempowered. But despite it all, there were folks that stayed, like my family, but you will see how all this disinvestment set the stage for the environmental burdens that were about to be heaped on it.

Our city and state regulatory agencies consistently used antiquated zoning regulations to justify putting burdensome facilities in my politically vulnerable community. The South Bronx was already home to a sewage sludge palletizing plant, two of our four power plants, more than two dozen waste facilities that handle approximately forty percent of the city's commercial waste, and if that's not enough, major concentrations of truck-dependent industries, including the world's largest wholesale food distribution center, which brings more than fifty-five thousand diesel trucks to the area each week, and a spaghetti-like network of highways built by New York's master builder, Robert Moses, which displaced more than six hundred thousand people—a neighborhood with a highway running through it.

South Bronx health statistics show the impact of environmental burdens on people's health. Don't think that we don't know how challenging our work is!

Even after a huge influx of housing dollars secured by dedicated South Bronx housing advocates in the 1970s and 1980s, the area could not have been confused with a livable community. In many respects the area hadn't changed much.

Yet this is a community with many strengths. For example, back in 1997, when I was working for another community organization, the city and state decided to privatize the city's waste-handling operations. They thought that the best use of our waterfront was to have a company—which existed only on paper—build a waste facility that would handle fifty-two hundred tons per day, or forty percent of the city's municipal waste, *despite* the fact that the South Bronx already handled forty percent of the city's commercial waste. That is an example of environmental racism.

We helped our community make the connection between how the land was being used in the community and their health, and many folks openly questioned why they were being singled out and the land was being ravaged. We mobilized the community to force the city and state to back down from their ill-conceived plan, and three years later, we won!

That process compelled me to do something about all this, so I started Sustainable South Bronx in 2001 to put a voice out there for these concerns. We are an environmental justice organization that helps make the South Bronx's visions for its own healthy future become realities. We work to create projects that improve the environmental and economic quality of life of the South Bronx community.

But I have gotten a little bit ahead of myself in terms of the story and the reason why I was invited here. Around the same time that we were battling this enormous waste facility, I kept getting phone calls and visits from a woman named Jenny Hoffner, who was the Bronx River coordinator for partnerships for parks, a program at the New York City parks department. Her job was to identify local groups that either were or might be interested in working along the Bronx River and let them know about a program that was offering $10,000 seed grants to do restoration projects along the river. Jenny was also charged with coordinating the assembled groups into a working group for the Bronx River as well. Like I said, Jenny kept reaching out to me, and I just thought, Sweet girl, but she's obviously not from around these parts, 'cause if she was, she'd know you can't get to the river from the South Bronx. Fortunately, I was dead wrong. Because you see, those seed grants and the Bronx River working group helped spur a green revolution along the Bronx River and especially in the South Bronx. The program that made that possible was the Urban Resources Partnership, which was funded by the U.S. Forest Service and the Natural Resources Conservation Service. Their goal for the partnership was to provide technical assistance and seed money to locally led urban forestry, parks, and waterfront development projects. They had a very clear understanding that local communities understood their own needs and how they wanted to develop their community. They made an investment in new leadership and talent because they understood the value of investing in *people*—a point that was apparently lost on this administration, as it's my understanding that the program has been completely gutted.

Back in the late 1990s, some of us in the South Bronx were at a point where we felt we had a choice: we could continue to be constantly *reacting* to the environmental injustices that were being thrust upon us—or we could take some time and develop *proactive* strategies that would allow us to develop our communities in a healthier way. And I stand proudly before you today as a living testament to the impact of the Urban Resources Partnership. The initial $10,000 investment that was made in us has been leveraged hundreds of times over in the South Bronx, and either directly or indirectly, that grant allowed us to dream and take actions that would help create a more sustainable future for the South Bronx. And I'd like to show you just a few ways we are doing that— and please consider this an open invitation to those inside and outside the Forest Service, we are always actively looking for new partners to collaborate and help build a more sustainable South Bronx.

A quick way to illustrate how being proactive can have a colossal impact on the future of an environmental justice community: this is the Bronx River, the only true freshwater river in all of New York City, and it travels through the entire length of the Bronx from north to south...I'd like to tell you a tale of two Bronx Rivers. What it looks like up north...and what it looks like down south, with debris that floats down to us.

The former management of one of the city's largest scrap metal yards used to believe that the river was a legal dumping ground. Fortunately, their new management is much more enlightened, and we will be working with them on another project, hopefully. How things can change....

Combined sewage outflows dump raw sewage into the river after a heavy rain. We have five of them in the South Bronx. Here is a preferred dumping site for cars. Seeing these disparities is what inspired folks to take action. A young boy petitioned the governor to get the National Guard to help them remove the cars from the river. Neighborhood youth are planting spartina. River heroes: the river nurtures us as we nurture it....

We have becomes "victims" of our own success as both parks are going under major reconstruction over the next two years.

Consistent with our mission, Sustainable South Bronx is always looking for physical ways for the South Bronx to view itself differently: Greenways!

We received $1.25 million in federal transportation funds for traffic congestion mitigation and air quality improvements to develop the first stage which is the production of a feasibility study and design. Our partners are my former agency, the Point and the New York City Economic Development Corporation.

The proposed waterfront esplanade has dedicated on-street bike paths and dedicated points of interest along the greenway. Economic development on the greenway is important to help support it as well as community needs. In the meantime, we are developing a community market which will open in spring of 2005; it will couple increasing community access to affordable, healthy produce direct from the Hunts Point Terminal Market and entrepreneurial opportunities for local folks who want to operate their own produce stands. We have already established relationships with major food distributors at the Hunts Point Market who have committed to mentoring vendors with training necessary to operate in the distribution-wholesaler environment. Last year, Sustainable South Bronx cosponsored a farmers' market at the Hunts Point "6" subway station plaza, as preparation for this year.

Green roofs are a new landscape type which are exactly what the name implies. Remember those combined sewage outflows? Green roofs are a roofing technique that uses soil and living plants instead of traditional Torchdown or tar materials. They last four or five times longer than traditional roofs; they are actually living plants, so they help to filter the air of pollutants instead of emitting pollutants like petroleum-based roofs do; they provide much better insulation; they are very effective in stormwater management, retaining up to seventy-five percent of rainfall, so they reduce a city's need to fund costly end-of-pipe solutions, which usually consist of expanded and/or new wastewater treatment facilities, the majority of which are then located in communities like the South Bronx; they provide habitat for migratory and insect-eating songbirds while denying a source of standing water where West Nile virus–carrying mosquitoes can breed; and they help minimize the urban heat island effect.

Urban heat island effect occurs when all those nonvegetated surfaces are reflecting heat back into the atmosphere. UHI and the extreme temperatures that it produces jeopardize public health, especially the very young and the elderly, and of course is helping to exacerbate global warming. Installing green roofs can help mitigate some of the impacts of UHI.

Our partnership with H.M. White Site architects and Columbia University Climate Change Project, with financial support from the utility ConEdison, is embarking on a demonstration project green roof, and we are exploring the creation of a training program and business opportunity in green roof installation geared toward local residents, and installing green roofs throughout the city and beyond.

People came out on an unseasonably cold Saturday, a week prior to a big community celebration. We remembered where we came from and were happy to be on our path.

The South Bronx is learning a lesson about loving itself enough to know that it deserves better than the burdens that have been foisted upon it. We have done some incredible work over the past few years, in large part by creating strategic alliances and partnerships that were beneficial to all concerned. Again, please consider this an open invitation to those inside and outside of the Forest Service, we are always actively looking for new partners to collaborate and help build a more sustainable South Bronx…and I really don't think it's going to take the next hundred years.

I would like to close with a little saying that we like to use in the social justice movement: communities don't plan to fail, they fail to plan. Those of us that are passionate about forestry—whether its urban forestry or protecting pristine wilderness—are all part of one community. Understand how the partnerships that we build can have an extraordinary impact on the land and the people that use it.

So what is your next hundred years going to look like?

Conservation Leaders:
Today and Tomorrow

January 6, 2005
11:00 am

Jim Oftedal *(Moderator)*
Alba Mercado
Jessica Farrar
Terry Baker
Alyse Charley
Daniel Delgado
John T. Vogel II

january 3-6
2005
washington dc

US Forest Service

Centennial Congress

A Collective Commitment to Conservation

Jim Oftedal

Director, Central California Consortium
USDA Forest Service, Clovis, California

Good morning. Thank you, Alba [Mercado], for that very warm introduction. It certainly is a pleasure and an honor to be introduced by a rising star from my program. I would like to thank the Centennial Congress for having the vision of bringing together young leaders from throughout the United States to be part of this once-in-a-lifetime event.

Let me tell you a little bit about myself. I was born and raised in Fresno, California, which is located between the Sierra and Sequoia national forests. I had never been to the forest until I actually began working for the Sierra National Forest twenty-four years ago. I started as a GS-1 engineering aide and had many jobs before becoming the director of the Central California Consortium over eight years ago. My job has allowed me to travel across the United States and speak to organizations on the importance of diversifying their workforce and educating their communities on natural resource issues. It has also allowed me to speak to youth and encourage them to continue their education, consider a career with the Forest Service, and most important, become productive citizens. I have done and been involved in many exciting things throughout my career, and being asked to moderate this event is certainly one of the highlights. This week I've had the opportunity to work with this group, leading them in workshops on networking, public speaking, teamwork, and leadership. I've gotten to know each one of them better; we've eaten together, laughed together, and shared some of our personal interests with each other. I've met some of their parents, and together we've grown from a group to a family.

Today, as we recognize a century of Forest Service accomplishments, we must face the challenges and opportunities presented in the next one hundred years of conservation and stewardship. "Conservation Leaders: Today and Tomorrow" is a panel of young women and men who are the future of the United States, the future of this agency, and the future of our natural resources.

These young women and men come to you today as representatives of their communities, cultures, and the next generation of conservation leaders. Through a national effort of Forest Service partnerships, these high school and college students were selected because of their exemplary dedication and participation in conservation, education, and community service.

Ladies and gentlemen, it is my pleasure to introduce to you some of the brightest stars around the nation, the leaders of today and tomorrow:

- from Florida, nominated by the Society of American Foresters, Mr. Terry Baker;
- from Illinois, nominated by the Girls Scouts, Miss Jessica Farrar;
- from Florida, nominated by Earth Force, Mr. John Vogel;
- from California, nominated by the Central California Consortium, Miss Alba Mercado;
- from California, nominated by the Central California Consortium, Miss Alyse Charley; and
- from New Mexico, nominated by the National Hispanic Environmental Council, Mr. Daniel Delgado.

Since Monday, we've been following the students into their workshops, getting their reactions from the centennial sessions that they've attended. We've put together a video clip of their week in Washington, D.C. I know you will enjoy this.

Note: The Central California Consortium is an environmental education–based program sponsored by the USDA Forest Service. The focus of the program is to educate the underserved rural communities on natural resources. Currently, the program has established Hispanic and Asian components with African American and Native American programs being established in the near future.

Alba Mercado

Student, College of the Sequoias

I am very pleased to be here today as a conservation leader in addressing some of the many issues confronting the Forest Service agency. To bring these issues to the floor and into perspective is our first action in improving the fundamentals of the matter. It is simply about telling the truth about our history and getting things right for our future.

My name is Alba Mercado, and I am currently a student at the College of the Sequoias in the process of completing my general education in pursuit of a bachelor's degree in anthropology. My parents migrated from Mexico into the San Joaquin Valley of California two decades ago, in search of jobs in agriculture, where they eventually settled and raised our family. My community is located at the base of the Sierra and Sequoia national forests. We are agriculturally based, richly diverse, and at times underserved. Growing up in the Central Valley has exposed me to the many issues which we face today, ranging from poverty-stricken communities to cultural barriers. We often face a struggle in which we are limited to certain opportunities, given the only chance to become a working class, instead of becoming a part of the prosperous few.

This past summer I was very privileged enough to work for the Forest Service in a summer internship program known as the Central California Consortium. This organization holds a strong commitment to building a better community and has set vast amounts of opportunities throughout the Central Valley and been a vital improvement for the Forest Service. And we have yet the need of improvement through programs like these that truly spark a difference to the agency, the land, and the people.

The program has since been a critical force in being inclusive and understanding the issues that are most effective to the Forest Service agency today. I would like to address much of the underlying factors that have been effective to these living issues. As humankind, we have a direct correlation to the root cause of our very own issues, and due to this, our society and our environment have suffered immensely. Thus it takes into big play the trust, understanding, and knowledge that we hold in connection with each other. As caretakers of our motherland and a part of our community, we are the core effect on the struggle against these issues. Our struggle for dignity, freedom, and land has yet to come. We have a responsibility understanding exactly who we are, what we want, and what we can do about it, primarily highlighting the needs of our community and looking at an agency with true representation of its population. That is the importance of the agency in meeting the needs of a culturally diverse society. For example, a state like California, one of the most culturally diverse places in the world, is surrounded by forests like the Sequoia and the Sierra, yet faces the need to be representative and inclusive of its people. As an agency, it is essentially important to manage our forests, beginning with the management of its surrounding communities, through encouragement, but more importantly to maintain a firm response by offering these opportunities. An increase of outreach toward our future leaders and bringing in a broader array of applicants to the agency will further construct a more realistic standpoint of the Forest Service. Because we are looking toward further expectations of the Forest Service, we should hold a strong focus toward the younger generations in order to invest in our leaders for the long run. It is fundamentally important that through these recognized issues we can embrace a change in which we value and respect one another, through color, gender, religion, and economic status. Because each and every difference of ours will truly hold a significant representation of our communities.

Through this inclusive, non-ethnocentric perception of an outlook toward a new century as an agency, we are accepting a change in better serving our public. And through the public's eye we can attain a new perception of the beauty and vitality of our national forests. And in response as leaders, environmentalists, and politicians, we have a responsibility to act upon these issues. We've reached a dangerous peak and our time to act is now! Thank you for your time and thank you for this opportunity.

Jessica Farrar
Student, Illinois Wesleyan University

Ralph Waldo Emerson once said, "The creation of a thousand forests is in one acorn," but I believe the creation of a thousand forests is also in one human. My goal is to highlight the individual programs that inspire humans to create forests, and the changes that have taken place in my Illinois Forest Service; I would like to emphasize the educational programs both inside and outside of the Forest Service.

To start off, I wanted to provide an introduction of myself. I am a nineteen-year-old business major at Illinois Wesleyan University. I am from a rural area of southern Illinois and currently live in central Illinois, where the only difference in landscape is the size of the cornfields. When I was growing up, I was lucky to be constantly educated and involved in learning about our environment. My mother is an interior landscaper and maintains a tree farm, and she has always requested my help in planting trees. Growing up, I was a part of Kids for Conservation, I benefited from Arbor Day grants, and I am still extensively involved in the Girl Scouts. All of these organizations not only brought a strict understanding of the importance of our environment but they showed me how wonderful it is to enjoy the environment.

Most youth don't even think about the environment, mainly because they are not introduced to the outdoors, and they are not educated on its benefits. It is important to spark interest from the youth in the ecosystem. I was fortunate to be extremely intimate with the outdoors from an early age. This was mainly due to my parents, Girl Scouts, and the Outward Bound program. I was lured into the wonderful world of the outdoors through Girl Scout camp in Illinois, canoe trips in Maine and Canada, as well as whitewater rafting and backpacking in Oregon. I then applied knowledge from these experiences to make a difference. When it came time to do my Girl Scout Gold Award project, I turned to the Forest Service to donate trees to help save the shoreline of my local lake. I owe all of my interest in the environment to the programs that groomed me as a youth.

Today, though, the youth do not understand the benefits that a healthy environment brings and therefore do not contribute the ecosystem. This problem is due to lack of education and participation in the environment. Outside programs are vital to capturing the hearts of the youth. They not only show how to maintain a strong ecosystem, but they show how to use and enjoy a healthy environment. These programs are the largest sources of outdoor education outside of the Forest Service, and even though they are huge national organizations, they are falling in membership, participation, and support. The Forest Service needs to establish stronger relationships with these outside organizations.

Programs geared toward youth that exist within the Forest Service are also slowly disappearing. In Illinois alone the Kids for Conservation program, the one that first educated me as a youth, is gone. The schoolyard habitat action grant, which was the single most important part of my Gold Award project, has also been cut. The few programs that still exist are only given to a certain audiences. In order to be effective and really make an impact, the educational programs must first of all exist, but they must also be carried out properly and fully. Repetitive programs that reach a larger audience would provide a better base for grasping support of the Forest Service from an early age.

The Forest Service is set up well and contains many valuable programs. But they are slipping away internally because the staff is decreasing, and the programs are leaving with the people. It is up to the Service to keep these programs alive and pull more support and interest, starting with the youth. They need to know that we can use our natural resources, and we can enjoy them. Supporting programs both inside and outside of the Forest Service will increase awareness and provide an educated population that will ensure the future of our forests.

Being accepted to speak at this conference has increased my knowledge of the great asset the United States has in its Forest Service. I arrived here educated in the environment, but extremely uneducated on the Forest Service. As I leave, I will leave with a wealth of knowledge to pass on to my fellow peers. Each and every one of you has so much knowledge and experience that needs to be passed on, not between yourselves but to the organizations that grasp the hearts of the youth. Pipa, Jodi, Jim, and the Centennial Congress, thank you for this opportunity and for being so welcoming to the youth. To end, I would like to share a quote. Now, I know what you are thinking—but it's not Pinchot. J. Sterling Morton wrote, "Other holidays repose on the past, Arbor Day proposes the Future."

Good morning. I don't want to break the cycle, so I will start off with a quote from Gifford Pinchot. "Many people do not know what the National Forests are. Others may have heard much about them, but have no idea of their true purpose and use. A little misunderstanding may cause a great deal of dissatisfaction."

My name is Terry Baker. I was born and raised in Marianna, a rural community in northwest Florida. I participated in and completed the Florida A&M University and University of Florida 2+2 Forest Service minority initiative program in May of 2004 with a B.S. in forest resources and conservation and a minor in botany from the University of Florida, and a B.S. in agricultural science from Florida A&M. I currently work as a forester trainee on the Apalachicola Ranger District of the Apalachicola National Forest. I have requested and received permission to take a leave of absence to pursue my graduate studies next fall. I plan on majoring in forest economics and policy.

The greatest concern facing the future of natural resource management is communicating with the public. Although it sounds like a simple task, it is one of the paths filled with detours that have to be taken and potholes that have to be stepped in to reach the true goal. One specific moment in my college education highlights this need. During my forestry studies at the University of Florida, I had to take a natural resource policy class. It is an interesting class because it is composed of forestry students, wildlife students, environmental science students, political science students, and other random students from across the university. Depending on the demographics of the class, the professor would choose recently proposed natural resource policies that would ignite a good debate. The above-mentioned moment was a result of a discussion of the proposed termination of commercial timber production on federal public lands. A student from a very urban part of south Florida said he could not respect someone who made a living with a chainsaw or someone who worked in a papermill. I don't know about the rest of you, but I don't think he thought that through very well. For one, those very reasons were printed on paper. Secondly, like many of you, when I am out in the middle of a forest, I definitely prefer toilet paper to any of the make-shift alternatives. When I first heard his comments, I was furious, but then I realized he just didn't understand. The gap between urban and rural communities means that neither side cares or wants to know about the other. How do you tell someone who has gone out, done hard physical labor, and comes home with a sense of accomplishment that he/she must survive by standing at an information kiosk and giving out pamphlets for six dollars an hour? Rural communities are composed of a culture that they do not want to change, and they shouldn't have to. All the policy makers in this room should realize and make an effort to include everyone in their decisions. That will be the first step in bridging the gap between urban and rural communities.

There is no single or simple answer to the questions of today and tomorrow, because every person is different. As each new individual is born, there is another variable added to the equation. This means we will never have the right answer, because the needs and wants of our nation's population will be in a constant state of change. What we are charged with, beyond being good stewards of the land, is communicating an understanding of our actions to the public and taking their concerns into consideration for decision making. We should teach those who believe that no tree should be cut that some trees must be cut for the social and economic stability of some communities, and those who feel we should cut as much as we please that areas need to be protected to maintain ecosystems. Proclaiming itself as the "Land of Many Uses," the Forest Service needs to exemplify this balance of use and preservation, as well as being at the forefront of disseminating knowledge of how such a balance works for the benefit of all. I would like to close with a very appropriate quote from Gifford Pinchot, who apparently could put my thoughts into better words than I can. "It is often necessary for one man to give way a little here, another a little there. But by giving way a little at the present they both profit by it a great deal in the end."

I would like to thank the Congress for this opportunity and all of you for taking the time to listen to what I have to say.

Alyse Charley
Student, Reedley High School, Dunlap, California

Good morning! It is a privilege for me to be here representing my family, my community, not only Native American young women but all young women. I want to thank my parents for being here to support me. I also want to thank the Central California Consortium for nominating me.

My name is Alyse Charley. I live in Dunlap, California, a small rancheria mountain community located at the base of the Sequoia National Forest. I'm a seventeen-year-old senior attending Reedley High School, in Reedley, California.

My mother's tribe is the Picayune Rancheria of the Chukchansi Indians; her tribe became recognized in 1983 but my father's tribe, the Dunlap Band of Mono Indians, have yet to be reestablished as a recognized tribe. A recognized tribe is what the government states is a legitimate group of people. We are working as a community on this tribe to become recognized as a tribe.

Culture is an important aspect in my life. I attend pow-wows to learn more about our tribe's history and discuss concerns that tribal members have. For Native American people the forest and life are sacred. We as people are users of the land. We gather food, materials for baskets, hunt and fish for food by following the seasons and caring for the land as well as depending on it for survival.

The Forest Service and the Native Americans have similar views on conserving and preserving natural resources. As more people take up residence in the mountains and forest communities, we as the American people along with the Forest Service must meet the challenges of the next century. As people we use the forest and land for recreational purposes such as skiing, hiking, and biking. We, as users of the forest, must work even closer with the Forest Service to help preserve and conserve our natural resources. This process will provide a vital component to our future.

I am a dedicated member of a USDA-funded program, known as Generation Green at Reedley High School. This program has broadened my view of the Forest Service and how it works. This program has influenced me to pursue my long-term goals.

One of the activities I was selected for was working at the Sacramento State Fair. I worked to demonstrate the hazardous effects that fire can cause. This was a rewarding experience for me. During my time at Camp Smokey, I had the chance to work beside a wildlife biologist, in which she discussed the benefits of pursuing this career.

Next year I plan to go away to college and study to become a wildlife biologist to help preserve the habitat and natural resources so that generations to come are able to enjoy the forest as we know it now.

I feel this experience has made me more appreciative of what I have, and opened my eyes to different aspects of the Forest Service. Not many people can say they came to this historic event. I feel there are many doors that are going to be opened for me. Once again, thank you for this wonderful opportunity!

Good morning. I would like to begin by stating what a pleasure and an honor it is for me to be here this morning. My name is Daniel Delgado. I am seventeen years old, and I am a senior at Cuba High School in Cuba, New Mexico, which is a rural community located in northern New Mexico surrounded by the Santa Fe National Forest, where every day, people in my community live with the possibility of a devastating forest fire. The efforts which the U.S. Forest Service puts forward can and will determine the economic future of my community. In some cases the very lives of our citizens are at the mercy of decisions which are made by the U.S. Forest Service. As more and more people move into our beautiful mountains, the more important a role the U.S. Forest Service plays in our community and around the Southwest.

The way that I became involved with the U.S. Forest Service is through projects involving our community, the environment, as well as water research within the Santa Fe National Forest. The Forest Service is important to our area not only because of fire control but also because our local Forest Service office is the second-largest job provider in our area, where the unemployment rate is close to forty percent. If the Forest Service was not in our area, I am sure that the percentage would be greater. I also feel that besides being a major job provider, the local forest district office is really involved with the community, and they also mirror the rich diversity of the community. They strive to be very approachable and have meetings with our community partners about issues that are important to us and our livelihood.

As you can tell, there are not very many opportunities in my area, especially for the youth. And a few months ago I was extremely lucky to be selected as one of four students from my high school to participate in the annual National Hispanic Youth Environmental Council Institute in Glorieta, New Mexico. The institute was truly an experience that I am sure none of the students who attended will forget. This institute opened my eyes to the wonder of the environment as well as important issues involving the lack of minorities in the environmental fields of study. I feel very lucky to have met Roger Rivera, as well as all the instructors and attendees of the training.

After attending the National Hispanic Environmental Council training, I had a spark to get more involved in conservation and the environment. I started looking for projects that I believed would have an impact in preserving our environment and getting the community to realize how lucky we are to live so close to a national forest. Just a few weeks later I found a large article in our local newspaper stating that a local conservationist was applying for a large grant to start a small-wood project area in Cuba. I immediately contacted her to offer my assistance. I already knew a little bit about the project because I represented the school in 2002 at a small-wood conference in Albuquerque, New Mexico, and after attending the conference, I was put on our local small-wood board. The small-wood project was developed to help reduce the amount of hazardous fuels, such as overgrown doghair thickets, and the use of the biomass to generate heat for buildings as well as making durable compounds used for signs and pressed-board materials. The small-wood project also encourages traditional uses of small-diameter timber materials such as *lattias* and *viggas*, used for herringbone roofing, and also materials for coyote fencing, which is a popular fencing style in New Mexico, as well as other traditional building materials that are desired especially in the Southwest for Santa Fe–style architecture. Small-wood project coordinators also work to restore watersheds by reforestation and erosion prevention. When they began to look at Cuba as a small-wood project area, I and many others in the community figured that it was too good of an opportunity to pass up. So our community really began to show interest and support, and if the project should come in and provide even a few more jobs, I would be proud to have helped bring any form of economic growth to our community. People in our area underestimate the risk that overgrowth in the forests poses, especially in the Southwest, where strong winds can turn a small fire into a firestorm. The risk of forest fires in New Mexico is very scary due to the fact that there are many homes and business communities intermingled with forestlands.

Like our community, I feel extremely lucky to live near a forest ranger office where they do all that they can to inform us of these important issues, and I also feel that forest offices that strive to mirror the diversity of the state help to make youth become more involved with the environment as well as conservation. And I believe that in the future, the Forest Service as a major government agency should strive to have the same diverse representation throughout the agency that our community is lucky to experience.

When I return to my hometown, I will have so much to inform the community of. The main message that I will take back to the community is that there are people in the Forest Service who are trying to make sure that rural communities have a voice, and I now know that. There are people who are watching out for small communities like ours and others. Thank you for this wonderful opportunity. I know that I will be able to draw from this experience for the rest of my life.

John T. Vogel II

Student, Jesuit High School, Tampa, Florida

First of all, I would like to say that it is a great honor to be here today, and I really appreciate the opportunity.

My name is John Vogel. I am seventeen, and I attend Jesuit High School in Tampa, Florida. I live in San Antonio, Florida, a small rural town of six hundred, about fifty miles north of Tampa. I feel that growing up in San Antonio has given me a good perspective on what it means to live an agricultural lifestyle and to appreciate the natural environment. The opportunity to go to school in Tampa has broadened my horizons and has made me accept the reality of a complex, rapidly urbanizing society. I've had the chance to travel all over the United States, to Europe, and to Central America. These opportunities to travel have also given me a vast array of experiences on which to draw and create my opinions.

I often ask myself, What sparked my interest in conservation and environmental awareness? Why do I have these concerns while most of my friends and peers show no real interest in matters relating to natural resource stewardship? My family's economic interests are closely tied to forestry. My hobbies and recreational pursuits are mostly tied to outdoor activities. I have had several teachers who have been catalysts in developing a growing passion for the protection of my natural surroundings. I have found that these influences have been good for me and are shaping my future pursuits. But I find it very lonely, being the only one in my peer group who has a serious interest in the public debate over the conflicting issues of natural resource conservation. What can one young person coming from a very small community in Florida really accomplish when trying to influence public opinion and trying to spread the message of responsible environmental activism?

My true challenge to a commitment to conservation activism was and is to find a way to draw young people such as myself into conservation activity. What vehicle could I use to bring a sense of excitement or a call to action and involve my friends and others into what I consider an extraordinarily important public debate? My conservation club activities in grammar school, while having some impact on my peers' awareness, did not develop long-term results. By luck or design, I am not sure which, I was drawn to an organization that believes in youth empowerment in how it relates to conservation concerns.

Earth Force, a national youth environmental movement based here in Washington, D.C., has enabled me to participate in an organization that has a real opportunity to create that excitement, commitment, and passion for conservation issues that have come to mean so much to me. I found in this organization a youthful environmental call to action done in a very responsible manner, without accusation or finger pointing. Conservation issues are first identified, then debated, and finally solutions to the problems are developed. It is fast-paced and appeals to the attention span of most young people.

I sincerely believe that youth education and awareness are essential to the mission of an informed, educated, and involved public. The foresters of this country will always have the ability to apply accurate science, based on sound research, to the management of our nation's natural resources. I know that if the public truly knows what it wants from our forests and rangelands, the U.S. Forest Service can deliver. As Gifford Pinchot once said, "What the people as a whole want will be done. To do it, it is necessary that the people carefully consider and plainly state just what they want and then take a very active part in seeing that they get it." Wouldn't it be best if the public based its desires and needs on sound information after intelligent debate? One can get an intelligent decision from the public first by education of its youth, second by involving their youthful enthusiasm, and last by allowing for their participation in the sometimes-contentious debate. Intelligent youthful conservation activists eventually become intelligent and connected adult participants in the development of public policy. They will also become intelligent and aware voters.

So upon entering its second century of existence, I implore the Forest Service to look toward youth education, involvement, and empowerment to solve its problems of the future. By having an interested, educated, and informed youth, this nation will be on the right track to solving its problems in a mature and intelligent manner.

Terry Baker, Alyse Charley, Daniel Delgado, Jessica Farrar, Alba Mercado, and John Vogel

Letter to the Centennial Congress

To the Centennial Congress: thank you for involving the youth. We want to congratulate you on growing over the past hundred years and seeking to incorporate the young people of our nation in the future. We come here from all over the country. From the hammocks of Florida, to the cornfields of Illinois, down to the Sangre de Cristo Mountains of New Mexico and back up to the great forests of central California, we join you today with different backgrounds but a common passion. This passion to provide wise use and preservation of our natural resources brought us together. Throughout the Congress we have sat in on sessions and have admired the great history of the Forest Service and the role models from our past. We have heard about the many challenges facing the Forest Service in the present and have discussed many opportunities that can help us continue the proud tradition of living in harmony with our natural resources.

Today we come to you representing the youth of our nation and to express our passion to work together and address the stresses on our natural resources. To do this it vital that the Forest Service focus on the youth, increase our involvement, and invest in integrating young people in natural resource management.

We come to you, the current leadership in the Forest Service, natural resources, and of the nation and ask you to help us. Your mentorship will develop us as leaders not only for the future, but for our peers today. We live in a generation ignorant to the role of the Forest Service in the nation, and through opportunities such as this one we are provided with the tools to share the depth of knowledge in the agency to our communities. When you share your expertise, knowledge, personal stories, and passion with us, we are both educated and inspired to continue to care for the land and serve people for the greatest good. All of you must take an active role in developing future leaders for the nation. To promote healthy local environments the leadership must be a product of the history of the people, communities, and the land.

Educate us! Involve us! Inform us! Although an anomaly among our peers we are asking that you increase educational opportunities to make our passions the norm. We ask that you trust us. By investing in us you will develop a lasting legacy that will care for the land and serve communities. Through active and flexible youth development and involvement programs you will soon create an educated, informed, and involved group of productive youth.

In closing, we would like to thank the organizations that nominated us: the Central California Consortium, the Society of American Foresters, Earth Force, Girl Scouts of the United States, and the National Hispanic Environmental Council. We thank the Congress for having us, for taking the time to hear our concerns. We need you to educate us, mentor us, and provide us with opportunities, today and tomorrow, so that we can ensure that the next one hundred years of conservation will prosper.

Summary Review

January 6, 2006
12:00 pm

Dale Bosworth

january 3-6
2005
washington dc

US Forest Service
Centennial
Congress
A Collective Commitment to Conservation

Dale Bosworth
Chief, USDA Forest Service

For most of you, your work at this Centennial Congress is over. Yesterday, you met in groups to offer your ideas in two general areas: first, how we can meet the long-term needs of the land and of the public we serve; and second, how we can work together more effectively. You came up with dozens of related issues and hundreds of ideas for addressing them.

You also came up with 242 suggestions of things you could personally do on behalf of conservation. That means almost everybody offered an idea of something they could personally do. I think that shows a real collective commitment to conservation.

Specific Findings

My job now is to report on your findings. I can't possibly do justice to everything you said in the few minutes I have, so I won't even try. I will just touch on a few key themes.

At least three general themes came out over and over again in various ways. The first has to do with ecological services—finding ways to attach market value to services from the land that were traditionally taken for granted and delivered for free, such as carbon sequestration, soil and water protection, biodiversity, and outdoor recreation.

It's based on a growing perception that top-down measures such as rules and fines aren't enough to conserve our natural resources. For example, we need to give private landowners positive incentives to protect threatened and endangered species, so when they find some on their land, it's a good thing, not a bad thing.

Market incentives can be part of the answer. Worldwide, markets today have acquired a whole new meaning for conservation. They aren't just for timber and other traditional forest products anymore. They now include various forms of payment for carbon sequestration, water delivery, soil protection, and biodiversity conservation. We need more.

A second set of themes revolved around better engaging the public in conservation. In our schools, we need curricula that can give us ecologically well-educated publics. We need to demystify the "cargo god"—the idea that everything we need originates in the cargo areas of our supermarkets and home improvement stores.

We need more nontraditional ways of reaching our kids, like using videogames or other media tied to pop culture. We also need to reach out to nontraditional constituencies, particularly to urban audiences, and that means connecting to issues and cultures that we've traditionally ignored.

Again, traditional top-down approaches from the expert point of view don't work. We need to treat our publics as equals. Instead of educating the public, we should work with them, involving them at every step of the way in our decision making. Our role at the Forest Service has changed: we still have an obligation to lead, but as organizers and facilitators rather than as experts who have all the answers, because we don't. Above all, we need to be clear with our publics about what we do, and then we must deliver on our promises. There can be no confounding examples.

A third—and related—set of themes revolved around partnership and collaboration. Perhaps we can reach out better to the public by finding nontraditional partners to deliver our conservation messages—partners who enjoy a high degree of public trust. But we often make it hard to be a Forest Service partner. We need to find ways to make it easier by simplifying our processes and getting new legislation to broaden our authorities. We need to reduce partnership liabilities and streamline our grants and agreements process.

We Heard You

Those are just some of the things we heard you say. Through the Forest History Society, we will publish your complete findings in detailed proceedings later this year. Everyone interested will have access to the proceedings.

But it shouldn't end there. I know a lot of folks sometimes think nothing concrete comes out of these events. But I believe that there's real value in coming together like this. The twelve regional forums we had last year and now this Congress have all had positive outcomes. I believe that the relationships we built at these forums have changed us all. I'm willing to bet that you don't see the issues we face—or each other—in quite the same way anymore.

It goes to the whole purpose of this centennial forum. For a number of years now, my biggest fear has been that the popular issues of the moment—like whether we're producing too much timber or not enough—are absorbing all our energy while more important things are falling by the wayside. Our collective energy is focused on things without a lot of collective impact, and we don't have the energy to address far greater issues where we have a lot of common ground—issues like global warming or ecological services or communicating the need for conservation.

That's why we started focusing on the Four Threats—fire and fuels, invasive species, loss of open space, and unmanaged outdoor recreation. These issues might not have as much popular appeal at the moment as things like timber or road building, but they are far greater long-term concerns. I think we need to change the national dialogue to focus on things like these that really count.

New Models for Collaboration

We stand at the beginning of a whole new century of issues. We don't even know for sure what the main issues will be twenty years from now, but we do know this: our way of dealing with issues in the past through top-down approaches and through conflict and gridlock doesn't work. We need to find new models for dealing with the issues we face today and the ones we'll face in twenty years, whatever they might be.

That's what I think this Centennial Congress and the regional forums we had last year are about. They're about finding new models for dealing with issues. How we approach each other is key. Do folks from outside the Forest Service come to the agency to get us to give them the solutions? Or do they come to us to help them work out the solutions for themselves?

I think this Congress has been a model of the latter, and the way you framed the issues yesterday shows it. You focused on huge issues that will matter for years to come, like ecological services. You focused on building our role as a convenor and facilitator instead of a top-down director of everything that happens. You focused on the need for engaging our publics in finding solutions for themselves, because they are the ones who are out there on the land and can truly make a difference. You focused on community-based forestry.

I think we need to follow up on that success. I'd like to see regional forums every few years where we focus on specific matters of common concern, like global warming or ecological services. We might also host a semiannual national meeting here in Washington to keep the momentum going.

The Forest Service doesn't necessarily have to take the lead. Our role in the new century will be to facilitate a collective commitment to conservation. Maybe we would work with the Bureau of Land Management or another agency, maybe with the states or nongovernmental organizations to host these meetings. The possibilities for collaboration are endless. But the only way to resolve the issues that truly matter in the long term will be through our collective commitment to conservation.

Continuing the Momentum

In closing, I just want to say how truly impressed I am by all the positive energy that has come out of this Congress. All the ideas you had for personally contributing to conservation showed that energy. I think we need to tap into that energy by continuing the dialogue, and I think last year's regional forums and this Congress itself are a good model for that. We are absolutely committed to working with you to resolve the issues you raised by treating each other with respect, by truly listening, and by seeking common ground. Thank you for showing the way.

Awards and Recognition

January 5, 2006
6:30 pm
Whitten Building Gala

Sally Collins *(Master of Ceremonies)*

January 6, 2006
12:45 pm
Awards Ceremony Luncheon

january 3-6
2005
washington dc

US Forest Service
Centennial Congress
A Collective Commitment to Conservation

Sally Collins
Associate Chief, USDA Forest Service

Remarks at the Whitten Building Gala

Welcome! It's a pleasure to be here. So much of the Forest Service tradition is reflected here…Theodore Roosevelt and Gifford Pinchot…Smokey and Woodsy and Lassie…our history timeline. I hope you are enjoying it all and maybe even learning something new.

PricewaterhouseCoopers sponsored this event, and I'd like to extend our warmest thanks to their representative here tonight, Mr. Don Christian. Mr. Christian.

We are here tonight to celebrate a century of conservation and to acknowledge the visionary public servants in Congress who made it possible. We'll make some special awards in a few minutes, but first I'd like to say a little about some of our great conservation leaders in the past.

The first is John Wingate Weeks, who served in the House and Senate from 1904 to 1919. At the time, all forestland in the East was privately owned, and a lot of it was in poor condition. To restore forests in the East, the government needed authority to purchase private lands, and Congressman Weeks sponsored the necessary legislation. As you enjoy any of our magnificent national forests in the East—and today there are dozens of them on tens of millions of acres—you and your children and their children have to thank Congressman Weeks.

Another visionary was Charles Linza McNary, who served in the Senate from 1917 to 1944. Senator McNary sponsored legislation that strengthened our cooperation with the states in areas such as reforestation and fire control. Thanks to his vision, we've had strong cooperative forestry programs with the states for many decades now. Senator McNary also helped expand our authority for acquiring new national forest land. He strengthened our ability to establish new national forests in the East.

The last public servant I'd like to mention is Hubert Horatio Humphrey, who served in the Senate from 1948 to 1978, except for four years as vice president under President Lyndon Johnson. Senator Humphrey was instrumental in passing such laws as the Multiple Use–Sustained Yield Act, the Wilderness Act, and the National Forest Management Act. He was an architect for much of the framework we operate under today in managing the national forests and grasslands.

Now it's time to recognize some of our conservation leaders today. I'll start by making the first award myself.

The Forest Service has a hundred years of caring for the land and serving people here in the United States. But from our very beginnings, we've also worked overseas, as Gifford Pinchot over there will surely tell you. Ask him about his trips to Europe and Asia. In fact, Gifford Pinchot envisioned conservation as a global peacemaker. He reasoned that if we can conserve our renewable natural resources worldwide, then we can eliminate one of the biggest incentives for waging war: to plunder the resources of other countries.

A good example of our overseas work is represented here tonight by the U.S. Agency for International Development—USAID. Our agencies have complementary resources—technical, financial, and programmatic. Through partnership, we have leveraged those resources to accomplish more than either of us could have accomplished alone.

For three decades, we have worked with USAID to help spread conservation and to provide disaster relief around the world.

- For example, the news is filled these days with the terrible tragedy caused by tsunamis in South Asia. We're collaborating with USAID to provide relief to the devastated areas. Forest Service and BLM personnel are already on the ground in Sri Lanka, Thailand, and here in Washington.
- You've probably also heard of the genocide going on in Darfur in the Sudan. We're working together with USAID to help resolve the conflict there and to alleviate some of the human suffering.
- And I guess you know the threat facing the Amazon's rainforests. We're working together with USAID to help spread sustainable forestry techniques there. It's really the only hope for protecting the region's vast rainforest resources for generations to come.

We have a distinguished guest from USAID here tonight, Ms. Emmy Simmons, assistant administrator at USAID. Ms. Simmons, in recognition of our longstanding partnership, and in hopes of continuing that partnership far into the future, I ask you to accept this award. We present this award to the U.S. Agency for International Development in recognition of your outstanding contributions in international cooperation and leadership for resource stewardship and disaster assistance during our first century of service.

A few more awards, and then you can return to enjoying everything you see around you.

As you might know, the Forest Service has a large and outstanding research organization devoted to conservation. It is essential for our researchers to keep abreast of research developments overseas, and one of our most important partners in doing so is the International Union of Forest Research Organizations, or IUFRO. Dr. Peter Mayer joins us tonight from IUFRO headquarters in Vienna, Austria, where he serves as IUFRO's executive secretary. Dr. Mayer will be making the first award.

The next award will be presented by a partner organization we've worked closely with for many, many years—The Nature Conservancy. I'd like to introduce the president of The Nature Conservancy, Mr. Steve McCormick. Mr. McCormick will be making the award.

The last award will be made by an organization with roots in the early conservation movement: the Jewish National Fund. I would like to introduce the CEO of the Jewish National Fund, Mr. Russell Robinson … and the vice president of government relations, Mr. Joe Hess. I'd also like to point out that the Israeli ambassador to the United States is present, Mr. Daniel Ayalon. He will be making a few remarks after the final award.

Now I'd like to invite you to enjoy the rest of the evening.

Centennial Congress Awards Ceremony, January 6, 2005

Public Service (External) Presented by Elizabeth Estill

The Ad Council

The Ad Council's Smokey Bear fire prevention campaign is the longest running public service campaign in history and has inspired several generations of Americans to take personal responsibility to prevent unwanted fires caused by humans. For more than sixty years, The Ad Council has worked pro bono with the Forest Service and the National Association of State Foresters to make Smokey's message contemporary and effective.

American Recreation Coalition

The American Recreation Coalition has long been a strong Forest Service partner and has sponsored numerous major programs for youth education, fire prevention, recreation management and information, public awareness, social science understanding, and customer service. The Coalition continues to be instrumental in supporting quality outdoor recreation programs for the public and supports the Agency in accomplishing that diverse challenge.

The Nature Conservancy

Founded in 1951, The Nature Conservancy (TNC), has been a special partner of the Forest Service in protection of plants, animals, and natural communities. TNC works across agencies, communities, and business in a non-confrontational approach using science and information as a strength of building understanding and support. TNC has been a major supporter of the Forest Service at all levels and across all parts of the country.

Rudolph (Rudy) Andrew Wendelin (1910–2000)

Rudy Wendelin was a Forest Service employee and the official Smokey Bear artist for many years. He provided national leadership in fire prevention with amazingly successful long-term and significant contributions. He produced more than four thousand Smokey Bear works of art in his twenty-seven-year career with the Forest Service.

Bob Marshall (1901–1939)

Bob Marshall was a pioneer in developing the recreation and wilderness programs in the Forest Service during the 1930s. He was instrumental in developing the institutional framework for protection of wild lands in America that eventually led to the establishment of the National Wilderness Preservation System.

Mark Reimers (retired)

Mark Reimers, in his thirty-eight-year career with the Forest Service, served the public in many different capacities with significant success, but his work and involvement in Legislative Programs is monumental. He worked tirelessly with Congress, interest groups, and six administrations on a variety of critically important legislation such as Renewable Resources Protection Act, National Forest Management Act, wilderness legislation in nearly thirty different states, and numerous others. Mr. Reimers, in a quiet, professional way, served the public in an exemplary manner which yielded long-term benefits to society.

University Leadership presented by Ann Bartuska

National Association of Professional Forestry Schools and Colleges

The National Association of Professional Forestry Schools and Colleges (NAPF-SC) consists of sixty-nine member colleges and universities and was formed to advance the science, practice and art of forest management through the encouragement and support of forest resource education, research, extension and international programs at the university level. Prior to the formation of forest research stations, university forestry schools played the primary role of providing research results to the Forest Service. Since World War II, NAPFSC members have been key partners in many Forest Service programs; within the National Forest System, State & Private Forestry, and Research & Development branches of the Agency. NAPFSC schools have played, and are still playing, major roles in the development of forestry policies affecting national forests and helping to improve the management of other public and private forests. NAPFSC schools work with State & Private Forestry to help deliver science to land managers and owners through extension forestry programs and other activities.

Tuskegee University

In the 1960s, Tuskegee University, College of Agricultural, Environmental and Natural Science entered into a Master Memorandum of Understanding with the U. S. Forest Service Southern Forest Experiment Station and placed Forest Service personnel on Tuskegee's campus. They assisted with outreach, recruitment, education, placement, and conversion of students (African Americans and other minority groups) into the Forest Service workforce. Since 1968, Tuskegee has graduated over 120 foresters and natural resources professionals, many of which whom are employed with the Forest Service. In the early 1990s, the Tuskegee University Forestry and Natural Resources Program Council was reestablished. The Council has over 30 active members including the USDA Forest Service, forestry industry, corporate America, alumni, and friends. The Council helps to provide scholarships, jobs, and placement of students in forestry, natural resources, agriculture, and related sciences. The Forest Service has been able to attract and retain many of the students under the USDA/1890 National Scholars Program. The Tuskegee University Forestry and Natural Resources Program has paved the way for other Forest Service "Multicultural Recruitment Initiatives."

Science Leadership Presented by Ann Bartuska

Raphael Zon (1874–1956)

Raphael Zon helped build the U. S. Forest Service organization by promoting the importance of scientific investigation. Mr. Zon was instrumental in the creation of Forest Experiment Stations, and without doubt, was the force behind science leadership in the Agency in its formative years.

Gene Likens, Institute of Ecosystem Studies
F. Herbert Bowman, Yale University
Robert S. Pierce, USDA Forest Service
Noye M. Johnson, Dartmouth College

Gene Likens, F. Herbert Bowman, Robert Pierce, and Noye Johnson founded long-term investigations of forest watershed ecosystems and the Hubbard Brook Experimental Forest in the White Mountain National Forest. They were among the first to apply the concepts of nutrient and energy flows to understanding forest watersheds. They used these studies to investigate the impacts forest management, road building, and air pollution have on the ecosystem. Their work has had global implications for forest and ecosystem management and conservation. Their ground-breaking approach set the stage for what has become the Long Term Ecological Network (LTER), a series of international ecosystem studies. The Forest Service is an active partner in these studies.

Jack Ward Thomas, Ph.D. (retired)

Dr. Jack Ward Thomas, Forest Service Chief from 1993 to 1996, has been instrumental in connecting management to science. Dr. Thomas has been influential in framing many of the science leadership issues that face the U. S. Forest Service today. He continues to use his science leadership to help reconcile the differences that exist in our society in viewing resource issues.

Leadership in a Diverse Society Presented by Chris Pyron

F. Dale Robertson (retired)

Dale Robertson has served in many leadership roles including Forest Service Chief from 1987 to 1993. Among Mr. Robertson's greatest contributions to the Agency was his passion and capacity to create an understanding and commitment to strengthening the U. S. Forest Service through diversity. During his time as Chief, Mr. Robertson not only changed the face of the Forest Service, but also changed our heart and future. He has set a leadership example that must be embraced at all levels and for all time.

Ellie Towns. J.D. (retired)

Ellie Towns was the Southwest Regional Forester until her retirement in 2002. Throughout her numerous roles, she set an example of positive leadership commitment to living, learning, and leading in a diverse society. She leads by example, and her commitment to the Agency and to the people who make it what it is exemplary.

Organizational Leadership presented by Chris Pyron

Overton W. Price (1873–1914)

Overton Price was the first Associate Forester of the Forest Service and was instrumental in developing the organizational structure of the Forest Service. He possessed a great capacity to organize and lead and created an efficient system of Ranger Districts, Forests, Regions, and National Office that in basic blueprint still remains today.

R. Max Peterson, Chief Emeritus

Max Peterson, Chief of the Forest Service from 1979 to 1987, symbolizes the leadership and commitment to organization that has held the Agency together for a hundred years. Mr. Peterson was instrumental in bridging new organizational realities brought about by the National Forest Management Act and responded to new challenges of immense proportion. In retirement, and as the former executive vice president of the International Association of Fish and Wildlife Agencies, he has continued to guide, counsel, and support the Agency through his seemingly infinite capacity to understand and lead the organization.

Lou Romero

For over forty years, Lou Romero has been a convener, facilitator, mentor, educator, communicator, and student of organizational leadership for the U.S. Forest Service. He has helped guide and transition numerous Forest Service leaders. He has had major roles in significant leadership gatherings, including all Forest Supervisor meetings since the first in 1985 and additional national meetings. He continues, in the private sector, to take special interest in providing organizational leadership to upcoming Forest Service leaders.

Society of American Foresters

Founded in 1900 by Gifford Pinchot, the Society of American Foresters has long been associated with and a solid supporter of the Forest Service. As the largest professional society for foresters in the world, their history in establishing professional standards has been invaluable to the Agency. The Society advances science, education, technology, and the practice of forestry. Their efforts on a continuing basis over a hundred years has made them leaders in advancing the conservation ethic to ensure the continued health and use of forest ecosystems for present and future generations.

Resource Stewardship (External) presented by Joel Holtrop

National Association of State Foresters

The National Association of State Foresters is a nonprofit organization that represents the directors of State Forestry agencies. State foresters have worked tirelessly with forestry, wildlife, wildfire, and other resource professionals promoting healthy sustainable forests that provide various uses, products and benefits for the public, landowners, and the Nation. The Association's partnership with the Forest Service has been essential in our mission of resource stewardship to meet the needs of present and future generations.

Trust for Public Land

The Trust for Public Land (TPL) has been a Forest Service partner for over thirty years, helping to conserve key land for watershed, public recreation, and resource protection. TPL has assisted the Forest Service with the Land & Water Conservation Fund (L&WCF) purchase and exchange program. Trust for Public Land has assisted in acquiring over five hundred thousand acres of land for the National Forest System, including nationally significant areas such as Columbia River Gorge National Scenic Area, Big Sur Coastline, and Hells Canyon National Recreation Area. They participated in over six hundred individual L&WCF acquisitions in thirty-four states in all nine regions.

William D. Hagenstein

William Hagenstein is a retired forest products association executive director from Portland, Oregon and a former president of the Society of American

Foresters (1966–1969). For many decades, he led efforts to further professional resource stewardship of our Nation's forests and was instrumental in working to resolve critical resource stewardship issues of the day. He was mentored by former Forest Service Chief William Greeley and was very engaged in policy dialogue as a professional, association representative, and as an advocate. He continues to be active and influential in resource management as an advisor and supporter.

Community Leadership presented by Joel Holtrop

Jack Shipley, Applegate Partnership

Jack Shipley founded and established Applegate Partnership in 1992 to encourage cooperation between communities and agencies on forest management issues in the Applegate River Valley. The Applegate Partnership is a community based nonprofit organization involving industry, conservation groups, natural resource agencies, and residents cooperating to encourage and facilitate the use of natural resource principles promoting ecosystem health and diversity. Mr. Shipley's accomplishments include: teaming with the Forest Service and BLM to implement forest health projects demonstrating how communities and agencies could work together; influencing the creation and inclusion of the Applegate Adaptive Management Area in the Northwest Forest Plan; and influencing the acquisition of over $100,000 in grant funding to initiate and complete the Applegate Fire Plan. He also played a significant role in coordinating a partnership between several parties, including the Forest Service, to raise over $100,000 to develop a collaborative demonstration project regarding fuels hazard reduction treatment effects and opportunities over a forty-thousand-acre landscape.

Volunteer Leadership presented by Tom Thompson

National Ski Patrol

Founded in 1938, the National Ski Patrol (NSP) has become the largest winter rescue organization in the world. The Patrol has been a strong partner of the Forest Service with largely volunteer patrollers promoting skiing and ski safety. Over the years many Forest Service employees and retirees have helped fill the volunteer ranks.

Appalachian Trail Conference

The Appalachian Trail Conference (ATC) has a long-term history as a volunteer based nonprofit organization which focuses on protection and promotion of the Appalachian Trail. The Forest Service and the ATC have been partners in management of the Trail since 1925, and the Conference was instrumental in ensuring the passage of the Volunteer Act of 1972. Each year more than 4,500 volunteers contribute more than 180,000 hours to maintain, manage, and administer the ATC. Total contributions are valued at over $3 million, with over a $1 million contributed annually on National Forest System lands.

Rocky Mountain Elk Foundation

The Rocky Mountain Elk Foundation (RMEF) has been a Forest Service partner for nearly 20 years. They have helped to fund and implement 1,667 resource stewardship projects, permanently protect 73,000 acres through land acquisition and protect over 50,000 acres through lease acquisitions. Additionally, they have assisted with research, elk restoration, and conservation education programs such as High Schools for Habitat, Becoming an Outdoors Woman, and the Wildlife Leadership Award Scholarship. RMEF has partnered with the Forest Service to enhance or protect almost 2 million acres across 83 national forests, 4 national grasslands, 5 National Recreation Areas, and involved 2 research stations on projects totaling nearly $90 million in total assets. RMEF has 140,000 members with 11,000 active volunteers contributing to work on the ground.

Resource Stewardship (Internal) presented by Tom Thompson and Dale Bosworth

Aldo Leopold (1887–1948)

Aldo Leopold, during his Forest Service career, made significant contributions to resource stewardship in the Agency's formative years. He pioneered new concepts and ideas of public land stewardship such as wildlife management and wilderness management. His philosophy of land ethic that matured in his years at University of Wisconsin and on his property in Sand County continues to lead resource managers throughout the world.

Floyd Iverson (1910–1998)

Floyd Iverson contributed to resolving major grazing issues in the Rocky Mountain and Intermountain West in the 1950s. His ability to bring resource stewardship concepts into the range business and his work in watershed management had a monumental impact on the U. S. Forest Service. He later became Regional Forester of the Intermountain Region and was very active in the Society of Range Management.

Jay Cravens (retired)

Jay Cravens has demonstrated a sustained commitment to resource stewardship of our Nation's forests. During his career with the Forest Service, he served in many capacities in the Southwest and as Regional Forester of the Eastern Region. During the Vietnam years, Mr. Cravens served in a significant AID tour. He also was a professor at the University of Wisconsin, the president of the Society of American Foresters, a consulting forester, and continues to be active in supporting the Forest Service.

Tom Thompson (presented by Dale Bosworth)

Tom Thompson, a thirty-six-year veteran and National Forest System Deputy Chief, has contributed significantly to the stewardship of National Forest System land resources. His leadership and commitment to diversity has provided the critical support, tools, and skills necessary to accomplish essential work on the ground. Tom is an avid connoisseur of Forest Service history and has a keen interest in examining and understanding the successes and disappointments of the past. Tom's infectious enthusiasm has been the catalyst behind the Agency's celebration of its one-hundred-year conservation legacy.

Centennial Legacy presented by Tom Thompson

Gifford Pinchot (1865–1946)

The first Chief Forester of the U. S. Forest Service, Gifford Pinchot, "Cared for the Land and Served the People." He was the Governor of the State of Pennsylvania, founder of the Society of American Foresters, and a professional forester who supported the U. S. Forest Service throughout his lifetime.

American Forests

For 125 years, American Forests has worked to find and develop the best science to identify conservation issues and solutions. They have been a leading voice for many Forest Congresses which helped establish the Forest Reserves and the transfer of those reserves to the USDA. They have supported the formation of state forestry associations and protection of eastern National Forests. American Forests has a proud history of support and partnership with the U. S. Forest Service. The organization has furthered communication of forestry issues and has been a convener of citizen activists, business, forestry professions and managers.

Congressional Recognition

The following Congressmen and Senators were recognized with a special Centennial award at the Whitten Gala on January 5, 2005.

John Wingate Weeks: U.S. Representative and Senator (1904–1919)

John Wingate Weeks is best known for his efforts at establishing the eastern national forest system. In the early 1900s all the forest lands in the eastern half of the United States were privately owned and many were in poor condition. There were no national forests in the east, and the government was not empowered to purchase private lands. Congress finally passed the Appalachian-White Mountains Forest Reservation Bill in 1911, largely due to the efforts of Representative Weeks. The Weeks Act authorized the federal government to purchase lands to be permanently reserved, held and administered as national forest lands, "for the protection, development and use of their natural resource."

Charles Linza McNary: U.S. Senator (1917–1944)

Charles McNary was a Senator from Oregon and Chairman of the Senate Select Committee on Reforestation. He sponsored the Clarke-McNary Act of 1924 which set the cooperative tone of the relationship between the Forest Service and the forest industry for decades to come. The act provided for cooperative opportunities with states on reforestation, fire control, farm woodlots, and expanded land purchase for new national forests under the Weeks Act of 1911. Senator McNary also co-sponsored the McSweeney-McNary Act of 1928 that expanded authorities for national forest land purchases.

Hubert Horatio Humphrey: U.S. Senator (1948–1964 and 1970–1978)
Hubert Humphrey, senator from Minnesota and vice-president under Lyndon Johnson introduced the Multiple Use Sustained Yield Act in 1956, which was passed in 1960. Senator Humphrey was instrumental in the passage of the Wilderness Act of 1964, the National Forest Management Act of 1976, and the Resource Planning Act of 1978.

Awards presented by the Regional Forums

The following Awards were given during the eleven regional forums held during November and December 2005.

International Institute of Tropical Forestry Forum
Michael Buck, *Partnership*
Geoambiente del Caribe, *Partnership*
University of Puerto Rico, *Partnership*

Region 1 Forum
Backcountry Horsemen of America, *Outstanding Partner Organization*
Carla Cline Belski, Bob Marshall Foundation, *Outstanding Forest Service Volunteer*
Smoke Elser, *Outstanding Private Sector Partner*

Region 2 Forum
Joe Chapman, *Outstanding Volunteer*
Laramie Bicycling Network (BikeNet), *Outstanding Partner Organization*
Volunteers for Outdoor Colorado, *Outstanding Volunteer Organization*
Recreational Equipment, Inc.(REI), *Outstanding Private Sector Partner*
Cheyenne River, Rosebud, Standing Rock, and Yankton Sioux Tribes, *Outstanding Youth Organizations*

Region 3 Forum
Sterling Tipton, *Outstanding contribution to the development of the Zuni Furniture Enterprise, which utilizes forest products from restoration treatments*
Cornelia Flora, *Outstanding contribution to developing community based collaborative approaches to natural resource management and conservation internationally*

Juan Manuel Frausto, *Outstanding contribution to the development and implementation of the Mexican Wildfire Prevention and Restoration Program*

Region 4 Forum
Stephen Steed, Skyline Forest Resources
Bethine Church
Idaho Department of Parks and Recreation, *Outstanding Partner*

Region 5 Forum
Rorie Gothan, *Outstanding Volunteer*
High Sierra Volunteer Trail Crew, *Outstanding Partner Organization*
Buck Rock Foundation, *Outstanding Partner Organization*
American Forest Resource Council, *Outstanding Private Sector Partner*

Region 6 Forum
Joan Hobson, The Hiking Grandmother, *In appreciation of her dedication in promoting the development and use of the Florida National Scenic Trail*
American Hiking Society, *In appreciation of our long-term partnership for the many collaborative efforts supporting trails, including promotion of National Trails Days events*
Tread Lightly!, Inc., *In appreciation of their many programs and services in promoting outdoor ethics for responsible recreation use of National Forest lands*

Region 8 Forum
Longleaf Alliance
National Wild Turkey Federation
Cecil Family and Biltmore Estate
Cradle of Forestry Interpretive Association

Region 9 Forum
Gerald Adelmann, *Chicago Open Space Preservation*
Northeastern Area Association of State Foresters, *Sustained Leadership*
The Pinchot Institute for Conservation, *Sustaining Pinchot's Legacy of Conservation*
The Nature Conservancy, *Restoring Natural Systems in the East*
Morton Arboretum, *Conservation Through Education*
Eastern National Forest Interpretive Association, *Quality Interpretive Programs*

The Society for the Protection of New Hampshire Forests, *Leadership in Establishing National Forests in the East*

Student Conservation Association, *Building Young Conservation Leaders*

American Forest and Paper Association, *Sustainable Forest Management*

The Engineered Wood Association, *Sustainable Forest Management*

CenterPoint, *Environmental Education and Stewardship of Prairies and Savannas*

Region 10 Forum

Bruce McCurtain, Alaska Recreation Management, *Outstanding Performance in Partnership*

Jeff Jahnke, Alaska State Forester, *Sustained Performance in Partnership with the Forest Service*

Art and Claire King, *Outstanding and Sustained Community Leadership*

Bob Ott, Alaska Northern Forest Cooperative, *Outstanding Leadership*

Roberta Wilfong, Manager, Kenai Peninsula Spruce Bark Beetle Mitigation Program, *Outstanding Support to the Interagency All Lands/All Hands Approach*

Tom Paragi, Cochair, Alaska Northern Forest Cooperative, *Outstanding Leadership*

Grey Towers Forum

F. Dale Robertson

Ann Forest Burns

Roger Sedjo

American Recreation Coalition

Ross Whaley, Ph.D., *Long-term Commitment and Support to Furthering the Pinchot Legacy*

Dennis LeMaster, *Long-term Commitment and Support to Furthering the Pinchot Legacy*

Char Miller, Ph.D., *Long-term Commitment and Support to Furthering the Pinchot Legacy*

The Forest History Society, *Sustained Partnership and Collaboration*

The Pinchot Institute, *Long-term Partnership and Cooperation*

Appendices

Background of Speakers
Sponsors
Exhibitors
Delegates and Attendees
Pinchot Principles

january 3-6
2005
washington dc

US Forest Service

Centennial
Congress

A Collective Commitment to Conservation

Background of Speakers

Dale Bosworth
15th Chief of the Forest Service, 2001–present

Dale N. Bosworth became the 15th Chief of the Forest Service on April 12, 2001. Bosworth began his career in the Northern Region as a forester on the St. Joe National Forest (now a part of the Idaho Panhandle National Forest) in Idaho, and later served on the Kanisksu, Colville, and Lolo National Forests. In 1990, he became Deputy Director of Forest Management in the Forest Service national headquarters in Washington, D.C., where he served until 1992, when he became Deputy Regional Forester for the Pacific Southwest Region. From that position, Bosworth was promoted to Regional Forester for the Intermountain Region in 1994 and the Northern Region 1997. Bosworth held this position until he was chosen to be Chief of the Forest Service in the spring of 2001.

David Bell
Chairman of the Board, National Forest Foundation

David Bell is vice chairman of the Interpublic Group of Companies, the world's largest marketing communications and services company. Mr. Bell was chairman and chief executive officer of True North Communications Inc. until its recent merger with Interpublic. Under his leadership, a culture of collaboration was established across True North brands on behalf of clients seeking broader solutions, significantly driving organic growth. He serves on the board of directors of Primedia Inc., the New York City Partnership and, the National Forest Foundation. In addition, he is a trustee of the Convent of the Sacred Heart school in New York City.

Elizabeth Agpaoa
Chief of Staff, Office of the Chief, USDA Forest Service

Liz Agpaoa is the new Chief of Staff for the Forest Service. Previously, Liz Agpaoa was the Forest Supervisor of the Cibola National Forest from 1998 to 2004. She was part of the Siskiyou National Forest Planning and Corporate Information Staff from 1996 to 1999 and a District Ranger from 1991 to 1996. Liz has also worked in the Pacific Northwest Region as an Environmental Specialist, and on the Willamette National Forest as a Planning Wildlife Biologist and District Biologist.

Terry Baker
Forester Trainee, Apalachicola National Forest, Marianna, Florida
Nominated by the Society of American Foresters

Terry recently graduated from the University of Florida with a B.S. in forest resources and conservation and a minor in botany, with an additional B.S. in agricultural science from Florida A & M University. Receiving two bachelor of science degrees, Terry completed the Florida A & M University and Florida University 2 + 2 Forest Service minority initiative program in April 2004. As a student, Terry served as the chair for the University of Florida's student chapter of the Society of American Foresters and was recognized as outstanding rising senior, outstanding graduating senior, and Diversity Scholar. Next fall Terry plans to take a leave of absence from his position as a forester trainee to pursue graduate studies in forest economics and policy to become, "a more effective Forest Service employee." He is especially active in informing the public about the Forest Service and natural resource management.

Arthur "Butch" Blazer
Director, State Forestry Division of the State of New Mexico's
Energy, Minerals and Natural Resources Department

Arthur "Butch" Blazer, New Mexico State Forester, is a member of the Mescalero Apache Tribe. Elected to the tribal council in 1998, he served on the executive committee as treasurer until the end of his second term in 2002. Prior to his State appointment by Governor Bill Richardson, Blazer held the position of director of planning and development for his Tribe, working on several economic and social initiatives, including the development of a tribal fish hatchery. Blazer carries a twenty-seven-year career with the Bureau of Indian Affairs (BIA) to his new position with state government. With the BIA, he served in the capacity of a range specialist, the Southwest regional natural resources manager, and as Agency Superintendent on two different reservations.

Edgar B. Brannon, Jr.
Former Director, Grey Towers National Historic Landmark

Ed Brannon spent the past fifteen years as director of Grey Towers National Historic Landmark, promoting the legacy of Gifford Pinchot through programs at Grey Towers, his service to the agency and, his affiliation with the Pinchot Institute for Conservation. In addition to his wide range of responsibilities and duties at Grey Towers, Ed served as coordinator of the Forest Supervisor's Leadership Forum, a leadership development program for field officers. Before coming to Grey Towers, Ed was the Forest Supervisor of the Flathead National Forest, Kalispell, Montana.

Deborah Campbell
Anchor, Regional Forum Reports
Deborah Campbell is a Nevada journalist, nonprofit executive, and civic volunteer with twenty-seven years of experience communicating, collaborating and connecting people. Ms. Campbell recently launched Deborah Campbell and Associates, a public relations, public affairs and philanthropy consulting firm. She is currently providing strategic planning, facilitation and fund development services to nonprofit, public agencies and private sector organizations. Deborah previously served as vice president and executive director of St. Rose Dominican Hospitals' Health Foundation located in Henderson, Nevada, one of the fastest growing cities in the country, and as senior vice president and chief operating officer of the United Way of Southern Nevada. Ms. Campbell's journalism background includes sixteen years of news, public affairs and morning show anchor duties at televisions stations in Chico, California and Las Vegas, Nevada.

Majora Carter
Founder and Director, Sustainable South Bronx
Majora Carter is founder and executive director of Sustainable South Bronx, an emergent community organization dedicated to the implementation of sustainable development projects for the South Bronx that are informed by the needs of the community and the values of environmental justice. She is also a co-founder of the group Greening for Breathing, an organization dedicated to increasing the number of street trees in Hunts Point. Majora Carter additionally co-designed the proposal for CityRiver, a job-creation, economic, and ecological development for the Bronx River. She is a board member of the NYC Environmental Justice Alliance and representative for the Organization of Waterfront Neighborhoods.

Alyse Charley
Reedley High School, Dunlap, CA
Nominated by the Forest Service Central California Consortium
Currently a senior at Reedley High School, Alyse Charley is maternally Mono Indian, and part Chukchansi and Choinumni Indian. Learning from her community, Alyse takes pride in her Native American heritage, and participates in

Dunlap Band of Mono Indian tribe meetings to become aware of the issues facing her tribe. In her community she accompanies her father, a Sergeant of Arms for the Dunlap Band of Mono Indians Tribal Council, to General Council. At school Alyse is a member of the Generation Green Club, where she was selected as one of fifteen students to participate in a Leadership Camp at the California State Fair in Sacramento, CA. There she worked as a Forest Service volunteer, spreading Smokey's message of fire safety. Next year Alyse plans on attending a forestry college, Feather River College in Northern California.

Sally Collins
Associate Chief of the Forest Service
Sally Collins was named Associate Chief of the USDA Forest Service in August 2001. Prior to her selection as Associate Chief, Collins had been the Associate Deputy Chief for the National Forest System since April 2000, and prior to that was the Forest Supervisor for the Deschutes National Forest in Oregon for seven years. Over her eighteen years in public service and resource management, Collins has worked for both the Forest Service and the Bureau of Land Management in Oregon and Colorado. In addition to serving as Forest Supervisor, she has held positions as Deputy Forest Supervisor, assistant planner, wilderness specialist, environmental coordinator, and mineral leasing coordinator.

Honorable Larry Craig (R)
Senator, Idaho
In 1974, the people of Payette and Washington counties sent Senator Craig to the Idaho State Senate, where he served three terms before winning the 1980 race for Idaho's First District Congressional Seat. He was re-elected four times before winning the U.S. Senate election in 1990 and was re-elected to the Senate in 1996 and 2002. Senator Craig is the Chairman of the Senate Special Committee on Aging and a member of the Committee on Energy and Natural Resources, where he is the Chairman of the Subcommittee on Public Lands and Forests, and a member of the Subcommittee on Energy and the Subcommittee on Water and Power. As a Westerner and a former rancher, Senator Craig plays a leading role in the formation of natural resource and energy policies, and he has gained a national reputation as a stalwart against environmental extremism.

Honorable John R. Crowell, Jr.
Former Assistant Secretary of Agriculture, Natural Resources and Environment

John Crowell served as Assistant Secretary of Agriculture for Natural Resources and Environment in President Reagan's first term, 1981–1985. Mr. Crowell came to the Department of Agriculture from a legal career in the natural resources field, having been general counsel for Louisiana-Pacific Corporation from 1972 to 1981 and an attorney with Georgia-Pacific Corporation from 1959 to 1972. From 1986 to 1999, Mr. Crowell was a partner in the Portland law firm of Lane Powell Spears Lubersky LLP, where he specialized in business and in matters affecting the forest products industry. His birding interest led him to serve twelve years as a volunteer regional editor for American Birds.

Honorable M. Rupert Cutler, Ph.D.
Former Assistant Secretary of Agriculture, Conservation, Research, and Education

Rupert Cutler of Roanoke, Virginia, currently is a member of the Roanoke City Council and the boards of directors of the Western Virginia Water Authority and the Virginia Outdoors Foundation. He has been assistant executive director of The Wilderness Society, senior vice president of the National Audubon Society, executive director of Population-Environment Balance, and president of Defenders of Wildlife. In 1977 President Jimmy Carter appointed him Assistant Secretary of Agriculture for Conservation, Research, and Education. Through 1980 he provided policy direction to the USDA Forest Service, Soil Conservation Service, and the USDA's research, extension, and library agencies. Since 1991, Dr. Cutler has resided in Roanoke, VA, where he has served as executive director of Virginia's Explore Park, an outdoor living history museum, and founding executive director of the Western Virginia Land Trust.

Todd Davidson
Executive Director, Oregon Tourism Commission

Todd Davidson was appointed executive director of the Oregon Tourism Commission in 1996. Under his direction, tourism in Oregon has become a $6.3 billion industry, employing nearly 89,500 Oregonians. Davidson is a member of numerous boards and commissions including the Travel Industry Association of America, the National Council of State Travel Directors (NCSTD), and the Western States Tourism Policy Council (WSTPC). As a member of WSTPC, he assisted with the development and implementation of the historic Memorandum of Understanding between five federal departments, eight federal agencies, and thirteen western states coordinating the management of tourism on public recreation lands.

Daniel Delgado
Cuba High School, Cuba, NM
Nominated by National Hispanic Environmental Council
Daniel Delgado is a senior at Cuba High School in Cuba, New Mexico, a small town where he grew up. Daniel currently works on a project identifying hazardous materials in the pit lake of the Nacimiento Copper Mine on the Santa Fe National Forest. Daniel has tested the water at New Mexico Tech and found that since beginning acid treatments he has raised the pH from 2.38 to 6.2. This project won recognitions for being one of the top environmental projects in the four corners region. He plans on attending University of New Mexico next year, where he will study environmental sciences.

Honorable Norm Dicks (D)
U.S. Representative, Washington
Norm Dicks, a native of Bremerton, Washington, was elected to Congress in November 1976. Having received a rare first-term appointment to the House Appropriations Committee, he currently serves as a senior member of that Committee. He is a member of three key Appropriations Subcommittees—Defense, Interior and Military Construction—which are all related to the interests of Washington State. In the 108th Congress he serves as the Ranking Democratic Member of the Interior Appropriations Subcommittee, which places him in a leadership position on federal environmental and natural resource policies as well as Indian Affairs.

Mike Dombeck, Ph.D.
14th Chief of the Forest Service, 1997–2001
Mike Dombeck's leadership in the Bureau of Land Management and as former Chief of the Forest Service impacted nearly five hundred million acres. He is most noted for significant efforts toward watershed health and restoration, sustainable forest ecosystem management, sound forest roads, and roadless area protection. Dr. Dombeck now serves as GEM Pioneer Professor and UW System Fellow of Global Conservation. He is helping to lead the planning and development of the Global Environmental Management Education Center in the College of Natural Resources at the University of Wisconsin-Stevens Point,

which aims to develop and share world-class educational programs in natural resources and environmental management for building a sustainable future locally and abroad.

Honorable Pete Domenici (R)
Senator, New Mexico

Pete V. Domenici, the longest serving U.S. Senator in New Mexico's history, began his sixth term in the Senate by taking on the major challenge of producing a comprehensive national energy policy for the United States. After more than two decades leading the federal budget process, Domenici assumed the helm of the Senate Energy and Natural Resources Committee. He is committed to bringing his hard-earned budget experience to play in setting a course for greater energy independence in the United States. Over the years, Senator Domenici has consistently supported balanced environmental initiatives to preserve our natural resources while permitting their best possible use. He has authored legislation to protect the wilderness in New Mexico, ranging from the creation of the Petroglyph National Monument near Albuquerque in 1990 to the Valles Caldera National Preserve and Trust in 2000.

Honorable Robert E. Douglas
Superintendent, Tehama County Department of Education
President, National Forest Counties and Schools Coalition

Bob Douglas currently serves as president of the National Forest Counties and Schools Coalition (NFCSC), a grass roots umbrella organization of eleven hundred local, state, regional, and national organizations representing thirty-seven states, which he helped develop in 1998. The National Forest Counties and Schools Coalition was the lead stakeholder advocacy group to develop and shepherd through Congress, PL 106-393, The Secure Rural Schools and Communities Revitalization Act of 2000. As president of NFCSC, Mr. Douglas has been a leader in the implementation of PL 106-393 and the integration of the Secure Rural Schools legislation with the Healthy Forest Restoration Act and other active forest management initiatives.

Honorable George Dunlop
Principal Deputy Assistant Secretary of the Army (Civil Works)
Deputy Assistant Secretary of the Army (Policy and Legislation)

George S. Dunlop assists the Assistant Secretary of the Army (Civil Works) in supervising the Army Civil Works program, including programs for conservation and development of the nation's water and wetland resources, flood control, navigation, and shore protection. Additionally, as Deputy Assistant Secretary of the Army (Policy and Legislation), he serves as the principal policy and legislative advisor to the Assistant Secretary of the Army (Civil Works). He is responsible for directing the Civil Works legislative program, including authorizing legislation to support Civil Works projects and programs, and the development and articulation of the Army's policies affecting the Civil Works program. He maintains extensive interface with the Executive Office of the President, Congress, Department of Defense, Department of the Army, other government departments, tribes, state agencies and other public and private parties interested in the Army Civil Works program.

M. Hosny El-Lakany, Ph.D.

Assistant Director General, Forestry Department, Food and Agriculture Organization (FAO)

Dr. M. Hosny El-Lakany was appointed Assistant Director General in charge of the FAO Forestry Department in 1998 after serving as the Director of Forest Resources Division. Prior to joining the FAO, Dr. El-Lakany was a consultant, inter alia, to the World Bank, UNDP, UNEP, FAO, IDRC of Canada, USAID, and undertook field missions in Africa, Asia, Australia, and Latin America. Currently, he chairs the Collaborative Partnership on Forests (CPR), composed of fourteen international, intergovernmental, and non-governmental organizations and supports the work of the U.N. Forum on Forests (UNFF). Dr. El-Lakany was awarded the International Forester of the Year Award (1988), the Alexandria University Gold Medal for Academic Achievements (1992) and the Order of The Two Niles, from the Republic of Sudan in 2001.

Sally K. Fairfax, Ph.D.

Department of Environmental Science, Policy and Management, College of Natural Resources, University of California, Berkeley

Sally Fairfax, Henry J. Vaux distinguished professor of forest policy, has taught natural resource law and policy at the University of California, Berkeley, College of Natural Resources for over twenty years. She specializes in land conservation and management and has published extensively on legal aspects of administration and related federalism issues. Sally Fairfax is co-author of *Forest and Range Policy, The Federal Lands, and State Trust Lands*. She is presently focused on changing institutions of land conservation and management, the dispersion and devolution of federal authority, and is co-author of *Conservation*

Trusts, forthcoming from University Press of Kansas. Working with several graduate students, she has just completed a new book entitled *Buying Nature: The Limits to Land Acquisition as a Conservation Tool From 1780 to 2002.*

Jessica Farrar
Illinois Wesleyan University, Bloomington, IL
Nominated by the Girl Scouts of America
Currently a sophomore enrolled as a business administration major and English minor at Illinois Wesleyan University, Jessica Ferrar has been described as a young and passionate Girl Scout. Recently she received the Girl Scout's Gold Award, "Young Woman of Distinction." Jessica has had a passion for the outdoors as long as she can remember, but two experiences with Outward Bound solidified her devotion to working for the environment.

Jo Ellen Force, Ph.D.
Head of Forest Resources Department,
College of Natural Resources, University of Idaho
Jo Ellen Force teaches and conducts research in the areas of forest social science and forest policy. Her research includes studies of public participation in forest planning, social change in forest resource-dependent communities, and development of the Human Ecosystem Framework (with colleagues Gary Machlis and Bill Burch). Jo Ellen has served on the Executive Committee of the National Association of Professional Forestry Schools and Colleges, Secretary Glickman's Forestry Research Advisory Council (1997–2000), and the Sustainable Forestry Initiative's External Review Panel.

Paul W. Hansen
Executive Director, Isaak Walton League of America
Paul Hansen is the executive director of the Izaak Walton League of America (IWLA), one of the nation's oldest and most respected conservation organizations. The League works closely with the nation's environmental groups, sportsmen groups, and the business community to find informed solutions to conservation and environmental problems. In February 1999, Mr. Hansen was named to the board of the Louisiana Pacific Corporation and is one of the first conservationists to sit on the board of a major corporation.

John Heissenbuttel
Vice President, Forestry and Wood Products Division, American Forest and Paper Association

John Heissenbuttel is currently responsible for managing the American Forest and Paper Association's Forest Resources Group, Wood Products International Department, and the American Wood Council. In this role he is responsible for identifying and pursuing issue priorities, strategic goals, and imperatives for ensuring fiber supply and access to wood product markets for member companies. John is known for providing the staff leadership to create and implement AF&PA's Sustainable Forestry Initiative® program.

Mavis C. Hill
Executive Director, Tyrrell County Community Development Corporation

Mavis Hill is one of the founders and the current executive director of the Tyrell County Community Development Corporation located in Columbia, North Carolina. As the executive director, Mavis is responsible for such programs as the Tyrrell County Youth Conservation Corps, Regional Business Incubator, Building Better Leaders Program, and fostered such partnerships with the Alligator Community Action and the Combined Communities Association. Mavis was also the recipient of the American Land Conservation Award for balancing economic development and the environment, Tarheel of the Week, and was featured in the June 1999 issue of *Audubon* magazine.

James B. Hull
Director and State Forester, Texas Forest Service

In 1996, James B. Hull, C.F., was named state forester and director of the Texas Forest Service, an agency of the Texas A&M University System. Under Hull's leadership, the agency was awarded the prestigious Gold Smokey for early successes in the Texas Wildfire Prevention Plan, the model for other state and federal organizations. James Hull holds numerous leadership positions on forestry boards and organizations at all levels and has served as chair of the Fire Protection Committee of National Association of State Foresters and co-chair of the National Blue Ribbon Commission on Aerial Firefighting. Currently, he is vice president of the National Association of State Foresters and will assume the position of president in September 2005.

Rob Keck
CEO, National Wild Turkey Federation
Rob Keck's passion is to leave an enduring legacy of progress as a deeply committed conservation leader. An avid hunter, fisherman, trapper, outdoor artist, and all around outdoorsman, he strives to promote wildlife conservation worldwide, with special emphasis across North America. He encourages all stakeholders to participate in conservation efforts. Under his leadership, the National Wild Turkey Federation (NWTF) has become one of the fastest growing single species conservation organizations in North America. Additionally, he hosts NWTF's three award-winning national television programs, Turkey Call, Turkey Country, and Get in the Game.

Lyle Laverty
Director, Colorado's Division of Parks and Outdoor Recreation
Lyle Laverty was appointed director of Colorado's Division of Parks and Outdoor Recreation in December 2001. As Director, Lyle oversees the operation of forty state parks as well as parks' programs including the State Trails Program, Boat Safety Program, Snowmobile Program, Off-Highway Vehicle Program, Commercial River Outfitters Licensing and Colorado Natural Areas Program. Prior to becoming Director of Colorado Parks and Outdoor Recreation, Lyle was the Associate Deputy Chief of the USDA Forest Service. Lyle has served as the Regional Forester of the Rocky Mountain Region and was the Director of Recreation, Heritage and Wilderness Resources.

Chuck Leavell
Keyboardist, The Rolling Stones
Chuck Leavell has been pleasing the ears of music fans for over thirty years now. His piano and keyboard work has been heard on the works of Eric Clapton, The Rolling Stones, The Black Crowes, George Harrison, The Allman Brothers Band, The Indigo Girls, Blues Traveler, and many, many more. His association with the Stones has been a long one, beginning back in 1982 and still going strong. In addition to his musical expertise, he is now a respected author, having penned a book on forestry and conservation called *Forever Green: The History and Hope of the American Forest*. He and his wife Rose Lane were given the ultimate honor for their outstanding management of their own forestland, Charlane Plantation, by being named National Outstanding Tree Farmers of the Year in 1999.

Patricia Limerick, Ph.D.
Center of the American West, University of Colorado at Boulder
Patricia Nelson Limerick is a Western American historian, with particular interests in ethnic history and environmental history. From 1980 to 1984, Limerick taught at Harvard University as an assistant professor before joining the faculty at the University of Colorado at Boulder. As a professor of history and environmental studies, she teaches a variety of undergraduate and graduate courses on the American West, including a team-taught course comparing the history of colonialism and imperialism in the American West, Africa, and the Middle East, and a team-taught course on the biological components of Western American history. Her best known work, *The Legacy of Conquest*, has had a major impact on the field of Western American History.

Ann Linehan
Director, Division of Program Support, Head Start Bureau
Ann Linehan has worked with young children and their families for nearly thirty years. From 1982 to 1992, Anne was the executive director of a Head Start and Child Care agency. In 1992, Ms. Linehan joined the Federal Government working in Region I, New England, as Program Manager for Head Start. In 1996, she joined the Head Start Bureau in Washington, D.C., as Director of Program Support devoting much of her time to the implementation of the Early Head Start Program. Currently she oversees the Education, Health, Mental Health, Disabilities and Family and Community Services.

Honorable Jim Lyons
Former Under Secretary, Natural Resources and Environment
Jim Lyons is currently the Executive Director of the Casey Trees Endowment Fund in Washington, D.C., and a Lecturer and Research Scholar at the Yale School of Forestry and Environmental Science. For eight years in the Clinton Administration, Jim was USDA Under Secretary for Natural Resources and Environment. In this position, he was responsible for USDA forestry, conservation, and environmental programs, with oversight of USDA's Forest Service and Natural Resources Conservation Service (NRCS). Jim was a principal architect of President Clinton's Northwest Forest Plan to conserve old-growth forests and promote sustainable forestry. He helped lead USDA efforts on the presidential initiative to protect remaining national forest roadless areas, to reform management of the Tongass National Forest, and to establish new policies to guide future national forest planning and management.

William H. Meadows
President, The Wilderness Society

President of The Wilderness Society since 1996, Bill Meadows has been active in conservation for over thirty years. He first became engaged in environmental issues as a volunteer leader in his home state of Tennessee, working through the Sierra Club, the Tennessee Environmental Council, and the Environmental Action Fund. Bill has become a national leader in public land conservation and wilderness protection, playing important roles in the protection of national forest roadless areas and the most recently designated national monuments. He has worked diligently on national efforts to protect the Arctic National Wildlife Refuge, the Rocky Mountain Front, the Northern Forests, and the Southern Appalachians and continues to provide leadership on wilderness campaigns in Utah, Alaska, California, and Washington State.

Alba Mercado
College of the Sequoias, Dinuba, CA
Nominated by the Forest Service Central California Consortium

Alba Mercado was inspired to become an anthropologist after experiencing ethnic discrimination and social marginalization in her own community. Currently she is studying anthropology and archaeology and frequently visits family in Mexico where she delves more deeply into learning more of her own culture. Last summer Alba participated in a USDA Forest Service Central California Consortium archeology project where she was able to learn artifact discovery and preservation processes as well as cultural resources management. After graduation Alba hopes to work for the Forest Service in order to preserve and conserve past and present cultures within the National Forests.

Char Miller, Ph.D.
History Professor, Trinity University, Texas

Char Miller is a member of the History Department and director of Urban Studies at Trinity University in San Antonio, Texas. He is the author of *Gifford Pinchot and the Making of Modern Environmentalism*, which has won many awards, including the 2003 Charles A. Weyerhaeuser Book Award from the Forest History Society, 2002 Independent Publishers Biography Prize, and the 2002 National Outdoor Book Contest Award for History and Biography. Char also is the co-author of the award winning, *The Greatest Good: 100 Years of Forestry in America*. He is a Senior Fellow at the Pinchot Institute for Conservation in Washington, D.C., and on the board of directors of the Forest History Society.

Robert Model
President, Boone and Crockett Club
Robert Model is the chairman of the American Wildlife Conservation Partners, a board member for the Theodore Roosevelt Conservation Partners, and a past director of the National Forest Foundation. He is also the president of the Boone and Crockett Club, owner and president of the Mooncrest Ranch in Cody, WY, and vice president of both Stillrock Management and Elmrock Capital. His memberships include the Rocky Mountain Elk Foundation, Izaak Walton League, Safari Club International, FNAWS, Quail Unlimited, Clove Valley Rod and Gun Club, and the Philadelphia Gun Club.

Honorable Jim Moseley
Deputy Secretary of Agriculture
Jim Moseley was sworn in as the Deputy Secretary by Agriculture Secretary Ann M. Veneman on July 17, 2001. Prior to this appointment, Moseley, an Indiana farmer with thirty-two years of hands-on farm experience, was the owner of Ag Ridge Farms, which specializes in grains, and managing partner of Infinity Pork, LLC, which raises hogs. From 1989–1990, Moseley served as agricultural advisor to the Administrator of the U.S. Environmental Protection Agency. Moseley previously served at USDA as the Assistant Secretary of Agriculture for Natural Resources and Environment from 1990–1992. In this capacity, he provided leadership to the Forest Service and the Natural Resources Conservation Service on a variety of issues including endangered species, old growth forests, livestock grazing on public lands, wetlands, and policy issues related to the conservation title of the 1990 Farm Bill.

Jim Oftedal
Director, Central California Consortium
Jim Oftedal is the Director of the Central California Consortium (CCC), the only known Forest Service-funded environmental education, outreach, and recruitment program working with Latino and Southeast Asian communities. He works tirelessly to educate and increase awareness about the Forest Service and natural resources to underserved communities. At the same time he works passionately and enthusiastically in assisting these communities in building capacity and providing life-changing opportunities to many youths, encouraging them to pursue higher education and professional careers in natural resources. Since the program's inception, the CCC has placed over four hundred fifty students in summer positions and about fifty in career positions. Jim

Oftedal has received the "Unsung Hero Award" from the USDA, the Forest Service Chief's "New Century of Service Award," and the Regional Forester's "Multicultural Award."

R. Max Peterson
11th Chief of the Forest Service, 1979–1987
In March 2004, Max Peterson retired for the third time after serving 10 months as interim executive director of the National Fish and Wildlife Zooquarium located in Springfield, Missouri. He previously served for 14 years as executive vice president of the International Association of Fish and Wildlife Agencies, an association that represents the state and provincial fish and wildlife agencies of the United States, Canada, and Mexico. Prior to his appointment as executive vice president, Mr. Peterson served for 37½ years in a variety of positions in the U.S. Forest Service, the last 7½ years as Chief. His assignments with the Forest Service included Deputy Chief for Programs and Legislation, Deputy Regional Forester and Regional Forester for the Southern Region, a variety of field assignments in the Pacific Southwest and Northern regions, and a previous assignment in the Chief's office. Upon his retirement in 1987, he was designated Chief Emeritus of the Forest Service by the secretary of Agriculture, the first person to be so designated.

Gifford Pinchot III
Co-founder, Bainbridge Island Graduate Institute
Gifford Pinchot is co-founder of the Bainbridge Island Graduate Institute (BGI), which offers the first M.B.A. program in the U.S. that focuses on socially and environmentally responsible business. Unlike other schools that offer a concentration in sustainability or the like, BGI weaves social and environmental responsibility into every course from finance and marketing to organizational systems. Ethics, cutting-edge sustainability practices, social justice, and students' spiritual perspectives, or what really matters, are part of the dialog in standard business subjects like marketing, finance and organizational design. He is also a speaker and consultant in innovation management and the author of the best seller *INTRAPRENEURING: Why You Don't Have to Leave the Corporation to Become an Entrepreneur*, which was published in fifteen languages, and co-author of *The Intelligent Organization: Engaging the Talent and Initiative of Everyone in the Workplace and Intrapreneuring in Action*.

Honorable Mark E. Rey
Under Secretary of Agriculture, Natural Resources and Environment
Mark E. Rey was sworn in as the Under Secretary for Natural Resources and Environment by Agriculture Secretary Ann M. Veneman on October 2, 2001. In that position, he oversees the U.S. Department of Agriculture's Forest Service and Natural Resources Conservation Service. Since January 1995, Rey served as a staff member with the U.S. Senate Committee on Energy and Natural Resources and was the lead staff person for the committee's work on national forest policy and Forest Service administration. He was directly involved in virtually all of the forestry and conservation legislation considered during the past several sessions of Congress, with principal responsibility for a number of public lands bills during this period.

F. Dale Robertson
12th Chief of the Forest Service, 1987–1993
F. Dale Robertson began his Forest Service career in 1961 and served in the South, Washington, D.C., and the Pacific Northwest. After the retirement of Max Peterson in January of 1987, Dale Robertson was appointed Chief of the Forest Service. Several new resource programs were developed under Robertson's leadership including the highly successful "Rise to the Future," a program designed to enhance the production of fish on the national forests. Robertson also led efforts by the Forest Service to find new and creative ways to manage the national forests, especially by emphasizing non-timber resources, new forestry, new perspectives, and ecosystem management.

Emilyn Sheffield, Ph.D.
Chair, Department of Recreation Administration, California State University, Chico
Emilyn Sheffield has worked for over twenty years with federal, state, and local public land partners to increase support for public lands. She is currently directing a wide-ranging program of applied research, strategic planning, and cooperative marketing projects throughout California and the western U.S. Dr. Sheffield is the director of the Tourism and Communication Design Partnership, an interdisciplinary project group comprised of faculty, staff and students at California State University, Chico. She is also the chairperson of the Recreation and Parks Management Department at CSUC, the largest undergraduate recreation department in the west. Sheffield has written extensively

about tourism, cooperative marketing, entrepreneurship and public lands and is a frequent speaker at gatherings of public land managers.

Stuart J. Shelk, Jr. (John)
Managing Director, Ochoco Lumber Company
John Shelk has been employed with Ochoco Lumber Company for over thirty years and is the current managing director. He also is the vice chairman of the World Forestry Center and a member of the Oregon State Board of Forestry. In the past, he was Chairman of the Western Wood Products Association, the Timber Operators Council, and the High Desert Museum.

Debra Shore
Director of Development, Chicago WILDERNESS Magazine
Debra Shore has served as editor of *Chicago WILDERNESS* magazine since its debut seven years ago. *Chicago WILDERNESS* is the first-ever magazine dedicated to providing news and information about the native animals, plants, and ecosystems of the Chicago region, and the remarkable people who cherish and protect them. Shore also serves as director of development for the Chicago Wilderness consortium of 178 public and private agencies. She is an active volunteer in the efforts to restore habitat in the Cook County forest preserves and serves on the Community Advisory Council on Land Management in Cook County.

James Gustave Speth, Ph.D.
Dean and Professor in the Practice of Environmental Policy and Sustainable Development, Yale School of Forestry and Environmental Studies
From 1993 to 1999, Dean Speth served as administrator of the United Nations Development Programme and Chair of the UN Development Group. Prior to his service at the UN, he was founder and president of the World Resources Institute, professor of law at Georgetown University, Chairman of the U.S. Council on Environmental Quality, and senior attorney and cofounder of Natural Resources Defense Council. Throughout his career, Dean Speth has provided leadership and entrepreneurial initiatives to many task forces and committees whose roles have been to combat environmental degradation, including the President's Task Force on Global Resources and Environment, the Western Hemisphere Dialogue on Environment and Development, and the National Commission on the Environment.

Jack Ward Thomas, Ph.D.
13th Chief of the Forest Service, 1993–1996

Jack Ward Thomas began his long career as a wildlife researcher with the Texas Game and Fish Commission in 1957, moving in 1966 to join the Forest Service in Morgantown, WV, as a research wildlife biologist and then in 1969 to the Urban Forestry and Wildlife Research Unit at Amhurst, MA. In 1974, he became the chief research wildlife biologist and project leader at the Blue Mountains Research Lab in La Grande, Oregon. In the late 1980s and early 1990s, Jack was a member of several studies concerning the northern spotted owl and old growth habitat in the Pacific Northwest. In the spring of 1993, in the wake of the President Clinton Forest Conference in Portland, Oregon, Jack Ward Thomas was named to head the Forest Ecosystem Management Assessment Team (FEMAT) to present a resolution based on the best scientific evidence to resolve the spotted owl crises in the Pacific Northwest and northern California. It was partially as a result of his work on this project that Thomas was chosen to be the new Chief of the Forest Service.

Tom L. Thompson
Deputy Chief, National Forest System, Forest Service

Tom Thompson started his thirty-six-year career with the U.S. Forest Service in Alaska with assignments on the Tongass National Forest, the Chugach National Forest, and the Institute of Northern Forestry, a unit of the Pacific Northwest Experiment Station. He served on the Mt. Hood and Willamette National Forests in Oregon, and in 1983, Tom moved to the Legislative Affairs Staff in Washington, D.C., with principal responsibility for wilderness legislation. During his time in that position, wilderness bills were enacted for twenty-two states. Tom was selected to be Forest Supervisor of the Siuslaw National Forest in 1985 and Deputy Regional Forester for the Rocky Mountain Region from 1989 until 2001. In October 2001, Tom was named Deputy Chief for the National Forest System, responsible for management of the 191 million acres of National Forest System land and all programs and policies for National Forests and Grasslands throughout the United States.

Honorable Mark Udall (D)
U.S. Representative, Colorado

Mark Udall is serving his third term representing Colorado's Second Congressional District. A member of the House Resources Committee, House Science Committee, and House Agriculture Committee, Mark has championed environmental, energy, education and health care issues. His position as ranking member on the Subcommittee on Environment, Technology, and Standards has given him a platform to address many issues important to Colorado's economy, including technology, transportation and homeland security. Mark's operating style has been to avoid burning bridges with people and has allowed him to work in a bipartisan fashion to pass legislation to turn Rocky Flats, the former nuclear weapons facility, into a wildlife refuge, protect many of Colorado's wilderness areas, establish a math and science scholarship program, and secure transportation funding for high-priority projects in Colorado.

Honorable Ann M. Veneman
Secretary of Agriculture

Ann M. Veneman was sworn in as the 27th Secretary of the U.S. Department of Agriculture (USDA) on January 20, 2001. Her lifelong commitment to food and farm issues, along with her bipartisan approach to solving problems and confronting new challenges, are reasons that explain why she was chosen by President George W. Bush to serve in his Cabinet and unanimously confirmed by the U.S. Senate. Veneman served as USDA's Deputy Secretary from 1991 to 1993 and as Deputy Under Secretary of Agriculture for International Affairs and Commodity Programs from 1989 to 1991. Secretary Veneman's extensive background and experience has been valuable since taking office as American agriculture has confronted critical issues such as new farm policy, international trade, homeland security, environmental stewardship and food safety.

John T. Vogel II
Jesuit High School, San Antonio, FL
Nominated by Earth Force

John Vogel, a junior at Jesuit High School in Tampa, Florida, is an active participant in environmental leadership. Recently named to the Earth Force National Board of Directors, he has also worked with the organization's development programs. The son of a professional forester, John is passionate about the environment as well as informed and knowledgeable about proper forest management, prescribed burns, and game management. A leader in academic, social, and parochial programs as well, John works hard to serve his community and uses these opportunities to broaden his horizons.

Honorable Greg Walden (R)
U.S. Representative, Oregon

Greg Walden was elected as the U.S. Representative for the Second Congressional District of Oregon on November 3, 1998. During his first term in the U.S. House, Greg's premier legislative accomplishment was the passage of legislation to protect Steens Mountain in Harney County. During the 108th Congress Greg has joined three new subcommittees. Following his efforts to pass the Healthy Forests Restoration Act, Greg was appointed Chairman of the House Resources Forest and Forest Health Subcommittee in March of 2004. The subcommittee is responsible for shaping the nation's forest policy and will allow him to influence a number of issues of importance to the Second District and the eleven national forests in southern, central and eastern Oregon.

Ross S. Whaley, Ph.D.
Chairman, Adirondack Park Agency

The New York State Senate approved the Governor's nomination of Dr. Whaley as chairman of the Adirondack Park Agency on September 16, 2003. He brings to that position more than thirty years of experience as a university teacher, researcher and administrator. He also served as Director of Economics Research for the United States Forest Service for six years. Ross Whaley has served as a consultant or member of several state, national and international commissions devoted to natural resource and environmental issues. In recognition of these activities, he has been awarded the Pinchot Medallion by the Pinchot Institute for Conservation, the Professional Conservationist Award by the New York Conservation Council, the Heiberg Memorial Award by the New York Forest Owners Association, and Honor Alumnus of Colorado State University.

Special Guests

Gary Hines
as Gifford Pinchot

Gary Hines began seasonal work with the U.S. Forest Service in fire and recreation while attending college. After several years with an acoustic folk group in San Francisco and composing a film score for the 1974 Spokane World's Fair, he accepted public information work on a National Forest in California. Twelve years later, in 1988, Gary's performance of Gifford Pinchot, intended only for local campers, took off, and he was soon performing it nationally. After working for eleven years at Grey Towers National Historic Landmark,

Gifford Pinchot's ancestral home, Gary changed careers and "retired" from the Forest Service but still performs the production.

Keith McGough
as President Theodore Roosevelt

Keith McGough is the creator of Theodore Roosevelt Today. As a lifetime admirer of the not-often-found ideals of America's hero one hundred years ago, Theodore Roosevelt, an avid sportsman and conservationist, Keith ended his career at age fifty to professionally portray President Theodore Roosevelt as a national professional speaker. While getting established was a great challenge, Keith has spoken to over one hundred fifty national and state associations, many U.S. and state agencies and Fortune 500 companies.

Lassie
America's Top Dog

Since her theatrical film debut in 1943, Lassie has starred in ten major motion pictures, her own radio show, and nearly six hundred TV episodes. From 1964 to 1969 Lassie played an important role in increasing public awareness of national forest and environmental issues during the "Ranger Corey Stuart" years. She also worked with the U.S. Forest Service on an anti-litter campaign and was given a conservation award by the U.S. Department of Agriculture for significant public service to conservation education.

Fiddlin' Foresters

The Fiddlin' Foresters are proud to be known as the "official old-time string band of the U.S. Forest Service." They are a special musical group composed of Forest Service employees and volunteers from the Rocky Mountain Region. Since 1994 they have performed over one hundred eighty inspirational, educational and entertaining interpretive programs illustrating the importance of natural resource conservation and public land stewardship throughout the country. The Fiddlin' Foresters have developed several interpretive musical programs, including presentations on New Century of Service and Wildland Fire, which use old-time music, songs of the American west, and novelty tunes. The group recently received the prestigious Forest Service Chief's Award and the Rocky Mountain Region's Regional Forester's Honor Award for their unique interpretive musical program.

Centennial Congress Sponsors

The National Forest Foundation in partnership with the USDA Forest Service is deeply grateful to those who have generously contributed time and success of the 2005 Centennial Congress.

Event Sponsors

PricewaterhouseCoopers LLP
1301 K Street NW Suite 800W
Washington, DC 20005
www.pwc.com

900 Frames
12910 Culver Blvd. Suite G
Los Angeles, CA 90066
www.900frames.tv

Classic Media TV
860 Broadway, 6th Floor
New York, NY 10003
www.classicmedia.tv

Schieffelin and Company
2 Park Avenue
New York, NY 10016
www.schieffelin.com

Golin Harris
2200 Clarendon Blvd. Suite 2200
Arlington, VA 22201
www.golinharris.com

Event Contributors

American Recreation Coalition
1225 New York Ave. NW Suite 450
Washington, DC 20005-6405
www.funoutdoors.com

National Wild Turkey Federation
770 Augusta Road
Edgefield, SC 29824-0530
www.nwtf.org

Rocky Mountain Elk Foundation
2291 W Broadway P.O. Box 8249
Missoula, MT 59807
www.rmef.org

Event Supporters

Forest Fire Lookout Association
374 Maple Ave. East Suite 310
Vienna, VA 22180
www.relookout.org

The Jewish National Fund
42 E. 69th St
New York, NY 10021
www.jnf.org

National Ski Areas Association
133 S. Van Gordon Street Suite 300
Lakewood, CO 80228
www.nsaa.org

The Nature Conservancy
4245 North Fairfax Drive, Suite 100
Arlington, VA 22203-1606
www.nature.org

Special Thanks to:

Adirondack Park Agency
American Forest and Paper
  Association
American Forests
American Wildlife Conservation
  Partners
Bainbridge Graduate Institute
Boone and Crockett Club
California State University, Chico,
  Department of Recreation
  Administration
Central California Consortium
Char Miller—Trinity University
Chicago Wilderness
Deborah Campbell and Associates
Earth Force
The Fiddlin' Foresters
Forest History Society
Food and Argiculture Organization,
  Forestry Department
Girl Scouts of America
The Head Start Bureau
The Interpublic Group of
  Companies
The Izaak Walton League
The Job Corps
Lisa Day
National Commission on Science
  for Sustainable Forestry
National Forest Counties and
  Schools

National Hispanic Environmental
  Council
National Park Service
New Mexico State University,
  Department of Fishery and
  Wildlife Sciences
Ochoco Lumber Company
Oregon Tourism Commission
The Pinchot Institute
Ruben Aronin
Society of American Foresters
State of New Mexico Forestry
  Division
Student Conservation Association
Sustainable Forestry Board
Sustainable South Bronx
Tehama County Department of
  Education
Texas Forest Service
Tyrell County (NC) Community
  Development Corporation
University of California, Berkeley,
  College of Natural Resources
University of Colorado at Boulder,
  Center of the American West
University of Idaho, College of
  Natural Resources
Western States Tourism Policy
  Council
The Wilderness Society
Yale School of Forestry and
  Environmental Studies

Exhibitors

American Fisheries Society, Society for Range Management, Society of American Foresters, and The Wildlife Society

These four societies of natural resource professionals meet information needs through periodicals, meetings, books and more.

Forest History Society

The Forest History Society preserves forest and conservation history for present and future generations, encourages scholarship in forest and conservation history, and conducts a comprehensive applied history program that brings the lessons of history to bear on the most pressing issues in natural resource management. It is the foremost library and archives of forest and conservation history in the world and repository of the Forest Service Headquarters History Collection.

Girl Scouts of America

Girl Scouts of the USA's Linking Girls to the Land initiative encourages Girl Scouts to become involved in issues related to conservation and natural resources through partnerships with federal agencies on national and local levels.

Jewish National Fund

Jewish National Fund is caretaker of the land of Israel. Their exhibit will focus on their environmental work as well as relationships with the USDA Forest Service and mutual partnerships. They also sell trees to be planted in the Holy Land and issue certificates.

National Fish & Wildlife Foundation

The National Fish & Wildlife Foundation promotes healthy populations of fish, wildlife and plants by leveraging public dollars with non-federal funds through the awarding of conservation grants.

The Nature Conservancy

The mission of The Nature Conservancy is to preserve the diversity of life on earth. Their many partners include the U. S. Forest Service.

PricewaterhouseCoopers

PricewaterhouseCoopers has been a leader in providing both assurance and advisory services to the Federal Government for over 75 years. PricewaterhouseCoopers serves the federal government through our Washington Federal Practice (WFP). WFP professionals bring direct hands-on knowledge of federal standards for systems, internal controls and financial reporting. Our mission is to deliver the full capabilities and expertise from PWC globally to assist government agencies solve complex business issues, manage risk and add value to performance through our comprehensive service offerings in financial management, program management, operations improvement, and security and data management.

Roundtable on Sustainable Forestry

The Roundtable on Sustainable Forestry is an open and inclusive stakeholder process committed to the goal of sustainable forest management on public and private lands.

United Four Wheel Drive Association

United Four Wheel Drive Association brings together four-wheel drive owners to share stimulating experiences through organized events. The Association acts to keep 4x4 roads and trails open so that people can continue to enjoy four wheeling in the great outdoors. Through united efforts, the opinions and beliefs of four-wheel enthusiasts are heard by land management agencies and by our elected officials.

USDA Forest Service, Geospatial Service & Technology Center

The Forest Service Geospatial Service & Technology Center provides geospatial services, data and map products to all organizational elements of the agency in support of the Forest Service mission.

USDA Forest Service, Global Change Research

Climate change is partially driven by increasing emissions of greenhouse gases. Carbon dioxide, the most common greenhouse gas, is sequestered (absorbed) by forests during growth and emitted from disturbances, such as fire and harvesting.

USDA Forest Service, International Programs

The USDA Forest Service international work fosters good forest management in other countries and continually improves forest management at home by utilizing lessons learned overseas.

USDA Forest Service, National Fire Plan

The National Fire Plan represents a long-term commitment and investment designed to protect communities, natural resources, and most importantly the lives of firefighters and the public. This long-term commitment is shared among federal agencies, states, local governments, tribes, and interested publics. Collaboration, priority setting, and accountability are the guiding principles that will ensure the continued success of this program.

USDA Forest Service, National Partnership Office

The National Partnership Office is a Forest Service effort to improve and expand partnership efforts across the agency and with our partners. The Partnership Office offers tools and products for partnership efforts, works to streamline business processes, and builds national networks for partnerships and collaboration.

USDA Forest Service, Remote Sensing Applications Center

The Remote Sensing Applications Center (RSAC) provides national assistance to agency field units in the application of remote sensing for monitoring and mapping of natural resources.

USDA Forest Service Technology & Development Program

The USDA Forest Service Technology & Development Program uses innovation to help employees and partner agencies manage the Nation's natural resources safely, effectively and efficiently.

USDA Forest Service, Urban & Community Forestry Program

Urban and Community Forestry promotes the creation of healthier, more livable urban environments across the Nation. They maintain, restore and improve the health of urban trees, forests, green spaces and sustainable forest ecosystems.

Western Heritage Company

Western Heritage provides commemorative items for the USDA Forest Service and the Centennial Celebration.

Delegates and Attendees

Adelman, Gerald W., Founder, Corlands: Corporation for Open Lands, Chicago, IL

Agpaoa, Elizabeth, Chief of Staff, USDA Forest Service, Washington, DC

Ahern, Catherine A., Vice President, Member Services, American Recreation Coalition, Washington, DC

Aicher, Davis, Manager, Technology and Development Program, USDA Forest Service, Missoula, MT

Allgeier, Andrew, Student, University of Alaska-Fairbanks, Casper, WY

Anderson, Jim, Director, United Four Wheel Drive Associations, Happy Jack, AZ

Anderson, Steven, President and CEO, Forest History Society, Durham, NC

Anderson, Ted, Commissioner and Vice Chair, Skagit County NACo Public Lands Steering Committee, Mount Vernon, WA

Andrews, Elaine, Environmental Education Specialist, University of Wisconsin Environmental Resources Center, Madison, WI

Applegate, Beth, Executive Director, National Tree Trust, Washington, DC

Archuletta, Phil, CEO, P&M Plastics, Inc., Mountainair, NM

Arcularius, Howard, Bishop, CA

Arcularius, Linda, District 1 Supervisor, Inyo County Board of Supervisors, Bishop, CA

Argow, Keith, President, National Woodland Owners Association, Vienna, VA

Arnn, Matthew, Officio of the Secretary's Rep, NYC Urban Forestry, U.S. Department of Housing and Urban Development, New York, NY

Asbury, Donna, Executive Director, Association of Partners for Public Lands, Wheaton, MD

Atwood, Walter, President, National Association Civilian Conservation Corps Alumni, Columbia, SC

Aune, Philip, Vice President, California Forestry Association, Sacramento, CA

Bailey, John, Danvers, MA

Bailey, Margaret, Federal Practice Manager, PricewaterhouseCoopers, Danvers, MA

Bailey, Ralph E., Chairman and CEO, American Bailey Corporation, Greenwich, CT

Baker, Terry, Forester, The Apalachicola Ranger District, USDA Forest Service, Marianna, FL

Banzhaf, William H., President, Sustainable Forestry Board Inc., Arlington, VA

Barber, John, Dr., U.S. Forest Service (retired), Warsaw, VI

Barnett, James, Project Leader, Southern Research Station, USDA Forest Service, Pineville, LA

Barrett, Gary, Program Specialist, International Programs, USDA Forest Service, Washington, DC

Bartuska, Ann, Deputy Chief, Research and Development, Forest Service Washington, DC

Baughman, John, Executive Vice President, International Association of Fish and Wildlife Agencies, Washington, DC

Beasley, J. Lamar, President, American Wetlands, Reston, VA

Beck, Jennifer, Coordinator, Federal Lands, National Cattlemen's Beef Association, Washington, DC

Beckley, Bob, Project Leader, Technology and Development Program, USDA Forest Service, Missoula, MT

Beddoe, Paul, Associate Legislative Director, National Association of Counties, Washington, DC

Bell, David, Chairman, The Interpublic Group of Companies, New York, NY

Bendick, Jr., Robert, Managing Director, Southern U.S. Region, The Nature Conservancy, Altamonte Springs, FL

Bergeron, Elizabeth, Executive Director, Pacific Crest Trail Association, Sacramento, CA

Bernabo, Chris, Program Director, National Commission on Science for Sustainable Forestry, Accokeek, MD

Berry, John, Executive Director, National Fish and Wildlife Foundation, Washington, DC

Berry, Joyce K., Dean, Colorado State University, Fort Collins, CO

Berry, Michael, President, National Ski Areas Association, Lakewood, CO

Bingaman, Jeff, U.S. Senate (D-NM), Washington, DC

Bittleman, Sarah, Office of Senator Ron Wyden, Natural Resource Counsel, Washington, DC

Blackwell, Jack, Regional Forester, USDA Forest Service, Vallejo, CA

Blazer, Butch, State Forester, New Mexico, Santa Fe, NM

Bobbe, Tom, Manager, Remote Sensing Applications Center, USDA Forest Service, Salt Lake City, UT

Bosworth, Dale, Chief, USDA Forest Service, Washington, DC

Boucher, Carla, Attorney, United Four Wheel Drive Associations, Chesapeake, VA

Bown, Kimberly, Director, Recreation, Lands and Minerals, Pacific Northwest Region, Forest Service, Portland, OR

Bradley, Jeni, USDA Forest Service, CEO-Recreation Solutions, Troy, MT

Brady, Charles, President and CEO, Memphis Zoo, Memphis, TN

Brannon, Edgar, President, Brannon and Associates, Inc., Milford, PA

Breault, Henri, Owner, Salt River Tubing and Recreation, Mesa, AZ

Breault, Lynda, Owner, Salt River Tubing and Recreation, Mesa, AZ

Brett, Linda, Policy Analyst, USDA Forest Service, Woodbridge, VA

Brierley, Harold, CEO, Brierley and Partners, Dallas, TX

Briese, Garry L., Executive Director, International Association of Fire Chiefs, Fairfax, VA

Brinker, Richard, Dean, Auburn University, Auburn University, AL

Brouha, Paul, Director, Strategic Planning, USDA Forest Service, Falls Church, VA

Brown, Bruce R., Partnerships Coordinator, Bureau of Reclamation, Washington, DC

Brown, David, Executive Director, America Outdoors, Knoxville, TN

Brown, Dean N., Deputy State Forester, Alaska State Forestry, Anchorage, AK

Brown, George, Professor, Center for Forestry and Ecology, Alabama A&M University, Normal, AL

Brown, Gloria, Forest Supervisor, Los Padres National Forest, Goleta, CA

Brown, Perry, Dean, College of Forestry and Conservation, University of Montana, Missoula, MT

Brown, Timothy, Research Associate, Center of the American West, Boulder, CO

Bryant, Arthur R., Business Operations, USDA Forest Service, Arlington, VA

Bryce, Philip, State Forester, New Hampshire Division of Forests and Lands, Concord, NH

Bryson, Nancy, General Counsel, USDA Office of the General Counsel, Washington, DC

Bschor, Dennis, Regional Forester, USDA Forest Service, Juneau, AK

Budd, Bob, Director of Land Management, The Nature Conservancy, Lander, WY

Burgess, Wells, Assistant Section Chief, Environment and Natural Resources Division, U.S. Department of Justice, Washington, DC

Burnett, Kelly, Research Fish Biologist, Pacific Northwest Research Station, USDA Forest Service, Corvallis, OR

Buscaino, Mark, Director, Urban and Community Forestry, USDA Forest Service, Washington, DC

Cables, Rick, Regional Forester, Region 2, USDA Forest Service, Golden, CO

Camarena, Abel, Deputy Regional Forester, USDA Forest Service, Los Lunas, NM

Camp, Ann, Senior Lecturer and Research Scientist, Yale School of Forestry, New Haven, CT

Campbell, Deborah, President, Deborah Campbell and Associates, Henderson, NV

Campney, Sara, USDA Forest Service, Washington, DC

Carlson, Paul, Executive Director, Land Trust for the Little Tennessee, Franklin, NC

Carrera, Jacqueline, Executive Director, Parks and People Foundation, Baltimore, MD

Carroll, Robin, Manager, Geospatial Service and Technology Center, USDA Forest Service Salt Lake City, UT

Carter, Majora, Executive Director and Founder, Sustainable South Bronx, Bronx, NY

Cassady, Ginger, Campaigner, Greenpeace, Washington, DC

Caswell, James, Administrator, Office of Species Conservation, Boise, ID

Cates, Rosalie, Executive Director, Montana Community Development Corporation, Missoula, MT

Charley, Alyse, Student, Reedly High School, Dunlap, CA

Charley, Ronda, Mother and School Bus Driver, Dunlap, CA

Chavez, Deborah J., Social Scientist, Pacific Southwest Research Station, USDA Forest Service, Riverside, CA

Chojnacky, Cindy, Policy Analyst, USDA Forest Service, Falls Church, VA

Clarke, Kathleen, Director, Bureau of Land Management, Washington, DC

Cleaves, David, Director, Resource Valuation and Use Research, USDA Forest Service, North Potomac, MD

Cleaves, Ellen, North Potomac, MD

Cline, Keith, Urban and Community Forestry, USDA Forest Service, Washington, DC

Collins, Gary, President, Mni Sose Intertribal Water Rights Coalition, Rapid City, SD

Collins, Sally, Associate Chief, USDA Forest Service, Washington, DC

Collins, Vaughn, Director of Public Policy, Ducks Unlimited, Washington, DC

Cooley, Rob, Executive Director and CEO, Catherine Freer Wilderness Therapy, Albany, OR

Cooper, Debora, District Ranger, Chugach National Forest, Seward, AK

Cope, Robert, Vice President, Western Interstate Region, Salmon, ID

Cornelssen, Curtis, Director, Washington Federal Practice, PricewaterhouseCoopers, Newton, MA

Coufal, James, Professor Emeritus, SUNY College of Environmental Science and Forestry, Cazenovia, NY

Coulombe, Mary, Director, Timber Access & Supply, USDA Forest Service, Oakton, VA

Crandall, Derrick, President, American Recreation Coalition, Washington, DC

Crandall, Doug, Majority Staff Director, Resources Committee, Forests and Forest Health Subcommittee, Washington, DC

Crowell, John, USDA Former Assistant Secretary of Agriculture, Natural Resources and Environment, Lake Oswego, OR

Cruz, Phil, District Ranger, Deschutes National Forest, Bend, OR

Curkendall, Jennifer, Watershed Forestry Planner, USDA Forest Service, Annapolis, MD

Cutler, Dr. M. Rupert, Former Assistant Secretary of Agriculture, Natural Resources and Environment, Roanoke, VA

Cutts, Jan, Assistant Forest Public Affairs Officer, Inyo National Forest, Bishop, CA

Daley Laursen, Steven, Dean, College of Natural Resources, University of Idaho, Moscow, ID

Daly, Calli, Legislative Assistant to Senator Craig, U.S. Senate, Washington, DC

Daniels, Orville, USDA Forest Service (retired), Missoula, MT

Daschle, Tom, Minority Leader (D-SD), U.S. Senate, Washington, DC

Davidson, Todd, CEO, Oregon Tourism Commission, Salem, OR

Davis, Lori, Executive Director, Tread Lightly!, Ogden, UT

Dearstyne, Joyce E., Director, Framing Our Community, Inc., Elk City, ID

Dechter, Michael, Program Specialist, USDA Forest Service, Rio Rancho, NM

DeCoster, Kathy, Director, Federal Affairs, Trust for Public Land, Alexandria, VA

DeCoster, Tim, Director of Legislative Affairs, USDA Forest Service, Washington, DC

DeHayes, Donald H., Dean, School of Natural Resources, University of Vermont, Burlington, VT

Del Rio, Valerie, Human Resources Specialist, USDA Forest Service, Region 4, Roy, UT

Delgado, Javier, Fire Program Specialist, Fire and Aviation Management, Region 9, USDA Forest Service, Milwaukee, WI

Delgado, Daniel, Student, Cuba High School, Cuba, NM

Delost, Susan, Cartographer, Remote Sensing Applications Center, USDA Forest Service, Salt Lake City, UT

Dersch, Judy, Illustrator and Graphic Designer, Region 2, USDA Forest Service, Lakewood, CO

Dessecker, Dan, Senior Biologist, Ruffed Grouse Society, Rice Lake, WI

Diamant, Rolf, Superintendent, Marsh-Billings-Rockefeller National Historical Park, National Park Service, Woodstock, VT

Dilks, Nicholas, Vice President, The Conservation Fund, Arlington, VA

Dixon, Antoine, Staff Assistant, USDA Forest Service, Washington, DC

Dombeck, Mike, Former Chief, USDA Forest Service, Stevens Point, WI

Donoghue, Linda, Station Director, North Central Research Station, USDA Forest Service, St. Paul, MN

Douglas, Robert, President, National Forest Counties and Schools Coalition, Red Bluff, CA

Drake, Joe, Rancher, National Grazing Lands Conservation Initiative, Davis, OK

Draper, Robert, Team Leader, Byways, Bike-Ped, Trails and Enhancements, Federal Highway Administration, Washington, DC

Duke, Cliff, Science Director, Ecological Society of America, Washington, DC

Dunlop, George S., Former Assistant Secretary of Agriculture, Natural Resources and Environment, Washington, DC

Dunn, Julie Anton, Director of Program Development, The Wild Foundation, Great Falls, VA

Dunn, Walter, Program Coordinator, USDA Forest Service, Albuquerque, NM

Dunsky, Ann, Video Producer, USDA Forest Service, Vallejo, CA

Dunsky, Steven, Video Producer, USDA Forest Service, Vallejo, CA

Eav, Bov, Associate Deputy Chief for Research and Development, USDA Forest Service, Washington, DC

Ehnes, Russ, Executive Director, National Off-Highway Vehicle Conservation Council, Great Falls, MT

Eisenberg, Jeffrey, Director, Federal Lands, National Cattlemen's Beef Association, Washington, DC

El-Lakany, M. Hosny, Assistant Director-General, Forestry Department, UN Food and Agriculture Organization, Rome

Emerson, Kirk, Director, U.S. Institute for Environmental Conflict Resolution, Tucson, AZ

Emmett, Brian, Assistant Deputy Minister, Natural Resources Canada, Ottawa, ON

Engert, Jan, Director, National Partnership Office, USDA Forest Service, Washington, DC

Estill, Elizabeth, Deputy Chief for Programs, USDA Forest Service, Washington, DC

Evans, Keister, Executive Director, Tropical Forest Foundation, Alexandria, VA

Faeth, Lori, Policy Advisor, Natural Resources, Office of the Governor, Arizona, Phoenix, AZ

Fairfax, Sally Kirk, Professor, University of California–Berkeley, Berkeley, CA

Farrar, Gloria, Mount Vernon, IL

Farrar, Jessica, Student, Illinois Wesleyan University, Mount Vernon, IL

Farrell, Dianne, Vice President, Government Affairs, Recreation Vehicle Industry Association, Reston, VA

Fedkiw, John, Volunteer, USDA Forest Service (retired), Bethesda, MD

Fehr, John, Manager, San Dimas Technology and Development Center, Missoula, MT

Finlayson, Karen, Outdoor Recreation Planner, USDA Forest Service, Camino, CA

Fisher, Larry, Senior Program Manager, U.S. Institute for Environmental Conflict Resolution, Tucson, AZ

Force, Jo Ellen, Department Head and Professor, Department of Forest Resources, University of Idaho, Moscow, ID

Forsgren, Harv, Regional Forester, Southwest Region, USDA Forest Service, Albuquerque, NM

Fowler, John M., Executive Director, Advisory Council on Historic Preservation, Washington, DC

Franklin, Thomas, Executive Director (Acting), The Wildlife Society, Bethesda, MD

Fraser, Teresa, Project Manager, Recreation Solutions, USDA Forest Service, Camino, CA

Frausto, Juan Manuel, Program Coordinator, Mexican Fund for Nature Conservation, Mexico,

Frazer, Nat B., Professor and Chair, Department of Wildlife Ecology and Conservation, University of Florida, Gainesville, FL

Freemuth, John, Professor of Political Science and Senior Fellow, Boise State University, Cecil Andrus Center for Public Policy, Boise, ID

Furnish, Jim, Consulting Forester, Rockville, MD

Gaines, Glen, District Ranger, USDA Forest Service, Double Springs, AL

Gale, Margaret, Dean, School of Forest Resources and Environmental Science, Michigan Technological University, Houghton, MI

Gangloff, Deborah, Executive Director, American Forests, Washington, DC

Gans, John, Executive Director, National Outdoor Leadership School, Lander, WY

Gardner, Lori, Marketing Director, Society of American Foresters, Bethesda, MD

Gaskin, Jennifer, Ocala, FL

Gasser, James, Office of Policy, National Park Service, Washington, DC

Gause, Kathleen, Director, Civil Rights, USDA Forest Service, Washington, DC

Gibson, Terry, Chair of Tribal Council, Shoshone-Paiute Tribes, Owyhee, NV

Gilbert, Thomas, Director, Eastern Forest Conservation Funding, Highlands Coalition, Doylestown, PA

Gladics, Frank, Member, Energy and Natural Resources Committee, U.S. Senate, Washington, DC

Glauthier, Roy, President, National Forest Homeowners, Costa Mesa, CA

Gomes, Stephanie Lynn, Public Affairs Specialist, Region 5, USDA Forest Service, Vallejo, CA

Gonzalez, Grizelle, Research Ecologist, International Institute of Tropical Forestry, San Juan, PR

Goodlatte, Bob, U.S. House of Representatives (R-VA), Washington, DC

Goodman, Linda, Regional Forester, USDA Forest Service, Portland, OR

Grace, James R., State Forester, Bureau of Forestry, Department of Conservation and Natural Resources, Harrisburg, PA

Graff, Walter, Deputy Director, Appalachian Mountain Club, Gorham, NH

Graham, Christy, Accountant, Colville National Forest, Colville, WA

Grann, Douglas, President and CEO, Wildlife Forever, Brooklyn Center, MN

Grenfield, Paul, Remote Sensing Applications Center, USDA Forest Service, Salt Lake City, UT

Guldin, Richard, Director, Science Policy, Planning, Inventory, and Information, Research and Development, USDA Forest Service, Rosslyn, VA

Guzman, Frank, District Ranger, USDA Forest Service, Watford City, ND

Guzman, Jeraline, Watford City, ND

Gyant, Barnie, Deputy Forest Supervisor, White Mountain National Forest, Laconia, NH

Hafer, Harry, Executive Director, Cradle of Forestry Interpretive Association, Brevard, NC

Hafer, Mae Lee, Brevard, NC

Hagood, Flip, Senior Vice President, Student Conservation Association, Arlington, VA

Hanka, Henry, Director, America's Byways Resource Center, Duluth, MN

Hansen, Paul, Executive Director, Izaak Walton League of America, Gaithersburg, MD

Harbour, Thomas, Deputy Director, USDA Forest Service, Washington, DC

Hardesty, Jeffrey L., Director, Global Fire Initiative, The Nature Conservancy, Gainesville, FL

Hardy, Yvan, Chief Scientist, Natural Resources Canada, Ottawa, ON

Harnik, Peter, Director, Center for City Park Excellence, Washington, DC

Harper, Carla, Program Manager, Colorado Wood Utilization and Marketing Assistance Center, Cortez, CO

Harrington, John Thomas, Professor, New Mexico State University, Mora, NM

Harris, Jennifer, Recreation and Public Affairs Staff, Malheur National Forest, Prairie City, OR

Harwood, Peggy, National Program Manager, Urban and Community Forestry, USDA Forest Service, Washington, DC

Hawley, Karla, Executive Assistant, USDA Forest Service, Washington, DC

Hayes, Jennifer, Presidential Management Fellow, Southern Research Station, USDA Forest Service, Asheville, NC

Hays, Misty, Deputy District Ranger, USDA Forest Service, Douglas, WY

Hecker, Linda, Regional Interpretive Services Coordinator, USDA Forest Service, Golden, CO

Heissenbuttel, Ann, Executive Director, National Association of State Foresters, Washington, DC

Heissenbuttel, John, Vice President, Forest and Wood Products, American Forest and Paper Association, Washington, DC

Helin, William, Business Operations Budget Coordinator, USDA Forest Service, Washington, DC

Helms, John, President, Society of American Foresters, Bethesda, MD

Henry, Mark, Manager, General Dynamics C4 Systems, Phoenix, AZ

Hess, Joseph, Vice President of Government Relations, Jewish National Fund, Garden Grove, CA

Hessel, David, Staff Forester, Colorado State Forest Service, Westminster, CO

Hessel, Sally, Westminster, CO

Hiatt, John, Chairman, Eastern Nevada Landscape Coalition, Las Vegas, NV

Hill, Mavis Colleen, Executive Director, Tyrrell County Community Development Corporation, Columbia, NC

Hilliard, Marisue, Director, Renewable Resources, USDA Forest Service, Golden, CO

Hines, Gary, USDA Forest Service (retired), Gualala, CA

Holland, Carolyn, Cartographer, Forest Service Geospatial Service and Technology Center, Salt Lake City, UT

Holland, David, Director, Recreation, Heritage and Wilderness Resources, USDA Forest Service, Washington, DC

Holmer, Steve, Communications Coordinator, The Wilderness Society, Washington, DC

Holtrop, Joel, Deputy Chief, State and Private Forestry, USDA Forest Service, Washington, DC

Hom, John, Global Change Program, Northeastern Research Station, Newtown Square, PA

Honeycutt, Karen, Fishery Biologist, USDA Forest Service, Colville, WA

Hoppus, Michael, FIA, Northeastern Research Station, Newtown Square, PA

Houghland, Paul, Executive Manager, National Hardwood Lumber Association, Memphis, TN

Hubbard, William, Southern Regional Extension Forester, Cooperative Extension Service, Athens, GA

Huffaker, Wellington, Executive Director, Aldo Leopold Foundation, Inc., Baraboo, WI

Hull, James B., State Forester and Director, Texas Forest Service, College Station, TX

Humphreys, David, President, Recreational Vehicle Industry Association, Reston, VA

Hunger, Don, Senior Director for Partnership Development, Student Conservation Association, Bellingham, WA

Hurst, William, Regional Forester (retired), USDA Forest Service, Albuquerque, NM

Ice, George, Principal Scientist, National Council for Air and Stream Improvement, Corvallis, OR

Imbergamo, Bill, Majority Staff, Committee on Agriculture, Washington, DC

Iwamoto, Y. Robert, Forest Supervisor, USDA Forest Service, Eugene, OR

Jacobs, Bob, Regional Forester, USDA Forest Service, Atlanta, GA

Jiron, Daniel, National Press Officer, USDA Forest Service, Washington, DC

Johnson, Myrna, Vice President, Government Affairs, Outdoor Industry Association, Boulder, CO

Jourdain, Christine, Executive Director, American Council of Snowmobile Associations, East Lansing, MI

Kaaumoana, Barbara, Executive Director, Hanalei Watershed Hui, Kilauea, HI

Kaden, Timothy, Land Preservation Specialist and Forester, Delaware Department of Natural Resources and Environmental Control, Dover, DE

Kahn, Brian, Director, Artemis Common Ground, Helena, MT

Kaiser, Janette S., Director, Rangeland Management, USDA Forest Service, Churchton, MD

Kanen, Dale, Director, Office of Tribal Relations, USDA Forest Service, Washington, DC

Kannalley, Elizabeth, Forest Service Geospatial Service and Technology Center, Salt Lake City, UT

Kavanaugh, Stephanie, Research Associate, Pinchot Institute for Conservation, Washington, DC

Keck, Rob, Executive Vice President, National Wild Turkey Federation, Edgefield, SC

Kendrix, Brenda G., Public Affairs and Communication Staff, USDA Forest Service, Vallejo, CA

Kenny, Alexandra, Director, Grants Program, National Forest Foundation, Washington, DC

Kenops, Darrel, National Council, Society of American Foresters, Springfield, OR

Kenops, Lynn, Springfield, OR

Kessler, Winifred, Director, Wildlife, Fisheries, Ecology, Watershed, and Subsistence, Alaska Region, USDA Forest Service, Juneau, AK

Khung, Kevin, Recreation and Lands Staff Officer, Bighorn National Forest, Sheridan, WY

Kimbell, Abigail, Regional Forester, USDA Forest Service, Missoula, MT

King, Aubrey, Washington, DC, Representative, Western States Tourism Policy Council, Bowie, MD

King, Belina, Fairfax, VA

King, Jesse, Associate Deputy Chief and CFO, USDA Forest Service, Fairfax, VA

Klim, Edward J., President, International Snowmobile Manufacturers Association, Haslett, MI

Kotar, John, Senior Scientist Emeritus, University of Wisconsin–Madison, Madison, WI

Kothmann, Merwyn, Professor, Texas A&M University, and President, Society for Range Management, College Station, TX

Kotschwar, Lance, Majority Staff, Committee on Agriculture, Nutrition, and Forestry, Washington, DC

Kovarovics, Scott, Director, Natural Trails and Waters Coalition, Washington, DC

Kozlowski, Steve, Facilitator and Wildlife Biologist, Medicine Bow–Routt National Forest, Laramie, WY

Krause, Richard L., Regulatory Counsel, American Farm Bureau Federation, Washington, DC

Kroenke, Loren, District Ranger, Wasatch-Cache National Forest, Salt Lake City, UT

Laferriere, Leo, Consulting Forester, Waitsfield, VT

Lancaster, Arlen, Senior Policy Advisor, Senator Michael Crapo's Office, Washington, DC

Lavendel, Claire, Forest Supervisor, Gifford Pinchot National Forest, Portland, OR

Laverty, Lyle, Director, Colorado State Parks, Arvada, CO

Leahy, Michael, Natural Resources Counsel, Defenders of Wildlife, Washington, DC

LeMaster, Dennis, Pinchot Institute for Conservation, Everett, WA

Leonard, George, USDA Forest Service (retired), Fairfax, VA

Lesko, Larry, National Fire Plan, Washington, DC

Lester, Michael, Assistant State Forester, Bureau of Forestry, Department of Conservation and Natural Resources, Harrisburg, PA

Lewis, Jamie, Historian, Forest History Society, Durham, NC

Lewis, Richard, President, Forest Resources Association, Rockville, MD

Libbrand, Lou, USDA Forest Service Technology and Development Program, Missoula, MT

Limerick, Jeffrey, Boulder, CO

Limerick, Patricia Nelson, Chair of the Board, Center for the American West, Boulder, CO

Linehan, Ann, Division of Program Support, Head Start Bureau, Director, Washington, DC

Link, Gerladine, Director of Public Policy, National Ski Areas Association, Lakewood, CO

Loesel, James, Secretary, Citizens Task Force, Roanoke, VA

Loggers, Chris, Wildlife Biologist, Colville National Forest, Kettle Falls, WA

Loucks, Andrea Bedell, Director of Conservation Studies, Pinchot Institute for Conservation, Washington, DC

Lucier, Alan, Senior Vice President, National Council for Air and Stream Improvement, Research Triangle Park, NC

Lugo, Dr. Ariel E., Director, International Institute of Tropical Forestry, USDA Forest Service, San Juan, PR

Lunney, Elizabeth, Executive Director, Washington Trails Association, Seattle, WA

Lynch, Mike, President, Western Heritage Company, Loveland, CO

Lynch, Pat, Founder, Western Heritage Company, Loveland, CO

Lyons, James, Casey Tree Foundation, Former Under Secretary of Agriculture, Natural Resources and Environment, Washington, DC

MacCleery, Douglas W., Senior Policy Analyst, USDA Forest Service, Washington, DC

Maciel, Martha, Public Affairs Specialist, Sierra National Forest, Clovis, CA

Mackey, Craig W., Public Policy Liaison, Outward Bound, USA, Golden, CO

Maclean, John, Author and Journalist, Washington, DC

Maguire, Colleen, Winter Recreation Administrator, Washington State Parks and Recreation Commission, Olympia, WA

Malis-Clark, Karen, Deputy Public Affairs Officer, Coconino National Forest, Flagstaff, AZ

Maloney, Kathryn, Director, State and Private Forestry, Northeastern Area, USDA Forest Service, Newtown Square, PA

Mangold, Robert, Director, Forest Health Protection, USDA Forest Service, Washington, DC

Maniella, Fran, Director, National Park Service, Washington, DC

Manning, Gloria, Associate Deputy Chief, USDA Forest Service, Washington, DC

Marita, Butch, Regional Forester (retired), USDA Forest Service, Townsend, MT

Marosy, Melissa, Dispute Resolution Specialist, Pacific Northwest Region, USDA Forest Service Woodland, CA

Marr, Jerri, District Ranger, USDA Forest Service, Silver Springs, FL

Marston, Edwin H., Former Publisher, High Country News, Paonia, CO

Mart, Eric, President, California Land Management, Palo Alto, CA

Matthews, Bruce, President and CEO, Recreational Boating and Fishing Foundation, Alexandria, VA

Mayer, Peter, Executive Secretary, International Union of Forest Research Organizations, Vienna

Maynard, Robert A., Attorney, Perkins Coie LLP, Boise, ID

McAvoy, Jacquellin, First Vice President, Idaho Women in Timber, Post Falls, ID

McCarthy, Laura, Program Director, Forest Guild, Santa Fe, NM

McCormick, Steve, President, The Nature Conservancy, Arlington, VA

McCurtain, Bruce, President, Alaska Recreational Management, Eagle River, AK

McElroy, James, State Forester, Washington Department of Natural Resources, Olympia, WA

McGuire, Marjory, spouse of former Chief John McGuire, Gaithersburg, MD

McIntyre, David E., Board of Directors, National Forest Foundation, Greer, SC

McKean, Lori, Public Affairs Officer, Grey Towers, Milford, PA

McKinney, Matt, Director, Public Policy Research Institute, University of Montana, Helena, MT

Meadows, William H., President, Wilderness Society, Washington, DC

Mealey, Timothy, Senior Partner, Meridian Institute, Washington, DC

Mercado, Alba, Student, College of the Sequoias, Dinuba, CA

Mezainis, Val E., Director, International Programs, USDA Forest Service, Herndon, VA

Milkman, Louise, Director of Federal Programs, The Nature Conservancy, Arlington, VA

Miller, Char, Professor and Chair, History Department, Trinity University, San Antonio, TX

Miller, Scott, Member, Energy and Natural Resources Committee, U.S. Senate, Washington, DC

Millet, Thomas, Assistant General Counsel, Department of Agriculture, Washington, DC

Mitchell, Nora, Director, Conservation Study Institute, Woodstock, VT

Mitsos, Mary, Director, Community Based Conservation, National Forest Foundation, Stevensville, MT

Mockenhaupt, Susan, National Program Manager, Urban and Community Forestry, USDA Forest Service, Washington, DC

Model, Robert, President, Boone and Crockett Club, Cody, WY

Monahan, Ruth, Forest Supervisor, Sawtooth National Forest, Twin Falls, ID

Montgomery, Michael, Research Entomologist, Northeast Research Station, USDA Forest Service, Hamden, CT

Moore, Randy, Regional Forester, USDA Forest Service, Milwaukee, WI

Morgan, Robin, Assistant Director, Northeastern Area, USDA Forest Service, Newtown Square, PA

Moseley, James, Deputy Secretary of Agriculture, Washington, DC

Motanic, Don, Technical Specialist, Intertribal Timber Council, Portland, OR

Mulder, Tom, Administrative Officer, Gifford Pinchot National Forest, Portland, OR

Murphy, Kym, Senior Vice President, Corporate Environmental Policy, The Walt Disney Company, Burbank, CA

Myers, Charles, Acting Director, Forest Management, USDA Forest Service, Sterling, VA

Myers, Peter C., Former Assistant Secretary of Agriculture, Natural Resources and Environment, Sikeston, MO

Naatz, Daniel, Director, Federal Resources, Independent Petroleum Association of America, Rockville, MD

Napier, Barry, Deputy Manager, Forest Service Geospatial Service and Technology Center, Salt Lake City, UT

Nelson, Wilke, Vice President, National Forest Foundation, Washington, DC

Nesselroad, Paul, Director, Public and Governmental Relations, Northern Region, USDA Forest Service, Missoula, MT

Newman, Corbin L., National Fire Plan Coordinator, USDA Forest Service, Washington, DC

Newman, Erin, Executive Assistant to the Deputy Chief, USDA Forest Service, Washington, DC

Noel, Frank, Public Relations Director, United Four Wheel Drive Associations, Happy Jack, AZ

Noel, Joanie, United Four Wheel Drive Associations, Happy Jack, AZ

Norbury, Frederick, Associate Deputy Chief, USDA Forest Service, Washington, DC

Nordin, Carol, Northeastern Research Station, USDA Forest Service, Newtown Square, PA

O'Connor, Patricia, District Ranger, Tongass National Forest, Yakutat, AK

Oakes, Maribeth, Director, Public Lands Program, Sierra Club, San Francisco, CA

Oftedal, James, Director, Central California Consortium, USDA Forest Service, Clovis, CA

Oliver, Chadwick D., Professor, Yale University, New Haven, CT

Omland, Mari, Conservation Director, Appalachian Trail Conference, Harpers Ferry, WV

Over, Stephen, Executive Director, National Ski Patrol, Lakewood, CO

Pagan, Shawn, Vice President, United Four Wheel Drive Associations, Happy Jack, AZ

Pandini, Cindy, Director of Marketing and Communications, National Forest Foundation, Missoula, MT

Paqueo, Liza, Outreach and Partnership Specialist, USDA Forest Service, International Programs, Washington, DC

Paro, Jeff, President, Primedia Outdoors, New York, NY

Parris, Luz, Program Manager, Urban and Community Forestry, USDA Forest Service, Washington, DC

Parsons, Robert, Vice President, North American Weed Management Association, Powell, WY

Partin, Tom, President, American Forest Resource Council, Portland, OR

Paterson, Richard, Director, Grey Towers, USDA Forest Service, Fairfax, VA

Patton, Roy, Assistant Director, Northeastern Forest Experiment Station, USDA Forest Service, Newtown Square, PA

Patton-Mallory, Marcia, Director, Rocky Mountain Research Station, USDA Forest Service, Fort Collins, CO

Payne, Larry, Director, Cooperative Forestry, USDA Forest Service, Washington, DC

Perez, Jerome E., Deputy Forest Supervisor, USDA Forest Service, Sonora, CA

Peterson, Jan, Leesburg, VA

Peterson, Max, Former Chief, USDA Forest Service, Leesburg, VA

Pfilf, Richard J., Executive Director, National Association of Forest Service Retirees, Alexandria, VA

Piltzecker, John, Chief Partnership Office, National Park Service, Washington, DC

Pinchot, Gifford III, Chairman, Bainbridge Graduate Institute, Bainbridge Island, WA

Piotrowski, Ruth, Executive Assistant, USDA Forest Service, Washington, DC

Pittman, Maggie, Assistant Director of Public Affairs, USDA Forest Service, Missoula, MT

Poling, Janet, Associate General Counsel, Department of Agriculture, Washington, DC

Pollock, Nadine, Staff Assistant, National Fire Plan, Washington, DC

Porterfield, Richard, Dean, School of Forest Resources, University of Georgia, Athens, GA

Possiel, William, President, National Forest Foundation, Missoula, MT

Poturalski, Raquel, Public Affairs Officer, USDA Forest Service, Flagstaff, AZ

Prouty, Sally, President, National Association of Service and Conservation Corps, Washington, DC

Pryor, III, Samuel F., Senior Counsel, Davis Polk and Wardwell, New York, NY

Puchlerz, Gerry, Lolo, MT

Puchlerz, Tom, Director, Recreation, Minerals, Lands, Heritage, and Wilderness, USDA Forest Service, Missoula, MT

Pyron, Christopher, Deputy Chief for Business Operations, USDA Forest Service, Washington, DC

Quigley, Thomas, Director, Pacific Northwest Research Station, USDA Forest Service, Vancouver, WA

Rains, Michael, Director, Northeastern Research Station, USDA Forest Service, Broomall, PA

Ramirez, George, CEO, Las Humanas Cooperative, Torreon, NM

Rapoport, Terrence, Executive Director, Colorado Fourteeners Initiative, Golden, CO

Rappe-Daniels, Olleke, Deputy Forest Supervisor, Tongass National Forest, Ketchikan, AK

Rasure, Nora, Forest Supervisor, Coconino National Forest, Flagstaff, AZ

Reaves, Adrienne, Upper Marlboro, MD

Reaves, Jimmy, Director, Vegetation Management and Protection Research, USDA Forest Service, Upper Marlboro, MD

Reed, Manuel Agustin, Director General, Comision Nacional Forestal, Zapopan, Mexico

Reid, Charles, Director and Professor, School of Natural Resources, University of Arizona, Tucson, AZ

Reilly, Tom, Forest Supervisor, Beaverhead-Deerlodge National Forest, Dillon, MT

Reimers, Diane, Clifton, VA

Reimers, Mark, USDA Forest Service (retired), Clifton, VA

Rey, Mark, Under Secretary of Agriculture, Natural Resources and Environment, Washington, DC

Reynolds, Gray, Deputy Chief (retired), National Forest System, USDA Forest Service, Davidsonville, MD

Richardson, Tim, Washington, DC, Representative, American Land Conservancy, Rockville, MD

Riley, James, President and CEO, Intermountain Forest Association, Coeur d'Alene, ID

Risbrudt, Christopher, Director, Forest Products Laboratory, USDA Forest Service, Madison, WI

Ritter, Lloyd, Minority Staff, Committee on Agriculture, Nutrition, and Forestry, Washington, DC

Robertson, F. Dale, Former Chief, USDA Forest Service, Sedona, AZ

Rodbell, Phillip, Program Manager, Urban and Community Forestry, Northeastern Area, USDA Forest Service, Newtown Square, PA

Roessing, Megan, Policy Analyst, USDA Forest Service, Washington, DC

Roffé, Sarina, Director of Communications, Jewish National Fund, New York, NY

Rogner, John, Field Supervisor, U.S. Fish and Wildlife Service, Barrington, IL

Romero, Louis D., Senior Consultant, DeLa Porte and Associates, Albuquerque, NM

Roussopoulos, Peter J., Director, Southern Research Station, USDA Forest Service, Asheville, NC

Rush, Keith, Yakutat, AK

Ruth, Celeste, Wildlife Partners Network Coordinator, Wildlife Management Institute, Washington, DC

Ruth, Dr. Lawrence W., Policy Specialist, University of California–Berkeley, Berkeley, CA

Salwasser, Hal, Dean, College of Forestry, Oregon State University, Corvallis, OR

Sample, V. Alaric, President, Pinchot Institute for Conservation, Washington, DC

Sanchez, Juan (Buck), District Ranger, Lincoln National Forest, Ruidoso, NM

Sanders, Wendy, Executive Director, Great Lakes Forest Alliance, Inc., Hayward, WI

Sandor, John, USDA Forest Service (retired), Juneau, AK

Scardina, Anthony, Budget Analyst, USDA Forest Service, Arlington, VA

Schieffelin, Tim, Board of Directors, National Forest Foundation, Greenwich, CT

Schilling, Sherri, Labor and Employee Relations Specialist, USDA Forest Service, San Francisco, CA

Sedell, James R., Director, Pacific Southwest Research Station, USDA Forest Service, Berkeley, CA

Sedjo, Roger, Senior Fellow, Resources for the Future, Washington, DC

Shimeall, Kirk, Wilderness Program Manager, Catherine Freer Wilderness Therapy, Albany, OR

Shirley, Jennie, Staff Assistant, Northeastern Forest Experiment Station, Newtown Square, PA

Shore, Debra, Director of Development, Chicago Wilderness, Skokie, IL

Simmons, Deborah, Professor, Northern Illinois University, DeKalb, IL

Sirmon, Jeff, USDA Forest Service (retired), Vienna, VA

Sloan, Mary Margaret, President, American Hiking Society, Silver Spring, MD

Smalley, Jim, Manager, Wildland Fire Protection, National Fire Protection Association, Quincy, MA

Smith, Cheryl, Penny Pine Chairman, National Garden Clubs, Inc., Huntington Beach, CA

Smith, Gregory C., Acting Director of Lands, USDA Forest Service, Washington, DC

Spivak, Randi, Executive Director, American Lands Alliance, Washington, DC

Sprague, G. L., Consultant, Boise, ID

Spriggs, Perdita, Program Analyst, Southern Research Station, USDA Forest Service, Asheville, NC

Sprinkle, Ron, Director, Law Enforcement and Investigations, USDA Forest Service, Arnold, MD

Stack, David, Vice President, National Museum of Forest Service History, Missoula, MT

Startzell, David, Executive Director, Appalachian Trail Conference, Harpers Ferry, WV

Steffenson, John, Account Manager, ESRI, Broomfield, CO

Steinke, Dave, Public Affairs Specialist, USDA Forest Service, Golden, CO

Stemler, Jodi, Director, Communications, Congressional Sportsmen's Foundation, Washington, DC

Stewart, Jodi, Elliott Wildlife Values Project Consultant, Girl Scouts of the USA, New York, NY

Stewart, Ronald, Associate Professor, George Mason University, Bowie, MD

Stewart-Kent, Deborah, Executive Director, Florida Trail Association, Gainesville, FL

Stockinger, Linda Lou, Public Affairs Specialist, Eastern Region, USDA Forest Service, Elm Grove, WI

Stokes, Turner, Washington, DC, Representative, American Association for Nude Recreation, Leesburg, VA

Stokes, Vaughn, Director of Engineering, USDA Forest Service, Washington, DC

Story, Donna, Chair, Colorado-Wyoming, Society of American Foresters, LaPorte, CO

Stubbs, Glenn, Forest Fire and Aviation Officer, Chugach National Forest, Anchorage, AK

Suenram, Peri, Planning, Budget, Information Staff Officer, USDA Forest Service, Dillon, MT

Swanson, Sue, Executive Director, Allegheny Hardwood Utilization Group, Kane, PA

Sweeney, Bernard, Director and President, Stroud Water Research Center, Avondale, PA

Sweeney, Sharon, Public Affairs Officer, Lolo National Forest, Missoula, MT

Swinford, Robert, Special Assistant to the Chief, USDA Forest Service, Washington, DC

Tarver, Charles, President, Forest Investment Associates, Atlanta, GA

Taylor, Charles H., U.S. House of Representatives (R-NC), Washington, DC

Tenny, David, Deputy Under Secretary of Agriculture, Natural Resources and Environment, Washington, DC

Tergeson, Erica, Legislative Staff, Forests and Forest Health Subcommittee, Resources Committee, Washington, DC

Theophile, Karin, Program Leader, Outreach and Partnerships, International Programs, USDA Forest Service, Washington, DC

Thomas, Jack Ward, Former Chief, U.S. Forest Service, Florence, MT

Thompson, Robin, Associate Deputy Chief, State and Private Forestry, USDA Forest Service, Falls Church, VA

Thompson, Tom, Deputy Chief, National Forest System, USDA Forest Service, Washington, DC

Tilotta, David, President, Coalition for Advanced Housing and Forest Products Research, Raleigh, NC

Titus, Kim, Staff Officer, Columbia River Gorge, NSA, USDA Forest Service, Hood River, OR

Todd, Albert, Watershed Program Leader, Northeastern Area, USDA Forest Service, Annapolis, MD

Toliver, John, Deputy Station Director, Rocky Mountain Research Station, USDA Forest Service, Fort Collins, CO

Toman, Tom, Director of Conservation, Rocky Mountain Elk Foundation, Missoula, MT

Tombaugh, Larry, Chairman, Board of Directors, Forest History Society, Cary, NC

Tooke, Tony, Deputy Forest Supervisor, USDA Forest Service, Tallahassee, FL

Tophooven, Tracy, District Ranger, Ottawa National Forest, Watersmeet, MI

Topik, Christopher, Professional Staff, House Appropriations Committee, Washington, DC

Towns, Eleanor, USDA Forest Service (retired), Westminster, CO

Troxel, Thomas, Director, Intermountain Forest Association, Rapid City, SD

Troyer, Jack, Regional Forester, USDA Forest Service, North Ogden, UT

Truman, Scott, Executive Director, Utah Rural Development Council, Cedar City, UT

Turbeville, Bruce, Chairman, California Fire Safe Council, Sacramento, CA

Umlauf, Pearse, Vice President, Jeep Jamboree USA, Georgetown, CA

Underwood, Karen, Arlington, VA

Underwood, Marvin, Director of Minerals and Geology Management, USDA Forest Service, Arlington, VA

Valdes, Michael, Resources Staff Officer, Eldorado National Forest, Placerville, CA

Vale, Abel, President, Citizens of the Karst, San Juan, PR

Van Abel, Mike, Executive Director, International Mountain Bicycling Association, Boulder, CO

Van Kleeck, Kathy, Vice President, Government Relations, Motorcycle Industry Council, Arlington, VA

Vann III, R.E., District Ranger, Nantahala National Forest, Murphy, NC

Vietzke, Gay E., Superintendent, Sagamore Hill National Historic Site, National Park Service, Department of the Interior, Oyster Bay, NY

Vogel, Jeanie, Senior Manager, Verizon Communications, San Antonio, FL

Vogel, John, Student, Jesuit High School, San Antonio, FL

Voorhees, Phil, Vice President and Director, National Parks Conservation Association Center for Park Management, Washington, DC

Vue, Bao, Asian Community Liaison, Central California Consortium, USDA Forest Service, Clovis, CA

Wachowski, Henry, Remote Sensing Applications Center, USDA Forest Service, Salt Lake City, UT

Wagner, Mary, Assistant Director, Wilderness, Backcountry and Trails, USDA Forest Service, Washington, DC

Ward, Bruce, Executive Director, Continental Divide Trail Alliance, Pine, CO

Watson, Rebecca W., Assistant Secretary, Land and Mineral Management, U.S. Department of the Interior, Washington, DC

Watts, Dana, Executive Director, Leave No Trace, Inc., Boulder, CO

Wear, David N., Project Leader, Southern Research Station, USDA Forest Service, Research Triangle Park, NC

Weingardt, Susan Alden, Centennial Partnership Coordinator, USDA Forest Service, Washington, DC

Welde, Allison, Program Coordinator, Sustainable Forestry Board, Arlington, VA

Werner, Gary, Executive Director, Partnership for the National Trails System, Madison, WI

Werner, Steve, Executive Vice President, American Land and Leisure, Orem, UT

West, Chris, Vice President, American Forest Resource Council, Portland, OR

West, Jay, Mediator, Meridian Institute Roundtable on Sustainable Forests, Washington, DC

Whaley, Ross, Chairman, Adirondack Park Agency, Ray Brook, NY

Wilbanks, Sam, District Ranger, USDA Forest Service, Sierraville, CA

Wilkerson, Randy, Public Affairs Specialist, Rocky Mountain Region, USDA Forest Service, Lakewood, CO

Williams, Steve, Director, U.S. Fish and Wildlife Service, Washington, DC

Williams, Tandra, Automation Clerk, International Programs, USDA Forest Service, Washington, DC

Williamson, Scot, Vice President, Wildlife Management Institute, Saint Johnsbury, VT

Wiseman, Laurence, President, American Forest Foundation, Washington, DC

Wolf, Robert, Congressional Research Service (retired), St. Leonard, MD

Wood, Michael, Environmental Liaison and Consultant, Missoula, MT

Yager, Thomas, Vice President, Specialty Vehicle Institute of America, Huntington Beach, CA

Yarie, John, Professor of Silviculture, University of Alaska–Fairbanks, Fairbanks, AK

Yates, Ryan, Majority Staff Assistant, Resources Committee, Forests and Forest Health Subcommittee, Washington, DC

Yonts-Shepard, Susan, Director of Ecosystem Management Coordination, USDA Forest Service, Washington, DC

Yung, Laurie, Interim Director, Wilderness Institute, Missoula, MT

Zackery, Joyce, Southern Regional Office, USDA Forest Service, Atlanta, GA

Zaksek, Melissa, National Fire Plan, USDA Forest Service, Washington, DC

Ziemann, Lois, Interpretive Planner, Rocky Mountain Region, USDA Forest Service, Victorville, CA

Zimmermann, Anne, Deputy Director, Watershed, Fish, Wildlife, Air and Rare Plants Staff, USDA Forest Service, Washington, DC

Pinchot Principles

A public official is there to serve the public and not to run them.

Public support of acts affecting public rights is absolutely required.

It is more trouble to consult the public than to ignore them, but that is what you are hired for.

Find out in advance what the public will stand for; if it is right and they won't stand for it, postpone action and educate them.

Use the press first, last and all the time if you want to reach the public.

Get rid of the attitude of personal arrogance or pride of attainment of superior knowledge.

Don't try any sly or foxy politics because a forester is not a politician.

Learn tact simply by being honest and sincere, and by learning to recognize the point of view of the other man and meet him with arguments he will understand.

Don't be afraid to give credit to someone else even when it belongs to you; not to do so is the sure mark of a weak man, but to do so is the hardest lesson to learn; encourage others to do things; you may accomplish many things through others that you can't get done on your single initiative.

Don't be a knocker; use persuasion rather than force, when possible; plenty of knockers are to be had; your job is to promote unity.

Don't make enemies unnecessarily and for trivial reasons; if you are any good you will make plenty of them on matters of straight honesty and public policy, and you need all the support you can get.

Note: Gifford Pinchot, the first chief of the Forest Service and first president of the Society of American Foresters, offered advice to guide the behavior of foresters in public office. They may have originated during one of his lectures on forest policy at the Yale School of Forestry in the early 1900s. Source: Journal of Forestry (February 1994): 12.

Photo Gallery

US Forest Service

*Centennial
Congress*

A Collective Commitment to Conservation

The Centennial Congress opened with a play about the establishment of the Forest Service. Gifford Pinchot (portrayed by Gary Hines) listens to President Theodore Roosevelt (portrayed by Keith McGough) address the crowd.
(Photo by Steven Anderson)

Bill Possiel, president of the National Forest Foundation, announced the purpose of the Congress. (Photo by Tami A. Heilemann)

Deputy Chief of the National Forest System Tom Thompson helped open the Congress on behalf of the Forest Service. (Photo by Tami A. Heilemann)

Jeffrey Stine of the Smithsonian Institution introduced a sneak preview of *The Greatest Good*, a documentary film produced by the Forest Service for its centennial. (Photo by Tami A. Heilemann)

After the Job Corps Color Guard presented the colors, musician and tree farmer Chuck Leavell performed the national anthem to open the second day of the Congress. (Photo by Tami A. Heilemann)

Waiting for the first speaker to begin are, from left to right, former chief Michael Dombeck, Associate Chief Sally Collins, Secretary of Agriculture Ann Veneman, Under Secretary of Agriculture Mark Rey, and Chief Dale Bosworth.
(Photo by Tami A. Heilemann)

Chief Dale Bosworth welcomed delegates on behalf of the Forest Service.
(Photo by Tami A. Heilemann)

After presenting the administration's welcome, Secretary of Agriculture Ann Veneman took questions at a press conference about the Centennial Congress. (Photo by Tami A. Heilemann)

Secretary of the Interior Gale Norton offered congratulations to the agency on its centennial. (Photo by Tami A. Heilemann)

Ed Brannon, former director of Grey Towers National Historic Landmark, provided historical perspective on the Forest Service. (Photo by Tami A. Heilemann)

The four former chiefs discussed their time in office as part of the Reflections and Visions from Forest Service Chiefs panel. Clockwise from upper left: Max Peterson (1979–1987), Dale Robertson (1987–1993), Michael Dombeck (1997–2001), and Jack Ward Thomas (1993–1996). (Photos by Tami A. Heilemann)

Outside Perspectives panel members: (left to right) John Shelk, Mavis Hill, Robert Model, Jo Ellen Force (moderator), Debra Shore, and Todd Davidson. (Photo by Tami A. Heilemann)

Debra Shore (left) of *Chicago WILDERNESS* magazine and Todd Davidson of the Oregon Tourism Commission. (Photo by Tami A. Heilemann)

Butch Blazer, Bill Meadows, John Heissenbuttel, Lyle Laverty, Robert Douglas, and Paul Hansen of the Public Policy panel listen to moderator Patricia Limerick. (Photo by Tami A. Heilemann)

Bill Meadows (left) of the Wilderness Society and John Heissenbuttel of the American Forest and Paper Association. (Photo by Tami A. Heilemann)

The Forest Service-produced documentary, *The Greatest Good*, premiered at the Centennial Congress. (Photo by Tami A. Heilemann)

Historian Char Miller introduced the film *The Greatest Good.*
(Photo by Tami A. Heilemann)

Associate Chief Sally Collins received autographs from filmmakers Ann Dunsky and
Steve Dunsky. (Photo by Gerald W. Williams)

From left to right, Greg Walden, Mark Udall, and Larry Craig of the Congressional Views panel. (Photo by Tami A. Heilemann)

Bruce Ward of Continental Divide Trail Alliance posed a question during the Congressional Views panel. (Photo by Tami A. Heilemann)

Former Forest Service and Congressional Research Service employee Bob Wolf made an observation during one of the panels. (Photo by Tami A. Heilemann)

The Forest Service in a Changing World panel: (left to right) Ross Whaley (moderator), Sally Fairfax, Gifford Pinchot III, Emilyn Sheffield, and Gus Speth. (Photo by Thomas Iraci)

Professor Sally Fairfax of the University of California and Gifford Pinchot III of the Bainbridge Graduate Institute. Pinchot is the grandson of Gifford Pinchot, the first Forest Service chief. (Photo by Tami A. Heilemann)

Deborah Campbell hosted those giving reports from the Centennial Regional Forums. (Photo by Thomas Iraci)

Discussions in the breakout groups were intense but productive. (Photo by Thomas Iraci)

Don Christian of PricewaterhouseCoopers, which sponsored the Awards Gala at the Whitten Building, offered opening remarks. (Photo by Tami A. Heilemann)

Chief Dale Bosworth accepted an award from Dr. Peter Mayer of the International Union of Forest Research Organizations. (Photo by Tami A. Heilemann)

Russell Robinson and Joe Hess presented Chief Dale Bosworth with an award from the Jewish National Fund. (Photo by Tami A. Heilemann)

Chief Dale Bosworth (left) and Regional Forester Harv Forsgren (right) of Region 3 received an award from Steve McCormick of the Nature Conservancy. The award was for the fuel reductions program. (Photo by Tami A. Heilemann)

Forest Service employees Tina Kingsbury (left) and Kissie Hopkins took time out to pose with Woodsy Owl and Smokey Bear. (Photo by Thomas Iraci)

Jon Provost (far left), who played Timmy on the television show *Lassie*, joined his former costar along with Doug Crandall, Sally Fairfax, and Mark Rey for a photo. (Photo by Tami A. Heilemann)

Steve Anderson, President and CEO of the Forest History Society, Joel Holtrop, Deputy Chief for State and Private Forestry, and Dave Steinke, co-director of *The Greatest Good*, discussed educational plans for the film at the Awards gala. (Photo by Tami A. Heilemann)

Attendees flocked to the Awards and Recognition gala at the Whitten Building. (Photo by Tami A. Heilemann)

Daniel Delgado, a high school student from New Mexico who appeared on the Conservation Leaders panel, received some advice from President Theodore Roosevelt, as portrayed by Keith McGough. (Photo by Tami A. Heilemann)

National Program Leader for Rangeland Ecology Research Ralph Crawford showed some lab specimens to Ariel Lugo, director of the International Institute of Tropical Forestry in Puerto Rico, at the awards party. (Photo by Tami A. Heilemann)

Jim Anderson of the United Four Wheel Drive Associations explained his group's mission to attendees. (Photo by Thomas Iraci)

The Nature Conservancy was one of eighteen exhibitors at the Centennial Congress. (Photo by Tami A. Heilemann)

Attendees look over literature from the Forest Service's National Partnership Office.
(Photo by Thomas Iraci)

Noretta Short (right) of the Forest Service's International Programs talks with Susan DeLong and Tom Bobbe of the Forest Service's Remote Sensing Application Center.
(Photo by Thomas Iraci)

Student attendee Terry Baker (far left) listens as Alba Mercado and John Vogel talk between sessions. (Photo by Thomas Iraci)

Perry Brown, Dean of Forestry at the University of Montana, (center) talks with Peter Mayer of the International Union of Forest Research Organizations (right) and John Toliver, Deputy Director of the Forest Service's Rocky Mountain Research Station. (Photo by Tami A. Heilemann)

From left to right, Jim Moseley (moderator), Rupert Cutler, John Crowell, George Dunlop, and Jim Lyons of the Assistant and Under Secretaries Panel.
(Photo by Tami A. Heilemann)

Former chief Max Peterson reconnected with his old boss, former Assistant Secretary of Agriculture, Conservation, Research & Education Rupert Cutler.
(Photo by Tami A. Heilemann)

Power of Participation panel members: (left to right) James Hull, Robert Keck, Ann Linehan, and Majora Carter. (Photo by Tami A. Heilemann)

Power of Participation panel member M. Hosny El-Lakany of the United Nations Food and Agriculture Organization. (Photo by Tami A. Heilemann)

Jo Santiago of the Monongahela (West Virginia) National Forest's Cranberry Mountain Nature Center lets Randy Moore of the Forest Service handle Anastacia, a redtailed hawk used in educational outreach programs.
(Photo by Tami A. Heilemann)

Conservation Leaders panel moderator Jim Oftedal with students Daniel Delgado, Alyse Charley, Alba Mercado, John Vogel, Jessica Ferrar, and Terry Baker.
(Photo by Thomas Iraci)

Dr. Walter Hill received a Centennial Congress award for university leadership on behalf of Tuskegee University. (Photo by Tami A. Heilemann)

Chief Bosworth and Associate Chief Sally Collins presented former Forest Service Regional Forester Eleanor Towns with an award for "Leadership in a Diverse Society." (Photo by Tami A. Heilemann)

Centennial Congress award winners and presenters. (Photo by Tami A. Heilemann)

The Fiddlin' Foresters, a musical group comprised of Forest Service employees, entertained at the awards ceremony luncheon. (Photo by Thomas Iraci)

Forest Service Law Enforcement Officers Robin Thies and Dallas Marroquin were among those who provided security for the event. (Photo by Thomas Iraci)

Staffing the Registration Desk were (left to right) Alexandra Kenny of the National Forest Foundation, and Susan Brooks, Yvette Shockley, and Mary Cook of the Forest Service. (Photo by Thomas Iraci)

Volunteers helped run the Congress smoothly. Back row, left to right: Steve Foley, Floyd Thompson, Susan Brooks; Ruth McWilliams, Susan O'Dell, Terri Cleland; Ted Beauvais, Mike Dechter, Susan Mockenhaupt; Debra Whiteall, Tom Thompson, Meg Roessing; Associate Chief Sally Collins, Sara Bickell; Cathy Carr, Meg Mitchell, Don Hansen; Sandy Forney, Chief Dale Bosworth, Jim Culbert; Brian Boyd, Yvette Shockley, Daina Apple, Linda Parker. (Photo by Thomas Iraci)

The second American Forest Congress in 1905 on the steps of the Navy Department. Gifford Pinchot (circled) helped organize it to pressure Congress to authorize the transfer of the forest reserves and create the Forest Service. (Photo courtesy of Grey Towers National Historic Landmark)

The 2005 Forest Service Centennial Congress gala at the Whitten Building. (Photo by Thomas Iraci)

The Planning Group put together the Congress. Back row, left to right: Erin Newman, Jan Engert, Karl Perry; Don Hansen, Kristen Thrall, Debbie Pressman; Patricia Woods, Tom Thompson, Karen Finlayson, Susan Alden Weingert; Jonathan Stephens, Associate Chief Sally Collins, Terri Cleland, Ralph Crawford; Sara Iverson, Theresa Fraser, Linda Brett, Jeff Waalkes; Dan Harkenrider, Chief Dale Bosworth, Jacqueline Leonard Emanuel, Floyd Thompson; Jim Gasser, Rita Gunther. (Photo by Thomas Iraci)